Practice and Precept in Psychoanalytic Technique

PRACTICE AND PRECEPT IN PSYCHOANALYTIC TECHNIQUE

SELECTED PAPERS OF RUDOLPH M. LOEWENSTEIN

WITH AN INTRODUCTION BY
Jacob A. Arlow

YALE UNIVERSITY PRESS
NEW HAVEN AND LONDON

Designed by James J. Johnson and set in Caledonia Roman type by The Composing Room of Michigan, Inc.

Printed in the United States of America by Halliday Lithograph, West Hanover, Mass.

Library of Congress Cataloging in Publication Data

Loewenstein, Rudolph Maurice.
   Practice and precept in psychoanalytic technique.

   Bibliography: p.
   Includes index.
   1. Psychoanalysis—Addresses, essays, lectures.
I. Title.
RC509.L63   616.89'17   81-21859
ISBN 0-300-02531-9   AACR2

10 9 8 7 6 5 4 3 2 1

The publisher gratefully acknowledges the following for permission to reprint previously published material:

Lucy Freeman for "Reflections on the Treatment of a Case of Obsessional Neurosis," first published in English in *Troubled Women*, ed. L. Freeman, World Publishing Co., 1959.

American Journal of Psychiatry for "Ego Development and Psychoanalytic Technique," vol. 107, pp. 617–22, 1951. Copyright 1951, The American Psychiatric Association.

International Journal of Psycho-Analysis for papers first published on dates indicated—"Some remarks on Defences, Autonomous Ego and Psycho-analytic Technique," vol. 35, 1954; "Some remarks on the Role of Speech in Psycho-analytic Technique," vol. 37, 1956; "Remarks on Some Variations in Psycho-analytic Technique" and "Variations in Classical Technique: Concluding Remarks," vol. 39, 1958.

Journal of American Psychoanalytic Association (published by International Universities Press) for papers first published on the dates indicated—"A Contribution to the Psychoanalytic Theory of Masochism," vol. 5, 1957; "The Silent Patient (Introduction)," vol. 9, 1961; "Some Considerations on Free Association," vol. 11, 1963; "Defensive Organization and Autonomous Ego Functions," vol. 15, 1967.

Psychoanalytic Quarterly for papers first published on dates indicated—"The Problem of Interpretation," vol. 20, 1951; "Ego Autonomy and Psychoanalytic Technique," vol. 41, 1972; "Bibliography of Rudolph M. Loewenstein," vol. 42, 1973.

Psychoanalytic Study of the Child for "Some Thoughts on Interpretation in the Theory and Practice of Psychoanalysis," vol. 1

Contents

Introduction

JACOB A. ARLOW

These essays represent the principal contributions of Rudolph M. Loewenstein to the technique of psychoanalytic therapy. For some twenty years he taught the subject at the New York Psychoanalytic Institute. This was during the time when interest in psychoanalytic training had reached its post–World War II zenith. Loewenstein had been a leading teacher in Paris before France fell to the Nazis. After his arrival in the United States, he contributed generously at one time or another to the training programs of practically all the institutes of the American Psychoanalytic Association. An entire generation of psychoanalysts in America and abroad owes much of its skill and its awareness of the theory of psychoanalytic technique to the efforts of this man.

Loewenstein was unique as a teacher and as a personality. His very presence had a therapeutic quality. In the classroom his manner was quietly confident, modest and assured at the same time. When a student struggled to formulate a problem of technique, Loewenstein would encourage him with a gentle, bemused smile, finally conveying his own views in a way that seemed to indicate that they were nothing more than reformulations of the very ideas that the student had been trying to express. He carried over into the setting of teaching the same tact and sensitivity that typified his work in the psychoanalytic situation. Bravura demonstration of his expertise was entirely foreign to his nature, despite the fact that he had an uncanny ability to articulate the most penetrating of insights in a clear and readily apprehensible fashion.

Even more significant and pervasive is the influence of his writing. Although he wrote about almost every phase of psychoanalysis, there

1

can be no question that the domain of his authority rested in the theory and technique of psychoanalytic therapy. Expressing himself with consummate grace and utmost clarity (a remarkable achievement for someone whose native tongue was not English), Loewenstein consistently drew upon his rich clinical experience as the source and foundation for his principles of psychoanalytic therapy. Accordingly, these introductory comments to this collection of the technical papers of Rudolph M. Loewenstein will concentrate on this aspect of his contributions to psychoanalysis.

Loewenstein repeatedly acknowledged the seminal influence upon him of his collaboration with Heinz Hartmann and Ernst Kris. The three began to work together shortly after Loewenstein arrived in the United States in 1941. As a group, they were concerned with the confused state of psychoanalytic theory current at the time. Noting that psychoanalytic hypotheses had undergone far-reaching modification in Freud's work as well as in the thinking of many of his co-workers, Hartmann, Kris, and Loewenstein (1946) began to asseverate that the significance of these changes had been underrated and that the implications of the new structural psychology had not been fully appreciated. They took it as their task to integrate the theoretical concepts of the structural theory into a consistent whole and to apply these concepts to hitherto unexplored areas. For psychoanalysis, as for other sciences, they maintained, coherent theory is an essential precondition for any worthwhile investigation. In 1965, Loewenstein wrote, "In each individual analysis, there is an interplay between observation and the application of some theoretical assumption or hypothesis, without which the observational data would remain in a state of chaos" (1965, p. 38; see also Hartmann, Kris, and Loewenstein 1953). This statement by Loewenstein clearly articulated the goal of these three collaborators. It was to resolve the chaotic state of psychoanalytic theorizing by bringing observational data and structural theory into the closest proximate relationship.

As the essays in this collection testify, Loewenstein's special contribution was to apply structural theory to that wide range of disparate psychoanalytic activity collectively labeled psychoanalytic technique. His special interest was to demonstrate how each particular therapeutic intervention related to the general framework of psychoanalytic theory and vice versa. This he did without permitting sensitivity to the requirements of the individual patient to be dissipated in a welter of technical generalizations. Thus, he warned that when the analyst achieves a certain insight into the patient's conflicts, it is not sufficient that he understands the nature of the unconscious id wish alone. Before the analyst transmits this knowledge to the patient, he must assess the effect of the interpretation against the other relationships of the ego and the superego. One does not transmit immediately and passively to the patient whatever comes to the analyst's mind, no matter how correct or consistent the insight may be (Loewenstein 1951a; reprinted here as chapter 1).

For Loewenstein, conclusions drawn from clinical data superseded all other considerations. Confronting the facts of analytic experience was the ultimate test of the validity of any conclusion. He conceded that, as important as the influence of ego psychology had been, it brought about no fundamental change in psychoanalytic technique; but what it did accomplish was "a shift in emphasis which, however, has had significant consequences" (1954, p. 189; reprinted here as chapter 3, p. 43). The consequences that he found especially noteworthy were the analysis of defense, the role of interpretation, and the handling of special situations in the transference.

According to the theory of technique that prevailed prior to Freud's "Inhibition, Symptom, and Anxiety" (1926) and Anna Freud's *The Ego and the Mechanisms of Defense* (1936), the goal of the analyst's technical procedures was to bring about the recovery of repressed memories. To accomplish this it was necessary to overcome the analysand's resistance. In this latter enterprise, the most effective ally of the analyst was the patient's positive transference. Enlisting the aid of the positive transference, the analyst can induce the patient to give up the resistance against associating freely, thereby facilitating and assuring the emergence of repressed memories. According to structural theory, on the other hand, the principal goal of the therapist is to modify the nature of the patient's ego (Freud 1933), to alter its mode of functioning by analyzing the automatic, usually unconscious, means the ego employs to defend itself against anxiety. Recollection of repressed memories is considered in a different light, and transference, positive or negative—if indeed these terms have any real meaning—is analyzed and understood as repetitions of experiences or fantasies from the past reenacted in the analytic setting on the person of the analyst. How these changes influenced Loewenstein's thinking may be illustrated from three areas that he considered most important in psychoanalytic technique. These are resistance, interpretation, and the management of the transference.

As regards resistance, Loewenstein (1963; reprinted here as chapter 11) challenged the concept that resistances manifest themselves only as obstacles to free association. In clinical practice one has to distinguish between resistances against verbalizing a particular thought or feeling and those difficulties that derive from the patient's fundamental conflicts that have eventuated in symptom formation or pathological character traits. There are practical consequences to this distinction. A patient may have resistance against expressing thoughts and feelings about the analyst; but once having expressed these feelings, he may resist conceptualizing these transferred reactions as repetitions of the past, as warded-off responses carried over from another person. In the first type of resistance, compliance with the basic rule to report freely what comes to one's mind may become extremely difficult, if not impossible. Resistance stemming from the latter kind of situation does not necessarily create obstacles to complying with the basic rule. These distinctions are pertinent to experience with certain patients in treatment. Some patients seem to get nowhere with their analytic work, whether they seem to accept or reject the analyst's interpretations. These patients, Loewenstein said, exhibit a resistance against an aspect of the analytic method which is not contained in the wording of the basic rule, namely, the requirement for the patient to cooperate with the analyst by reflecting on his own productions on the basis of hitherto warded-off information that has now been brought to his attention. Such self-reflection is a necessary step in achieving "dynamic insight." The foregoing is but one example of how Loewenstein combined structural psychology with precise examination of the clinical data that enabled him in this case to shed light on the phenomenon of intractable resistance and therapeutic impasse.

If one were to single out Loewenstein's principal interest in the area of technique, it would surely be the problem of interpretation. He returned to this topic repeatedly (1951a, 1951b, 1954, 1956, 1957b, 1963, 1967, 1972; reprinted here as chapters 1, 2, 3, 4, 7, 11, 12, 13, respectively). Interpretation is generally regarded as the analyst's essential contribution to the therapeutic process. As stated previously, Loewenstein pointed out that everything the analyst does must be assessed in terms of how it impinges on each part of the psychic apparatus—the id, the ego, and the superego. In regard to the ego, which is the principal locale of the analyst's functioning, one must take into account the nature of the patient's resistances, as well as the organized system of defense mechanisms, whether these mechanisms are part of the normal personality or embedded, as it were, in the structure of the patient's neurosis. In the adult one hardly ever observes isolated defense mechanisms, but groups of defenses working together. Loewenstein warned that, in giving deep interpretations, it is particularly important to assess the level of the total ego functioning. At the same time, interpretations do not represent the sum total of the analyst's interventions. Some interventions make it possible for interpretations to have the desired dynamic effect. There are many types of interventions. Some represent the preparatory work that leads from intervention to interpretation and from interpretation to insight. This preparatory work may take many forms. Some interventions serve to facilitate the patient's ability to communicate. Others lay the basis for provisional hunches that may be corroborated later or discarded in keeping with how the material unfolds in the course of the analysis. Some of the analyst's work represents organizing the patient's productions in such a way as to elicit additional material by bringing out similarities of themes or similarities of mechanisms for dealing with situations, people, or impulses. And finally the work of preparation may involve confrontation, clarification, and even, under certain circumstances, interpretation proper.

It follows from these considerations why Loewenstein thought of interpretation as a continuing process, taking the form of a layering or of a hierarchy of interventions or explanations that one communicates to the patient in order to increase his knowledge of himself. In keeping with such an approach, the analyst must work from the surface to the depth, the surface meaning not only what is conscious but also what is present and real and significant. "Interpretations deal with the individual experiences of a human being. They aim at widening the conscious knowledge of the individual about himself and should therefore deal with the psychological realities of the individual. . . . For example, interpretations . . . aim at uncovering not . . . the Oedipus complex, but specific individual experiences which constitute the manifestations of the Oedipus complex of the person" (Loewenstein 1951a, p. 5; reprinted here as chapter 1, p. 21). Interpretations cannot all be superficial. They must be an optimal distance from the surface, neither too close nor too far removed, and ultimately they must lead to an understanding of how the past is still active and dynamic in the patient's current real experience.

It would be a grievous error to conclude from these recommendations that Loewenstein advanced a fixed or rigid technical approach to every segment of analytic work. Loewenstein was not a systematizer, nor did he ever formulate a primer for psychoanalytic technique. He prized too highly the unique individuality of each patient and was much too aware of the multiple determination of psychological structures to formulate a specific set of didactic approaches. In addition to his exquisite sensitivity and humane nature, Loewenstein had a deep-seated, unwavering quality of practical common sense, which led him to declare that the analyst's personality and style are important variables in the therapeutic interaction. Although each analyst has his own way of analyzing, it is equally certain that he varies the way he works with each patient and even in different phases of the same analysis. Each patient is a unique individual with a unique combination of traits and problems and will therefore present a unique combination of patterns of behavior in the analysis. "These ... differences ... account for the various ways in which we must understand the material and accomplish the long preparatory work, so that our interpretations may favor the gaining of insight. Hence the difficulty of formulating general rules for interpretation. Psychoanalysis, nevertheless, has discovered a general framework of principles governing the interpretative work in analysis. However, within this general framework a large number of variations are inevitable" (Loewenstein 1958, p. 206; reprinted here as chapter 8, p. 156).

How the patient gradually develops insight into his conflicts parallels the analyst's progressive understanding of the analytic data. Commenting on the subject, Loewenstein wrote, "It is not as if the analyst knew everything and merely had to convey this knowledge via interpretations, according to rigidly established rules. In actual fact, during the analytic process the analyst gradually learns from his patient while attempting to convey to him what he thus learns, so that the process of gaining insight and conveying it is reciprocal to some extent" (1958, p. 206; reprinted here as chapter 8, p. 156). How the analyst learns to decode the "second message," the unconscious import of the patient's verbal productions, is not a magical or mystical process dependent upon some transcendent intuition of the well-analyzed therapist. In the verbal and nonverbal communications, there are hints and clues transmitted from the analysand to the analyst. If these were studied in a systematic and meticulous way, our understanding of the process of unconscious communication in the analytic situation would be immeasurably enhanced. In this respect, Loewenstein's approach differs fundamentally from that of Isakower (1963), who posited a hypothetical "analytic instrument," which in some vaguely defined way enabled the analyst to understand the unconscious significance of the patient's productions. Loewenstein's approach, on the other hand, was practical and empirical. For him the solution was to be found through meticulous examination of the objective data that emerged in the analytic setting. In this process the form and function of language plays a major role (Loewenstein 1956, 1957b; reprinted here as chapter 4 and chapter 7). His intimations concerning the use of figures of speech, especially metaphor, and their effect upon the analyst's intuition were later developed by Arlow and Beres (Beres and Arlow 1974; Arlow 1979).

Because his thinking was so deeply rooted in and directly related to clinical observation, Loewenstein frequently took issue with prevailing theories, even those advanced by Freud and by some of his own collaborators. This fact may have been overlooked because his style was as subtle as his manner was gentle. For example, in re-examining the psychoanalytic theory of masochism, Loewenstein wrote, "Femininity and female sexuality are not identical with masochism. . . . To equate masochism with femininity would not solve the problems presented by masochism. For all these reasons it seems preferable not to follow the classification of masochism, as proposed by Freud in 1924, which placed masochistic perversion under the heading of feminine masochism." And he continues, "Even if biological research were to confirm the validity of the concept of a death instinct, it is not certain that this would decisively add to the explanation of masochism" (1957a, pp. 207–09; reprinted here as chapter 5, pp. 77–79).

A further example of how Loewenstein differed with prevailing views concerns the concept of altered states of consciousness. For a time, analysts, stimulated by the dramatic advance in sleep research, tried to link the origin of psychopathology and the effectiveness of psychoanalytic therapy to their relationship to altered states of consciousness. They would point out, for example, that the patient's situation during free association may be likened to a dream state. Loewenstein took issue with this point of view. He pointed out that the analogy is far from a close one. Free association is not the equivalent of day-dreaming or even thinking aloud or following a stream of conscious-ness. These latter states are all characterized by wish-fulfilling trends directed toward a particular goal and are solitary in character. Free association in the analytic setting is different. "The requirement to curtail censorship and yet [at the same time] to verbalize, to tell all the resulting self-observations to another person, makes the psychic processes of the analysand different from anything else in his life" (1963, p. 458; reprinted here as chapter 11, p. 181).

Although it is difficult to predict what stand Loewenstein would have taken on some of the controversial issues at the center of analytic interest in our time, we do know his stand concerning two continuing controversies in psychoanalysis: the concept of the therapeutic or working alliance and the conceptualization of psychoanalytic metapsychology. For Loewenstein, structure and conflict were the main components of the principal investigative tool of psychoanalysis—the psychoanalytic situation. Cognizant of the influence of the therapeutic setting of the analyst's personality and style, Loewenstein nonetheless eschewed any intimation of role playing on the part of the analyst. In a discussion of Zetzel's (1956) concept of the therapeutic alliance, he rejected the notion that the analyst could or should depart from his neutral, objective attitude in order to supply a nurturing, supportive experience that the patient had missed in the earliest mother-child relationship. This latter nurturing experience was to Zetzel a precondition for any effective therapeutic alliance in psychoanalysis.

Loewenstein was equally clear concerning the definition and function of metapsychology. To Freud (1923), an explanation of phenomena that takes into account topographic, dynamic, genetic, and economic factors is a metapsychological one. Hartmann stated his ideas in more general terms: "Psychoanalysis [is] a psychology of motivation ... that takes into consideration the interaction of the individual with his environment, as well as his so-called 'inner psychic' processes. The study of these psychic processes constitutes what in analysis we call 'metapsychology,' a term that signifies not [as it may seem] that which is beyond psychology altogether but simply those psychological investigations that are not limited to conscious phenomena and that formulate the most general assumptions of psychoanalysis on the most abstract level of theory" (1959, p. 9). Rapaport and Gill (1959; Rapaport 1960) added additional dimensions to the criteria for a metapsychological explanation, especially the role of the function of adaptation. For Loewenstein, clinical relevance was paramount. Discussing psychoanalytic theories and hypotheses, he states, "Most, if not all of these generalizations and extrapolations can be validated or invalidated by use of the very method thanks to which they were arrived at—the method of psychoanalysis. However, there exist in psychoanalysis a number of other propositions which can never be either confirmed or invalidated by the psychoanalytic method proper. They can be formulated or discarded only on the basis of their usefulness and inner consistency. These propositions are the explanatory concepts and constructs which form the psychoanalytic metapsychology" (1965, p. 39). Loewenstein cites the authors just discussed and seems to be following them. Yet in fact he distinguishes very sharply between those inferences that can be derived from data obtained by the psychoanalytic method and those basic assumptions which go beyond (meta) to psychology. In this respect his views seem to be closer to those of Waelder (1962) and to Brenner's (1974) more recent contributions which emphasize that even the broader, more abstract principles of psychoanalytic theory, like instinct theory, fundamentally are based on psychological data derived from the analytic setting.

On the basis of the distinction between inferences derived from data in the psychoanalytic setting and assumptions which go beyond psychology, Loewenstein proposed two sets of concepts: (1) homologous concepts, that is, inferences derived from observational data, and (2) heterologous concepts, which belong to the category of fundamental (a priori) assumptions. Force, energy, cathexis, and neutralization would be examples of heterologous concepts. Such concepts are used when explanations in homologous terms prove unsatisfactory. "We use them when explanations of some data in homologous terms are not forthcoming, when an understanding of some connections appears to lie beyond the observable—hence, the term metapsychological for this kind of explanatory position" (Loewenstein 1965, p. 51). Loewenstein was aware of the pitfalls of the so-called heterologous concepts. For example, he noted that many analysts use the concept of psychic energy while neglecting to search for relevant clinical data which could account for the same phenomena in other terms. Nor did he avoid facing up to the fact that economic concepts in psychoanalysis are hard to sustain because we are not able to measure the hypothetical quantities of energy involved. In his view, Freud used such propositions as a "last resort" when other kinds of formulations proved inadequate to account satisfactorily for some particular phenomenon. While he followed Hartmann's (1950) concept of neutralized energy and its elaboration into the idea of intrasystemic conflict, Loewenstein could not rebut the evidence of his clinical experience and in the end was forced to say, "However, it must be assumed that intrasystemic conflicts probably exist only in conjunction with intersystemic ones" (1965, p. 47).

   If interpretation stood first in Loewenstein's interest regarding psychoanalytic technique, understanding and managing the transference was not far behind. Loewenstein (1969) objected to the tendency to use the concept of transference in an imprecise way, for he felt that such a procedure had serious consequences for the management and interpretation of the transference in the analytic situation. In contradistinction to Sandler and others (1967), he observed that the trend to widen the concept of transference and to use it as a general human reaction both within and outside of the analytic situation diluted and obscured the concept. The phenomena of transference in the psychoanalytic situation are special in the sense that they represent both a resistance and a vehicle for discovering a cure, something that exists only within the analytic situation. Outside of the analytic situation, one can only infer some facets of object relations or of neurotic behavior. In analysis, transference unfolds under controlled conditions with a minimum of contamination from real interactions. A logical consequence of the preceding quote concerning the therapeutic alliance was Loewenstein's opposition to the tendency to separate transference from the therapeutic alliance. In a cogent and pithy footnote Loewenstein observes, "The terms 'therapeutic alliance' and 'working alliance' may have the disadvantage of failing to cover the fact that some patients are willing to get well but not to work, while others are ready to work but not to get well" (1969, p. 585). Perhaps more than with any other aspect of therapy, when it comes to transference, it is of paramount importance to take a hard look at the facts. Not every reaction of the patient to the analyst represents transference, nor can transference interpretations be regarded as the only therapeutically valid ones, as Strachey (1934) maintained. This blurred concept of transference has caused Melanie Klein and her school to view any reactions of the patient to the analyst almost exclusively as repetitions of fantasies of earliest childhood. "This approach has often led to an unfortunate loss of distinction between past and present, reality and fantasy, between the values of dynamic and of genetic interpretations and reconstructions" (Loewenstein 1969, p. 586).

Adumbrating future developments in psychoanalysis, Loewenstein observed that the tendency to complete development is one element of the transference situation, but it cannot be subsumed entirely under the heading of transference. This observation of Loewenstein's relates directly to one of the controversial issues of our time. Those who stress the importance of distorted early object relations in the process of pathogenesis emphasize the effect of the nurturing attitude of the analyst in the transference. The so-called new object relationship with the beneficent analyst in the transference situation fosters the achievement of health, since it furthers the process of completing maturation during treatment by removing the blocks to the biologically preordained thrust towards maturity and normality (for further discussion, see Friedman 1978 and Arlow 1981).

Loewenstein's position on these issues was by no means entirely unequivocal. In another context, commenting on the fact that not every human being is capable of performing the complex ego functions required of an analysand, he went on to say that the essential condition for the successful pursuit of analysis is the basic trust in the analyst and in the psychoanalytic method. "The existence of this underlying stable object relationship . . . based upon aim-inhibited drives, enables the patient to develop intense transference reactions at times and yet to withstand their nongratification. . . . Greenacre [1954 and] Stone [1961] have stressed that the child-mother relationship is the ultimate paradigm [of the transference in] the analytic situation. It is characteristic of this transferred relation that when it appears, nonverbal elements of free associations tend to prevail. Not only is this due to the preverbal stage of development which is being relived at such moments, but it also expresses the longing to be understood by the analyst without talking, as the infant was by the mother" (1963, p. 467; reprinted here as chapter 11, p. 189–90). Loewenstein gives no clinical data to support or illustrate the very striking phenomenon of nonverbal elements of free association dominating this regressively reactivated form of transference. It would indeed be a worthy subject for the kind of systematic study of data derived from within the psychoanalytic situation that Loewenstein urged upon psychoanalysts.

Loewenstein remained convinced of the scientific validity and re-

liability of the psychoanalytic method. If he entertained any en-
thusiasm for extra-analytic methods that might prove superior as in-
struments to validate psychoanalytic hypotheses, it does not seem to
appear in his writings. In considering the following, one may observe
the range of topics that Loewenstein felt should be confirmed or invalidated by recourse to systematic examination of clinical data. For example, in the course of successful therapy, what happens to the energy of
the warded-off instinctual drives as a consequence of changes in the
balance between impulse and defense? Hartmann (1955) had suggested
that the energy required for purposes of defense was derived from the
aggressive drive and, when no longer necessary for this purpose, was
used to strengthen the cathexis of ego functions. Does a similar process
eventuate for the energy of the instinctual drives? Still on the subject of
defense, Loewenstein proposed that it would be useful to study the
defenses the ego institutes against superego demands, as well as to
trace the origin of the so-called primitive forms of superego functioning.

Primarily Loewenstein was interested in learning from clinical
investigation how to improve psychoanalytic technique in order to
achieve better therapeutic results. To this end he proposed a disci-
plined study of the patient's reactions to interpretations. Mere agreement or disagreement with the analyst's interpretations does not shed
sufficient light on the dynamic effect of the analyst's interventions.
Extending the principles of structural theory, it is more important to
observe the dynamic transformations that interpretations induce in the
functioning of the ego. A further step in this process would be to
understand the nature of the preparatory work, the hierarchy of interpretations that leads to understanding in the first place and subsequently to dynamic insight on the part of the patient. Obviously this
is not simply a matter of transformation of ego defenses. Accordingly,
Loewenstein suggested that it would be important to describe precisely and to understand the interaction of various ego functions at
different stages of analysis. This would represent an elucidation of how
the realm of the ego is extended in the course of treatment at the
expense of the id. The final item in this brief listing is probably the one
that would have concerned Loewenstein the most, namely, a study of
the nature of the traces on which inferences are made in the course of
psychoanalytic treatment. The subtle interaction between analyst and
analysand, the verbal and nonverbal communication which takes place

between them, and above all, the patterning of language, the use of
figures of speech, the modes of articulation, and the meanings of
silence—these were the elements to which he turned again and again
in his formulations of theory and technique.

No commentary on Loewenstein's contributions could be considered adequate without mentioning that unique quality of humanity he
brought to the treatment situation. Throughout all the penetrating and
sensitive recommendations on how to address problems of technique,
one perceives a never-failing respect and sympathy for the patient, an
attitude born of a rich and fluid empathy. Loewenstein emphasized
that every communication to the patient must be approached in this
spirit. That is why the style of the analyst is so important, why he must
think carefully of how best to convey his insights to the patient and
must appreciate the impact of the precise mode of communication
employed. Economy of communication should be the guiding principle
in order to make each interpretation count. In that spirit it is important
to avoid clichés and technical jargon, and not to fall into the use of the
same mechanisms of defense—for example, irony, humor, sarcasm—
that a patient may use. One has to circumvent the defenses in order to
really appreciate what it is the patient is feeling and to get the patient
to realize that. In this connection Loewenstein particularly emphasized
the importance of "reconstruction upwards," by which he meant to
alert the analyst not to overlook powerful emotional conflicts in the
present, which the patient may be fending off and which at the same
time may represent significant derivatives of childhood conflicts.

If each analyst has his own personal style of analyzing, it is equally
certain that every patient has his special problems. Hence, the difficulty of formulating general rules for interpretation. In this regard,
Loewenstein probably occupies a position midway between those who
pursue the principles of the psychoanalytic situation in the strictest
sense and others who tend to be more flexible and gratifying in the
transference interaction. In one of his most interesting and striking
contributions, "Remarks on Some Variations in Psychoanalytic Technique," Loewenstein states, "Maximal frustration is not always the
most favorable condition for analytical work" (1958, p. 204; reprinted
here as chapter 8, p. 152). In fact, Loewenstein cites a number of specific
situations in which he departed from fundamental principles, such as
having a patient sit up or suggesting that a candidate accept a small gift
from a patient. In the latter case, he explained that, to this near border-

line patient, the acceptance of a gift meant that she was accepted by the analyst as a worthwhile person. Implicit in these examples is Loewenstein's guiding principle for all approaches to psychoanalytic technique: "The applicability of a rule in a given case or at a given moment will depend on the patient's psychological state and on our estimate of the effect its application might have upon him at such time or in the future" (1958, p. 204; reprinted here as chapter 8, p. 152). To follow this principle one must appreciate the function of tact in psychoanalysis. This involves understanding one's motivation, conscious or unconscious, in deciding when and how to make a particular interpretation. One has to be in step with the patient's problems to understand what is relevant at a given moment, so that one can evaluate the direct and indirect impact of an interpretation, while taking into account the patient's autonomous ego and the transference. Much of this would fall under the heading of what recently has been described as empathy leading to intuition. A specific example would pertain to those cases where the analyst wishes to utilize particular gifts of his patient so as to convey his interpretation in a special, convincing way. Sometimes the right joke told at the right moment may be highly effective when a patient's sense of humor makes him accessible to a particular type of joke. Yet there are times when a joke not only falls flat but may even have the opposite effect on a patient. Loewenstein quotes some analysts who would never tell a joke to certain patients for various reasons, such as, competition or mutual seduction; and he observes that tact depends upon empathic understanding of the patient. It cannot be worked out blueprint fashion "on the spot."

When dealing with variations of technique, Loewenstein is at his best, for he demonstrates that quality which gave him mastery of this area of psychoanalysis, namely, delicate sensitivity to all aspects of the human condition, harnessed to a rigorous scientific methodology. It was in this spirit that he said—and his words are fitting ones with which to close this essay: "Every psychoanalysis can and perhaps ought to be conducted as though the theory were never completely taken for granted. This is a way to make new discoveries; it was the way Freud, in the past, discovered most of what we know now. It may also enable us in the future to effect possibly necessary realignments or modifications of our theoretical assumptions on the basis of new observations. The essence of psychoanalysis is that particular interplay between observational data, gathered from clean clinical work, and their interpretation within a scientifically valid conceptual framework—be it the one we have now or possibly a future, better one" (1957b, p. 149; reprinted here as chapter 7, p. 144).

REFERENCES

Arlow, J. A. (1979). Metaphor and the psychoanalytic situation. *Psychoanal. Q.*, 48: 363–85.
—— (1981). Theories of pathogenesis. Hartmann Lecture, New York Psychoanalytic Institute, October 14, 1980, in press.
Beres, D. & Arlow, J. A. (1974). Fantasy and identification in empathy. *Psychoanal. Q.*, 43: 4–25.
Brenner, C. (1974). On the nature and development of affects: a unified theory. *Psychoanal. Q.*, 43: 532–56.
Freud, A. (1936). *The Ego and the Mechanisms of Defense.* New York: Int. Univ. Press, 1946.
Freud, S. (1923). Psychoanalysis. *S. E.*, 18.
—— (1926). Inhibition, symptom, and anxiety. *S. E.*, 20.
—— (1933). New introductory lectures on psychoanalysis. *S. E.*, 22.
Friedman, L. (1978). Trends in the psychoanalytic theory of treatment. *Psychoanal. Q.*, 48: 524–67.
Greenacre, P. (1954). The role of the transference: practical considerations in relation to psychoanalytic therapy. *J. Amer. Psychoanal. Assn.*, 2: 671–84.
Hartmann, H. (1950). Comments on the psychoanalytic theory of the ego. *Psychoanal. Study Child*, 5: 74–96.
—— (1955). Notes on the theory of sublimation. *Psychoanal. Study Child*, 10: 9–29.
—— (1959). Psychoanalysis as a scientific theory. In *Psychoanalysis, Scientific Method, and Philosophy*, ed. S. Hook. New York: New York Univ. Press, pp. 3–37.
——, Kris, E. & Loewenstein, R. M. (1946). Comments on the formation of psychic structure. *Psychoanal. Study Child*, 2: 11–38.
—— (1953). The function of theory in psychoanalysis. In *Drives, Affects, Behavior, I*, ed. R. M. Loewenstein. New York: Int. Univ. Press, pp. 13–37.
Isakower, O. (1963). Minutes of the Faculty Meeting of the New York Psychoanalytic Institute, November 20.
Loewenstein, R. M. (1951a). The problem of interpretation. *Psychoanal. Q.*, 20: 1–14.
—— (1951b). Ego development and psychoanalytic technique. *Amer. J. Psychiat.*, 107: 617–22.
—— (1954). Some remarks on defenses, autonomous ego, and psychoanalytic technique. *Int. J. Psychoanal.*, 35: 188–93.

———— (1956). Some remarks on the role of speech in psychoanalytic technique. *Int. J. Psychoanal.*, 37: 460–68.

———— (1957a). A contribution to the psychoanalytic theory of masochism. *J. Amer. Psychoanal. Assn.*, 5: 197–234.

———— (1957b). Some thoughts on interpretation in the theory and practice of psychoanalysis. *Psychoanal. Study Child*, 12: 127–50.

———— (1958). Remarks on some variations in psychoanalytic technique. *Int. J. Psychoanal.*, 39: 202–10.

———— (1963). Some considerations on free association. *J. Amer. Psychoanal. Assn.*, 11: 451–73.

———— (1965). Observational data and theory in psychoanalysis. In *Drives, Affects, Behavior, II*, ed. M. Schur. New York: Int. Univ. Press, pp. 38–59.

———— (1967). Defensive organization and autonomous ego functions. *J. Amer. Psychoanal. Assn.*, 15: 795–809.

———— (1969). Developments in the theory of transference in the last fifty years. *Int. J. Psychoanal.*, 50: 583–88.

———— (1972). Ego autonomy and psychoanalytic technique. *Psychoanal. Q.*, 41: 1–22.

Rapaport, D. (1960). *The Structure of Psychoanalytic Theory: A Systematizing Attempt*. New York: Int. Univ. Press.

———— & Gill, M. M. (1959). The points of view and assumptions of metapsychology. *Int. J. Psychoanal.*, 40: 153–62.

Sandler, J. et al. (1967). Einige theoretische und klinische Aspekte der Übertragung. *Psyche*, 21: 804–26.

Stone, L. (1961). *The Psychoanalytic Situation—An Examination of Its Development and Essential Nature*. New York: Int. Univ. Press.

Strachey, J. (1934). The nature of the therapeutic action of psychoanalysis. *Int. J. Psychoanal.*, 15: 127–59.

Waelder, R. (1962). Review of *Psychoanalysis, Scientific Method, and Philosophy*, ed. S. Hook. *J. Amer. Psychoanal. Assn.*, 10: 617–37.

Zetzel, E. R. (1956). Current concepts of transference. *Int. J. Psychoanal.*, 37: 369–76.

1

The Problem of Interpretation

I shall limit myself to an inventory of how analysts actually interpret, mentioning cursorily those facts which are well known (Fenichel 1941), and emphasizing those problems which have not yet been formulated clearly enough and should become subjects of further research. I shall start by discussing the place of interpretation in analytic technique, from the point of view of those dynamic changes which we call insight (Freud 1920, 1922), produced in the patient by interpretations.

First I wish to stress that interpretations do not represent the sum total of the analyst's interventions. Some interventions of the analyst make it possible for interpretations to have the desirable dynamic effect. Other interventions create conditions without which the analytic procedure would be impossible. Among those that are necessary are all those which induce the patient to follow the fundamental rule (Freud, *Coll. Papers* 3), the purpose of which is to loosen the barrier or censorship existing normally between conscious and preconscious processes, and this, in turn, indirectly leads to loosening the barrier between preconscious and unconscious phenomena (Freud, *Coll. Papers* 4, chap. 6): in other words, it permits the patient's associations to be more decisively influenced by the primary process (Freud, *Coll. Papers* 4, chap. 7). The patient's adherence to the fundamental rule is facilitated among other conditions by—at least in the majority of cases suitable for psychoanalysis—the recumbent position (Freud, *Coll. Papers* 2, chap. 31). This we know is contraindicated in the analysis of children (A. Freud 1946) and sometimes of adolescents, and in the

Paper read at the meeting of the American Psychoanalytic Association, Montreal, May 1949.

treatment of schizophrenics (Federn 1943) and of some borderline cases (Stern 1938). Experience has proved it to be unsuitable or harmful in these cases; hence the conclusion that the recumbent position has a positive, dynamic function, and not only serves the convenience of the analyst. The recumbent position, indeed, tends, as Ernst Kris has said, to increase the proportion of projections over objective perceptions. Besides, it creates for the patient a situation where attention and reality testing are withdrawn from the outside (the analyst) and shifted onto the inner experiences of the patient. However, a certain balance between outward and inward reality testing, in which the ability of the patient to keep what we propose be called "differential reality testing," is a prerequisite for analytic treatment.

The withdrawal of reality testing from the external object facilitates the displacement of past reactions onto the analyst, creating transference phenomena, whereas the increased attention and reality testing centered upon the inner experiences of the patient favor, at least in the majority of cases, the flow of associations and the gaining of insight.

One knows that in certain cases and at certain moments of analysis, in which displacement and projective processes gain too much over objective perception, where withdrawal from reality becomes too intense, some analysts have the patient sit up to confront him with reality. Where there is, for whatever reasons, too much or too little mobility of displacement of this type, the management of transference becomes difficult or impossible. Thus the usual analytic procedure is most effective within an optimal range of conditions. At either end of this range, conditions may become such as to preclude analysis or necessitate a modification of the technique. This is one example of the well-known fact that the possibility of applying the analytic technique depends upon the conditions of the instinctual drives as well as the state of the patient's ego (Freud, A. 1942, Freud, S. 1920).

There are a great many methods of intervention by the analyst—other than interpretation—which at all times facilitate the flow of associations and prepare the ego to accept the interpretations. Some of these interventions fall under the heading of the rule of abstinence (Freud, *Coll. Papers* 2, chap. 34), others encompass all those which create the so-called analytic atmosphere. To the latter belong, for instance, the benevolent understanding or the objectivity of the analyst. One might say that these interventions contribute to strengthening the conflictless sphere of the ego (Hartmann 1939).[1] They diminish the intensity of the defenses which the patient's ego opposes to drives or their derivatives in the pathogenic conflicts, and also facilitate the establishment of transference.[2]

Other interventions include explanations given by the analyst as to procedure, or, for instance, questions asked concerning realities in which the patient finds himself; also, the analyst's silence which, as we know, has not only the effect of encouraging the flow of associations but, at certain moments, has an important dynamic effect on the patient.

The analyst uses a number of tacit interventions which may have various consequences. As a result, the reality of the analytic situation and the general attitude of the analyst tend to encourage the patient's need for unburdening his conscience and the verbal expression of all his needs and drives, whereas they tend to thwart actual gratification of aggressive, sexual, and self-punishing behavior in the analysis.

Some analysts have tried recently to shorten and simplify the analytic procedure by limiting themselves mainly to dynamic changes produced by interventions and by minimizing the use of interpretations. They thought that if the analyst behaved in certain psychological situations in a way which was the opposite of the behavior of an important person in the patient's past life, therapeutic results might be achieved. This is a devaluation of what is specifically psychoanalytic: i.e., of dynamic changes produced by insight gained from interpretations. Some limited dynamic changes may occur independently of insight, and some limited insight may be gained without interpretations or even without analysis. In analysis, some insight may be gained from the very fact of talking frankly. The gain of insight, however, is limited if the patient is merely left to associate and is not given any interpretations.

What defines interpretation and distinguishes it from other interventions? In psychoanalysis this term is applied to those explanations, given to patients by the analyst, which add to their knowledge about themselves. Such knowledge is drawn by the analyst from elements

1. As a matter of fact, the strengthening of the conflictless sphere of the ego is mainly brought about by interpretation.

2. Under this heading, also, fall those interventions which have an "educational" effect upon the patient.

contained and expressed in the patient's own thoughts, feelings, words and behavior. This is proposed in such general terms because I believe that the definition of interpretation should not be rigid.

Among the interventions there are many which may be called preparations for interpretation. It happens frequently in the beginning of analysis that a patient describes a number of events which strike the analyst as having certain similarities. The analyst's task is then to show the patient that all these events in his life have some elements in common. The next step is to point out that the patient behaved in a similar way in all these situations. The third step may be to demonstrate that this behavior was manifested in circumstances which all involved competitive elements and where rivalry might have been expected. A further step, in a later stage of the analysis, would consist, for instance, in pointing out that in these situations rivalry does exist unconsciously, but is replaced by another kind of behavior, such as avoiding competition.[3] In a still later stage of the analysis this behavior of the patient is shown to originate in certain critical events of his life encompassing reactions and tendencies, as, for example, those which we group under the heading of the Oedipus complex. The interpretation extends in installments throughout the analysis, and only in late stages of treatment does an interpretation become complete, encompassing the origin both of ego elements and id derivatives. There may be no convention as to where in the series of interventions preparation ends and interpretation begins, but the disagreement is of little importance compared with the acknowledgment that there is a gradual transition from a preparation to interpretation.

There are conditions to which interpretation must be subordinated in order to produce insight. In making interpretations, dynamic, economic, and structural points of view have to be taken into consideration (Fenichel 1941, Glover 1931). I should like to attempt a more detailed classification of these conditions, which at the same time will aim at encompassing in greater detail the role of ego psychology in psychoanalytic technique.

Interpretations deal with the individual experiences of a human being. They aim at widening the conscious knowledge of the individual about himself and should therefore deal with the psychological realities

---

3. In all these stages of analysis the interpretation of mechanisms, as opposed to that of content, is significant.

of the individual. Psychoanalytic interpretations give a patient insight at a more generalized level than the insight he might gain from pure introspection, but much less abstract than are scientific formulations. For example, interpretations during psychoanalytic treatment aim at uncovering not, for instance, the Oedipus complex, but specific individual experiences which constitute the manifestations of the Oedipus complex of the person.

Interpretations may be characterized by the distance from the surface. The material communicated by the patient may move from the surface to the so-called depths, and it is important for the analyst to make his interpretations conform to this progression (Freud, *Coll. Papers* 2, chap. 28). The optimal distance from the surface of an interpretation may mean: (a) the known (to be convincing an interpretation has to include elements known to the patient besides the unknown which the interpretation aims to convey); (b) the present (there are interpretations which deal with current events and those which deal with the patient's past).

If one supposes that to seek among the innumerable memories of a human life precisely those which are relevant and curative would be comparable to looking for a needle in a haystack, fortunately the relevant repressed memories may be compared to a magnetic needle in iron filings. The latter, which in this comparison are the patient's associations, are influenced in a specific way by the pathogenic events of his past. In this respect one might say that the patient's past is in the present.

It has been said that Ferenczi once gave the advice: when a patient talks about the present, the analyst should talk about the past, and vice versa. He obviously meant that the goal of analysis is to uncover how the patient's present is related to his past. This advice implies that, in analytic therapy, interpretations aim at connecting the one with the other, and that this connection works both ways. Interpretations, consequently, deal also with what connects the past with the present. One knows that this is one reason that interpretations of transference are so effective. Transference, indeed, reactualizes the past.

Other characteristics of interpretations deal with the optimal range or the distance from the present interest. One knows that an interpretation cannot be given while the patient is overwhelmed by emotional reactions. The patient's reactions can be interpreted only when there is a certain distance from the emotions aroused by the events to be interpreted. For example, reactions of acute mourning are not subject to interpretation. Conversely, when the present situation is too far removed from certain conflicts, their interpretation has hardly any effect. As an example, we may cite what Freud says about the impossibility of analyzing dormant conflicts (Freud 1937).

Distance is also used in the sense of the accessibility of a patient to a given interpretation, which might be partly included in the previous considerations, but which may also be based on quite different factors: for instance, on the degree of progress of the analysis, or on the so-called degree of "depth" of an interpretation.

One might distinguish at what interpretations aim: (a) resistance as opposed to historical material; (b) ego phenomena as opposed to id derivatives; (c) transference as opposed to material which does not deal with the analyst.

We know that it is favorable to give interpretations in a certain sequence—that there is a hierarchy of interpretations. Under this heading can be placed the preparation for an interpretation, the rules of analyzing the resistances or the defenses before the id derivatives, as well as the choice between the interpretations of the transference as opposed to that part of the material which is not included in the patient's relations to the analyst (Freud, *Coll. Papers* 2, chap. 28 and 33).

Two other rules about the sequence of interpretation are: first, the avoidance of analyzing an important neurotic symptom in the beginning; second, the advice given by Anna Freud (1942) (in disagreement with Wilhelm Reich 1945) to start analyzing still mobile defense traits in preference to the rigid, characterologic defenses of neurotic characters.

It has frequently been said that an analysis proceeds in layers corresponding to the layered structure of the personality, and in reverse chronology. Heinz Hartmann has recently pointed out that this hardly ever happens. The structural approach to an understanding of the personality shows very clearly that the well-known stages of instinctual and ego development overlap and commingle in the course of an individual's life. Hartmann also stressed the fact that during the analytic process further reshuffling occurs, so that the process of analysis is not a mirror image of the psychological ontogeny (Hartmann 1951).

In this connection we should remember the well-known fact that correct interpretations often remain ineffective for a long time. For instance, some of the patients who in their own estimation "underpay" the analyst might be refractory to the effect of the treatment. Although adequate fees have certainly no therapeutic value in themselves, the unconscious use of such factors by some patients may create resistances to the most correct interpretations. Indeed we know that certain interventions and interpretations derive their particular efficacy from what Kris has called their positional value.[4] Freud compared them with the battles around a village or a hill which in peacetime had little importance in the life of a nation, but around which in wartime hinges the fate of a whole country (Freud 1920). Pursuing Freud's simile, one may say that some interpretations have tactical values, others aim at strategic objectives. These considerations may furnish clues to the understanding of successes in relatively short analytic treatments, as well as in psychotherapies by talented therapists.

The sequence, or hierarchy, of interpretation is closely connected with another point of importance—the timing. Under this topic fall considerations of avoiding premature and prematurely deep interpretations that frequently create stubborn resistances. A parallel can be drawn to the resistivity or fastness of certain micro-organisms produced by an untoward administration of certain drugs. While we do not have a complete explanation, we may assume that these phenomena are connected with the ego's use of intellectualization as a special form of defense (Freud 1920). Properly timed, an interpretation is made neither prematurely nor belatedly. It is important not to delay the analysis of resistance, transference, and problems arising from current situations. Under the heading of timing one might also include the repetition of interpretations and the process of working through (Freud, *Coll. Papers* 2, chap. 32).

Freud used the word "tact" to describe the importance of the correct timing of interpretation (Freud 1949). We might add that analytic tact (not to be confused with social tactfulness) is important not only in the choice of a moment in which to give or avoid an interpretation; it plays a role in technique on many more accounts. The word, used for lack of a more precise one, may be approximately defined as that intuitive evaluation of the patient's problems which leads the analyst to choose, among many possible interventions or interpretations, the one which is right at a given moment. Consequently, tact

---

4. Ernst Kris, personal communication.

equally entails evaluation of the extent to which optimally a patient should be gratified or frustrated through an interpretation—referred to as "dosage." An instance of gross tactlessness was reported by a patient about an analyst with whom he had previously been in analysis. One day the patient saw this analyst's cigar quietly burning on the floor. The patient coughed to awaken the analyst, and to the patient's observation that he had been asleep, the analyst replied: "You always want everybody's attention." This was true of the patient; but said at that moment, it could hardly have had a beneficial effect (Loewenstein 1930–31), first of all, because an analytic patient is entitled to have the attention of his analyst; but also because the analyst misused the correct observation in order to displace the guilt about having been asleep onto his patient. Had he made this remark at another time, it might have increased the patient's insight.

It is known that the wording of an interpretation considerably determines its dynamic effect. For instance, it is important to avoid psychoanalytic and theoretical terminology and to use the idiom of the patient's individual experience. Interpretations should be specific and concrete; they should also be worded so as to fit the individual situation.

The analysis of a compulsive neurotic patient required interpretation of the significance of a number of newly formed symptoms. I had to supply the terms lacking in the elliptic language of her obsessional thoughts, as expressed in her symptoms. I would propose an interpretation, to which she would respond: "It's almost that, but not completely so." Modifying my wording slightly, so as to correspond with her own thought, I would then succeed in making a correct interpretation. Then she would have visible vasomotor reactions, laugh, and acknowledge with unmistakable joy, "That's it." In such instances the symptoms would disappear temporarily. Another of my patients once reacted to an interpretation by saying, "You missed it by a hair's breadth."

Two technical rules of interpreting are based upon the importance of wording. First, the analyst should avoid using the same defense mechanism which his patient uses: for instance, avoid ironical expressions with patients who use irony as a defense. Second, interpretations gain when their wording explicitly or implicitly contains elements of time: such adverbs or phrases as "now," "before," "at the age of," or "after this happened," etc. Such interpretations are genetic, connect-

ing the patient's past with his present, and vice versa. The importance
of the correct wording of an interpretation is based on the fact that a
neurosis, its symptoms, and the pathogenic conflicts are not static but
dynamic phenomena which evolve with the patient's life. The function
of interpretations is to put into words the hidden conflicts underlying
the patient's symptoms; consequently, they must be adapted to the
specific relationship existing between the ego and id derivatives at a
given moment.

A married patient talked, during several sessions, of being sexually attracted to several women and mentioned the effort he had to
make to struggle against this attraction. Immediately following, he very
clearly expressed a wish to be loved by his analyst. This need to be
loved by a man at that moment was interpreted as a wish to be pro-
tected against the temptation exerted by women. It would not have
been sufficient to point out the oscillation between heterosexual and
homosexual tendencies; it was necessary that the wording of the interpretation imply also the structural conflict of the patient.

Freud called a certain type of interpretation "reconstructions"
(Freud, *Coll. Papers* 5, chap. 31). From the history, from associations,
from dreams, etc., the analyst deduces the existence of significant
events in the patient's past. Aside from these typical reconstructions,
analysts sometimes use another type of reconstruction of which I
should like to give a few examples.

Hartmann told me of a patient who had previously been analyzed
by Freud. When the patient recounted that in his puberty he had once
dreamed of having intercourse with both his mother and his sister,
Freud remarked that the patient must have been very much in love
with a girl at the time when he had this incestuous dream.

A patient who was familiar with analysis complained repeatedly, in
the beginning of his treatment, that his wife's behavior castrated him. I
suggested that what he actually wanted to express was his doubt about
his wife's loving him. Although his remarks about the castrating effect
of her behavior might have been genetically correct, it was important
at the time when this interpretation was given to point out the relevant
psychic reality—to transpose from a regressive level to a more superficial one. I would like to call this type of interpretation "reconstruction
upwards," historically as well as structurally. It is useful in the presence of regressive material, and aims, for instance, at reconstructing a
relatively recent pathogenic conflict, whence the regression started.

Sometimes it is particularly valuable to reconstruct a specific point, as, for example, a forgotten emotional state which must have been present during the process that led from the defense against a pathogenic conflict to regression and symptom formation.

An example from a case history written by Mrs. Bornstein (1949), is a young boy who had severe phobic states related to the birth of a sibling. In analysis, the boy's fantasies centered on a scene of a lonely boy, sitting in a hospital that had been destroyed by a fire in which all the babies and most of the mothers had burned to death. Among many possible interpretations, Mrs. Bornstein chose to tell the boy that he must have been very sad when his mother left for the hospital where she had the little baby.[5]

Another example of this kind occurred in the case of a brilliant, sophisticated young man who had a contemptuous ambivalence toward men, particularly toward his own father and father figures. The outbreak of war was then expected (in 1939 in France), and I informed my patient that in the event of war I would have to interrupt his treatment to join the army. He was not to be mobilized at that time. His aloof and nonchalant attitude toward the political situation continued, without a trace of emotional reaction of any kind, and his hostile attitude toward me became more conspicuous. The patient defended himself rigorously against sharing any emotions with other men. One day he suddenly remembered that during the first World War, when his father was a soldier in the French Army, he had spent hours drawing up elaborate comparative statistics of the respective armies, navies, and air forces. It was clear that his adolescent statistics were a magic defense against his unconscious death wishes, but mainly an expression of the wish that his father might survive and be victorious. My only interpretation at that point was to tell him that during the first World War he had been patriotic. The function and the aim of this interpretation were to bring to consciousness the strongly warded-off emotions and positive feelings both toward his father and toward the analyst, who like his father had to leave him to join the army.

The value of this particular type of interpretation is based upon the fact that an emotion partakes, as it were, of both ego and id derivatives and thus gives access to roads leading in both directions.

5. Anna Freud's examples of analysis of defense against emotions (1942).

We cannot conclude our inventory of interventions and interpretations without stressing that they cannot be studied independently from their corollary, the patient's reactions to them. Indeed, the dynamic effect of insight produced by interpretations manifests itself in the patient in an active psychic process. Interpretations bring forth new material, either in the form of resistance or in the form of additional details, memories, the flow of associations, information, and various changes in the intensity and in the form of symptoms, etc., revealing the dynamic effect of the interpretations. The therapeutic effects of analytic interpretations are displayed not only in objective and subjective changes in the patient, but also in verbal manifestations of, for instance, recollections formerly repressed.

It would be worth while to make a systematic study of the reactions of patients to interpretations, which might guide analysts in their successive interventions and interpretations. From such reactions analysts derive new knowledge about the patient for use in subsequent interpretations as the analysis progresses.

It has been discussed whether the remembering of forgotten events or only the work of overcoming resistances has a curative effect. The formulations given in this paper aim at a synthesis of these points of view by stating that the therapeutic effect of the analysis is due to a psychic process in which each part—the overcoming of resistances, the working through, as well as the remembering and reliving of repressed material and the effect of analytic reconstructions—has its respective place. They represent steps in the process of solving pathogenic conflicts.

I should like to add a few words about the peculiarities of interpretations and their effects. They are both based on the importance of speech in this peculiar interpersonal relationship—the psychoanalytic treatment. Freud's definition of the curative effect achieved by making the unconscious conscious was correctly supplemented by Nunberg when he stressed the importance of verbalization in analytic therapy (Nunberg 1948). This may be best illustrated by the example of cases of acting out. There we know that the therapeutic change can be achieved only when the tendency gratified in the acting is first inhibited and then verbally expressed: then its motivation can be transformed into insight. If the utterances of the analyst have this quite unusual, I would say unique, function of inducing dynamic changes in the patient by revealing to him new aspects of his own psychic reality, the patient's utterances, his communications to the analyst, contain emotional discharges in addition to mere thought; yet, they yield insight where acting alone does not. They are social acts binding for the individual. Is it not said that unspoken words are our slaves and spoken ones enslave us? Words, then, also subserve superego functions. Spoken words become social realities; verbalized thoughts and emotions of patients lead to socialization. In contrast to solitary thoughts or dreams, spoken words become objects created by the act of speaking. Hartmann stressed the importance of objectivation for the therapeutic effect of analysis. Freud said that thinking is a trial action. One could say of speech that it is a substitute for action. Speech, being between emotional expression and action, partaking of both, is an essential prerequisite of those dynamic changes which are produced by psychoanalytic treatment.

REFERENCES

Bornstein, B. (1949). The analysis of a phobic child. *Psychoanal. Study Child,* 3/4.

Federn, P. (1943). Psychoanalysis of psychosis. Part I: errors and how to avoid them. *Psychiatric Q.,* 17:3–19.

Fenichel, O. (1941). *Problems of Psychoanalytic Technique.* Albany: Psychoanal. Q.

Freud, A. (1946). *The Psychoanalytic Treatment of Children.* London: Imago Publ. Co.

——— (1942). *The Ego and the Mechanisms of Defense.* London: Hogarth Press.

Freud, S. (1920). *General Introduction to Psychoanalysis.* New York: Boni & Liveright.

——— (1922). *The Interpretation of Dreams.* London: Allen & Unwin.

——— (1937). Analysis terminable and intermination. *Int. J. Psychoanal.,* 18:373.

——— (1949). *The Question of Lay Analysis.* New York: Norton.

——— Papers on technique. The dynamics of transference. *Coll. Papers* 2, chap. 28.

——— Papers on technique. Recommendations for physicians on the psychoanalytic method of treatment. *Coll. Papers* 2, chap. 29.

——— Further recommendations in the technique of psychoanalysis. On beginning the treatment. The question of the first communications. The dynamics of the cure. *Coll. Papers* 2, chap. 31.

———— Further recommendations in the technique of psychoanalysis. Recollection, repetition and working through. *Coll. Papers* 2, chap. 32.

———— Further recommendations in the technique of psychoanalysis. Observations on transference-love. *Coll. Papers* 2, chap. 33.

———— Turnings in the ways of psychoanalytic therapy. *Coll. Papers* 2, chap. 34.

———— Fragment of a case of hysteria. *Coll. Papers* 3.

———— Notes upon a case of obsessional neurosis. *Coll. Papers* 3.

———— Papers on metapsychology. The unconscious. *Coll. Papers* 4, chap. 6.

———— Metapsychological supplement to the theory of dreams. *Coll. Papers* 4, chap. 7.

———— Constructions in analysis. *Coll. Papers* 5, chap. 31.

Glover, E. (1931). The therapeutic effect of inexact interpretation. *Int. J. Psychoanal.*, 12.

Hartmann, H. (1939). Ich-Psychologie und Anpassungsproblem. *Int. Ztschr. Psa.*, 24:parts 1/2.

———— (1951). Technical implications of ego psychology. *Psychoanal. Q.*, 20.

Kris, E. (1951). Ego psychology and interpretation in psychoanalytic therapy. *Psychoanal. Q.*, 20.

Loewenstein, R. M. (1930–31). Remarques sur le tact dans la technique psychoanalytique. *Rev. Franç. Psychanal.*, 4:266–75.

Nunberg, H. (1948). *Practice and Theory of Psychoanalysis.* New York: Nervous and Mental Disease Monographs.

Reich, W. (1945). *Character Analysis.* New York: Orgone Institute.

Stern, A. (1938). Psychoanalytic investigation of and therapy in the borderline group of neuroses. *Psychoanal. Q.*, 7:467–89.

2

Ego Development and Psychoanalytic Technique

For many years scientific interest in psychoanalysis was mainly concerned with the instinctual aspects of pathogenic conflicts. These studies culminated in the discovery of childhood sexuality, its development, and its impact on adult life.

Although from the beginning Freud stressed repeatedly the importance for therapy of analyzing the patient's resistances, the study of these resistances was not systematically undertaken until the 1920s. This became possible through the introduction of the structural point of view.

It was to Anna Freud's work that we owe the practical application of the structural concept to psychoanalytic therapy. We observe in every patient what types of defense mechanisms exist in him, whether repression, projection, identification, etc. We study patients' motives and their aims; we analyze what they achieve and what consequence their presence has for a given individual. We also observe in the history of each patient the various types of dangers that the ego tries to avert.

It is indeed possible to discern, in conflicts, anxiety centered around the fear of loss of love, the fear of loss of an object, castration anxiety, and so-called superego anxiety, which is best known as guilt feeling.

A frequent symptom of compulsion neurotics is anxiety that something dreadful might happen to someone close to them. We know that these fears are generally based on warded-off unconscious aggressive

Paper read in the section on psychoanalysis at the 106th Annual Meeting of the American Psychiatric Association, Detroit, Mich., May 1–5, 1950.

tendencies toward the person concerned. The aim of psychoanalytic treatment is the patient's gaining of insight into these aggressive tendencies, because this leads to the disappearance of the symptom. One possible way of achieving this result would be to tell the patient that his anxiety is based on aggressive and hostile feelings toward the person concerned. Usually such an interpretation would do more harm than good. Indeed, the symptom is based on the fact that the patient's ego is unable to tolerate the existence of such tendencies. An interpretation of the kind we have just mentioned does not make the ego more capable than before of solving the conflict between the warded-off tendency and the powerful forces that oppose it.

Long ago Freud established this important rule of psychoanalytic technique: namely, that the resistances should be analyzed first, that is, those forces that the ego opposes to the repressed drives. However, for a long time there existed no detailed and systematic study of how to proceed to analyze these resistances. Nowadays we are better equipped.

I remember the case of a girl in her twenties, who presented the symptom just mentioned—the anxiety that some harm might occur to her beloved mother. The analysis went through a prolonged, circuitous route, through various aspects of the patient's complicated relationship toward her mother, before the girl was able to become aware of strongly warded-off hostile feelings toward her. In the analysis gradually the at first vague content of the anxiety became more concrete, more precise. First we encountered the fear of being punished by her mother's disappearance or death, with which the patient was threatened in childhood when she misbehaved. The patient as a girl and adolescent was afraid not only of being abandoned by the beloved mother, but also of being left unprotected against her own sexual desires, which the mother's presence helped to ward off. The dreaded danger also meant something else: it represented the terrible, mysterious sexual things that the father would do to the mother, and that the jealous little girl frantically wished to prevent from happening. Only then was it possible to approach the other side of this patient's feelings toward her mother: namely, that in all these situations there was not only love for her mother, fear of losing her, but also the opposite feeling: resentment for standing in the way of gratification of the various instinctual drives connected with the situations just mentioned.

This extremely brief summary of various steps in the analysis of a patient is an example of the way we gradually achieve a greater tolerance of the patient's ego toward the warded-off drives.

Now, as a matter of fact, the example just cited shows that there has been no fundamental change in the analytic technique. The increase in the tolerance of the patient's ego to his unconscious drives has always been sought for. It is now, however, being achieved with greater security and greater ease. This also makes accessible to analysis certain patients or certain of their symptoms that hitherto were not. Moreover, the example described reveals a shift of emphasis as compared to the past. Indeed the area of interest of the psychoanalyst is widened; it is not exclusively concerned with the uncovering of the earliest forms of pathogenic conflicts. The interest of the analyst dwells for a long time on all the intermediates between the original conflict and its present manifestations. That is actually no fundamental change in the psychoanalytic technique either. Freud formulated the relationship of the past and the present in the pathogenesis of neurosis by comparing it to a damage wrought by fire to a building. The original source of the fire does not always cause the greatest damage. This might very well result from a secondary site of the fire. The therapist has to take this into account.

The scientific interest in the importance of very early stages of instinctual development formerly led some analysts to concentrate their interest, even during treatment, exclusively on them. We do not nowadays minimize their importance, but we know better that the neglect of later events and phases is not only unwarranted but might even have unfavorable therapeutic consequences. Let me give you another example:

Many years ago I saw a patient in a state of violent anxiety. This man in his early fifties, when first entering my office, started by repeatedly asking me, with tears in his eyes, what it meant to be castrated and what castration was. I learned that this man had been in analysis for many years in another country. The symptoms that had led him to treatment five years before were obsessional preoccupations with sensations in the rectum in the presence of other men. During the years of his previous treatment his anxiety did not diminish; on the contrary, it seemed to worsen. His previous analyst had explained to him that his rectal sensations were based on passive homosexual desires, originating in early childhood. He told the patient that in order to overcome his symptom, he had to recall the wish to be castrated and to relive feminine sexual desires of an anal nature toward his father, which he was supposed to have experienced at the age of two. The poor patient could never remember having had wishes or sensations of that kind. However, when we talked about his conflicts of a moral and religious nature, centering around masturbation and sex life in puberty, he soon told me of an event that apparently had been completely neglected by the other analyst. The patient, having in adolescence struggled for years vainly against masturbation, went to a big city and had intercourse with a prostitute. Immediately after intercourse, he thought he had contracted gonorrhea. He soon consulted a so-called "specialist," whose advertisement he had read in a paper. The doctor told him that he did have gonorrhea, and added that he would give the patient a massage, during which he would experience a special sensation in the rectum. The patient underwent a very painful prostatic massage, and, terrified, left the city. Fortunately, he was able to consult another doctor in his home town, who found him in perfect health. This event at the age of seventeen was essential in the structure of his later symptom, consisting of rectal sensations in the presence of men. They appeared years later, when the patient for the first time had satisfactory heterosexual activity. To the patient this traumatic event unconsciously meant that rectal sensations inflicted by another man were punishment for forbidden heterosexual activity. The later obsessional symptoms, indeed, were not just a break-through of passive homosexual tendencies. The patient's anxiety rather expressed his guilt feelings, the fear of punishment for prohibited heterosexual gratifications, so that one could speak in this patient of a partial regression that served as a defense against the danger of castration.

What we have been dealing with up to now was mainly the shift of emphasis in the understanding of the structure of neuroses, which has been brought about by the introduction of ego psychology. We would now like to emphasize that it also led to improvements in the details of the technical procedure itself. Psychoanalysis brings about insight in patients by means of various interventions. Among the interventions, interpretations are characteristic and specific for the psychoanalytic technique.

Webster's Dictionary defines interpretation as the act of explaining, elucidating, telling the meaning of, translating orally into intelligible language. In analysis we apply this term to those explanations we give patients that add to their knowledge about themselves from elements contained and expressed in the patient's own thoughts, feelings, words, and behavior.

The analyst uses interpretations in order to produce those dynamic changes that we call insight. Interpretations are given to patients in analysis to produce insight into thoughts and feelings of which the patient is not aware. Among other things, the patient must gain insight into the resistances that he opposes to his treatment.

This might seem paradoxical. Are not resistances due to defenses of the ego, and is not the ego something essentially conscious? This is not so; indeed patients have only a very incomplete awareness of their resistances. A patient might at a certain time be reluctant to continue his treatment. Of this he may be perfectly aware. It is the analyst's task to show him that this sudden reluctance to continue is, for instance, due to the fact, concealed by the patient at first, that he would have to tell the analyst some unpleasant thought he had about him. When we speak of resistances, we mean to have the patient gain insight into the connection between his reluctance to continue and the fear of revealing a hostile thought. And at a later stage this resistance will be linked to other instances in the patient's life in which he would choose to remain sick rather than express hostility and competition with another man.

Since resistances are in themselves partly unconscious, one must take into account that a very important part of the ego remains unconscious, so that an important part of the analyst's interpretations aim at bringing to consciousness unconscious ego phenomena. As we know, bringing to consciousness is not merely an intellectual process; it presupposes and implies dynamic changes that are prerequisites for what we call analytic insight.

Ego psychology had deep effects on the special criteria that analysts try to establish for the correctness and effectiveness of their interpretations. If one compares the character of interpretations as they were given in the early phases of psychoanalysis with those used more recently, one is struck by one obvious difference: formerly, symbolic interpretations played a much greater part in the analyst's everyday work than they do nowadays. This change is not due to the fact that we consider symbolism less true than before. It is not the frequency of symbolic expressions that has changed; it is the frequency of the use that the analyst makes of symbolic interpretations of the patient's material. If a girl has a phobia of being run over by cars, the car as a symbol for a man is as true now as it was thirty years ago. Our interest, however, is centered not only on this fact, but equally on the motive and the reasons for this patient's fear.

Nowadays analysts are very much concerned with what one might call the hierarchy of interpretations. In the cases I have described earlier, there are examples in point. Indeed, I have stressed in one example the importance of analyzing defenses before analyzing the id derivatives—the motives for the fear of hurting a beloved person before analyzing repressed hostility against this person. In the other example, the one in which it was so essential for the cure of the patient to relate his symptoms to the prostatic massage, it was a concern with another aspect of the hierarchy of pathogenic events and consequently of interpretations. Analytic interpretations now follow more deliberately the general rule enunciated by Freud, in which he advised the analyst to follow the patient's material from the surface to the so-called depth. In this respect, what we call the surface of the patient's material has various meanings. It relates to what is conscious to the patient, as opposed to what is unconscious. It relates to the present or the recent past, inasmuch as it is influenced by the patient's past; and the interpretations must take into account this specific relationship between the past and the present. One might say that in respect to all these various aspects, which we call the psychological surface, interpretations in order to be effective must be at an optimal distance from the surface. Their effectiveness is impaired if they are too close to the surface, or if they are too far removed from it. This notion of optimal distance or range of interpretations for their effectiveness is a direct result of what we know now about the ego's defensive functions.

The wording of interpretations is sometimes an essential factor in promoting insight. The importance of wording is due to the fact that interpretations must deal with concrete psychological realities of a given individual. The interpretation must also take into account the same conflict in one and the same patient, varied in its significance from one moment in life to another, so that the interpretations have to take into account the specific relationship of the conflict between the ego, superego, and the id, at a given moment.

Tact is an important factor in the way interpretations are given in analysis. Timing, which is part of the problem of tact, is essential because the therapeutic procedure, like the neuroses itself, is not a static phenomenon but a dynamic process. And you know that in this dynamic process, which is the psychoanalytic therapy, a complex rela-

tionship develops between the patient and the analyst, of which transference phenomena are the core. Interpretations, consequently, have
to take into account the fact that, in the transference, ego defenses,
superego, and id functions operate. This explains the fact that frequently patients react to interpretations in a way not directly connected with the actual meaning of an interpretation: lack of
psychoanalytic tact in the sequence of interpretations brings about
quite unexpected results, sometimes. If a patient's aggressive reactions
are being interpreted before his defensive reactions to them have been
analyzed, certain patients respond not to the actual meaning of an
interpretation, but react as though the analyst were reproaching them
for their alleged nastiness. This might have a bearing on certain types
of patients who are being analyzed for psychosomatic disturbances. If
their psychosomatic symptoms are being interpreted as expressing
their unconscious tendencies, they sometimes react with a serious in-
tensification of their symptoms. For these patients it means that they
are not only sick but that they are made responsible—that means
blamed—for their illness.

One important consequence of the impacts of ego psychology on
the psychoanalytic technique, introduced by Anna Freud, is the
analysis of defenses against emotions. Pathogenic conflicts between
instinctual drives and defenses do not stop there. They are being carried on to conflicts about emotions. Anna Freud pointed out that in
certain cases it is impossible to achieve any therapeutic result, to reach
the deeper pathogenic conflict, without first having overcome defenses
against emotions connected with the past. Sometimes this process
takes the form of what I proposed calling "reconstruction upwards." A
beautiful example of it is from a case history written by Mrs. Berta
Bornstein.

The patient, a young boy, had severe phobic states related to the
birth of a sibling. In the treatment the boy's fantasies centered around
an imagined scene of a lonely boy, sitting in a hospital that took fire,
during which all the babies and most of the mothers were burned to
death. Mrs. Bornstein chose, among many possible interpretations, to
tell the boy that he must have been very sad when his mother left for
the hospital, where she had the little baby.

Nowadays, when one sees so many patients who have read
psychiatric or psychoanalytic books, this procedure of reconstructing
upwards is sometimes essential. These patients indeed start by talking

about their Oedipus complex, their unconscious homosexuality, they interpret their dreams symbolically, and evade by this very fact all the so-called more superficial but actual psychological realities of their emotional life. The task of the analyst then is to bring the patient's attention to this part of his life, which is the only real and relevant part. Reconstructions upwards are a most helpful type of interpretation in those cases.

We know that the ego develops gradually, and we assume now that both ego and id develop gradually through differentiation from a previous common, undifferentiated stage. However, it has not been possible to find as yet specific correlations between the formation of defense mechanisms and specific stages of instinctual development.

It is striking that certain types of defense mechanisms are, as it were, preferred by certain individuals and not by others. These defense mechanisms can be found at work in them again and again at various periods and in various situations in their lives. The predominance of certain types of defense mechanisms is probably not so much the question of individuals as of neurotic types. One knows, for instance, that isolation, undoing, and regression are found particularly among obsessional neurotics, and that in neuroses of the hysterical type repression seems to play a predominant role. However, repression is never absent in compulsive neurotics either. One knows the intimate relationships that exist between projection and paranoid symptoms, and the frequency of introjection in depressive states. Unfortunately, it does not seem possible for the time being to make a nosological classification of mental illnesses on the basis of distribution of defense mechanisms. As a matter of fact, in adults one hardly ever observes isolated defense mechanisms, but groups of them working together. So it might well be worthwhile to look in given patients for certain characteristic "patterns of defense used against certain patterns of instinctual drives."[1]

In successful psychoanalytic treatment of neurotic patients we know what happens to their warded-off instinctual drives. Some of these drives, hitherto repressed, are being made available to the individual. Another part is supposed to remain unsatisfied, but instead of being repressed is being consciously suppressed. We imply thus that at least to a certain extent the defensive mechanism of repression is being

1. As Dr. Ernst Kris put it in a discussion.

replaced by another defensive mechanism, conscious suppression. We also know that sometimes the defense through repression is being partly replaced by sublimation. One might hope that studies will be made of what happens to the other defensive mechanisms during the psychoanalytic treatment. It will certainly be a worthwhile object of research. However, one might already state that psychoanalysis does not result in doing away with them. The existence of all mechanisms of defense—even repression and projection—are necessary functions of the normal human mind. Here, as in all other areas of medical re-search, it can be found that the difference between normal and pathological is not one of essence but only one of degree.[2] It is certain that those ego mechanisms that function as defense mechanisms exist also in the normal functions of the ego for the very reason that conflict is not identical with mental illness. For this very reason, further re-search on the vicissitudes of these mechanisms in psychoanalytic treatment will also be important in a study of what Hartmann called various forms of mental health.

The functions of the ego are not limited to defense mechanisms. Among the authors who have made important contributions to normal ego psychology, I should like to name: Paul Federn, Thomas M. French, Edward Glover, Heinz Hartmann, Ives Hendrick, Ernst Kris, Herman Nunberg, Robert Waelder. More recently Heinz Hartmann introduced the important concept of the conflictless sphere of the ego, or of autonomous ego functions, and studied their role in problems of adjustment.

Psychoanalysis, since its inception, has always had a two-fold func-tion: If on the one hand it was a therapy, on the other hand it was a method of scientific research, which has had a tremendous influence on other psychotherapeutic procedures and on general psychopathology. The study of the ego development has enriched the psychoanalytic therapy. It has widened the area of its application; it has considerably improved its results. That this progress in psychoanalysis will have an equally stimulating influence in psychiatry, there can be no doubt.

2. This does not exclude the fact that quantitative differences might lead to qualita-tively different phenomena.

REFERENCES

Alexander, F. (1930). *Psychoanalysis of the Total Personality*. New York and Washington: Nervous and Mental Disease Publ. Co.

Bornstein, B. (1949). The analysis of a phobic child. *Psychoanal. Study Child*, 3/4.

Breuer, J., & Freud, S. (1936). *Studies in Hysteria*. New York: Nervous and Mental Disease Publ. Co.

Fenichel, O. (1941). *The Problem of Psychoanalytic Technique*. Albany: Psychoanal. Q.

―――― (1945). *The Psychoanalytic Theory of Neurosis*. New York: Norton.

Freud, A. (1942). *The Ego and the Mechanisms of Defense*. London: Hogarth Press.

Freud, S. (1947). *The Ego and the Id*. London: Hogarth Press.

―――― (1948). *Inhibitions, Symptoms, and Anxiety*. London: Hogarth Press.

―――― (1933). *New Introductory Lectures*. New York: Norton.

―――― (1920). *General Introduction to Psychoanalysis*. New York: Boni and Liveright.

―――― Fragment of a case of hysteria. *Coll. Papers* 3.

―――― Notes upon a case of obsessional neurosis. *Coll. Papers* 3.

―――― (1922). *The Interpretation of Dreams*. London: Allen & Unwin.

―――― The dynamics of transference. *Coll. Papers* 2.

―――― Recommendations for physicians on the psychoanalytic method of treatment. *Coll. Papers* 2.

―――― Further recommendations in the technique of psychoanalysis. *Coll. Papers* 2.

―――― Turnings in the ways of psychoanalytic therapy. *Coll. Papers* 2.

―――― (1949). *The Question of Lay Analysis*. New York: Norton.

―――― (1937). Analysis terminable and interminable. *Int. J. Psychoanal.*, 18:373.

―――― (1938). Constructions in analysis. *Int. J. Psychoanal.*, 19:377 and *Coll. Papers* 5.

Glover, E. (1947). *The Basic Mental Concepts*. London: Imago Publ. Co.

Hartmann, H. (1947). On rational and irrational action. In *Psychoanalysis and the Social Sciences*, ed. Geza Roheim.

―――― The Relationship between the Theory of Analysis and Psychoanalytic Technique, in press.

Hartmann, H., Kris, E. & Loewenstein, R. M. (1946). Comments on the formation of psychic structure. *Psychoanal. Study Child*, 2.

―――― (1949). Notes on the theory of aggression. *Psychoanal. Study Child*, 3/4.

Loewenstein, R. M. (1951). The problem of interpretation. *Psychoanal. Q.*, 20.

Reich, W. (1945). *Character Analysis*. New York: Orgone Institute.

3

Some Remarks on Defenses, Autonomous Ego, and Psychoanalytic Technique

I. HISTORICAL INTRODUCTION

Psychoanalytic treatment since its very beginning has been used as an experimental set-up which permits generalizations applicable not only to therapy and to psychopathology, but beyond these, to normal psychology as well. The present report will take account of all these aspects of psychoanalysis.

In most of the fundamental and pathogenic conflicts which he found to be at the origin of neurotic disorders, Freud studied at first more completely that side of the conflict which encompassed the instinctual drives. The study of the forces opposing the drives was undertaken later. These forces are observable, in the experimental set-up represented by the psychoanalytic treatment, in the phenomena of resistance. Although the concept of defense mechanisms in the pathogenesis of neuroses had been used by Freud very early, and although the study of the main defense mechanism (repression) was very far advanced (Freud 1915), the application of this concept to psychoanalytic technique did not go beyond a purely descriptive classification of resistances.

Freud's theoretical contributions in the twenties brought about a decisive advance (Freud 1921, 1923, 1926). His reformulation of the theory of anxiety—leading from, as it were, a physiological to a more biological plane (Kris 1951c)—was better apt to describe man in relation to his environment. Furthermore, by introducing the structural

Paper read in the symposium "Mechanisms of Defense and their Place in Psychoanalytic Technique" at the 18th International Psychoanalytical Congress, London, July 29, 1953.

point of view, Freud created the conceptual tools necessary for this shift. The introduction of the concepts of id, ego, and superego permitted a more adequate description of the psychic functions of man within his physical, biological, and social environment. Moreover, the conception of anxiety as a signal of danger encompassed the individual history of danger situations and, consequently, of motives for defense. Thus it laid the basis for our present concept of defense mechanisms; i.e., of the various means by which the ego deals with the outside world, the instinctual drives and the moral forces within.

Among the authors who in the late twenties and the thirties contributed in important degree to the application of these advances in ego psychology to the psychoanalytic technique, I should like to mention here Franz Alexander (1930), Wilhelm Reich (1927, 1928), and, most particularly, Anna Freud (1937). Anna Freud's contribution has been the most decisive and the most fruitful for the progress in psychopathology and normal psychology, as well as in psychoanalytic technique.

Turning now to the more recent developments in the field of ego psychology, I have time only to emphasize Hartmann's concept of the conflictless sphere of the ego, or, as he has since decided to call it, of the autonomous ego functions (Hartmann 1939, 1950; Hartmann, Kris, and Loewenstein 1946). I believe that we can apply this concept with great advantage to the understanding of certain problems of psychoanalytic technique.

II. APPLICATIONS TO TECHNIQUE

1. Defense Mechanisms in the Analytic Situation

We know that a precondition for psychoanalytic work is a certain integrity of the patient's ego, whose alliance with the analyst is essential for the success of the psychoanalytic treatment (Freud 1917). This alliance enables the patient to overcome his unconscious resistances against the treatment and the cure (Sterba 1934). It is obvious that this alliance is not made with that unconscious part of the patient's ego which comprises the defenses, but with its conflictless sphere. Indeed, the intactness of the patient's perceptions, of his memory, his thinking, his reality testing, of his capacity for self-observation and understanding of others, and of his faculty for verbal expression, is indispensable in psychoanalysis. To be sure, we know that our alliance with the patient's autonomous ego would be precarious without the transference; i.e., without the tendency of the drives to come to the fore, to find gratifications in the outside world. It is in the analysis that one best observes how much the functioning of the autonomous ego can be impaired by the unconscious. But, on the other hand, we know that only this alliance with the patient's intact ego functions permits us to overcome the power of his resistance.

In the analytic situation, the analyst plays a double role for the patient. From the point of view of the id, he becomes the object of his drives in the transference. From the point of view of the ego, the analyst represents to the patient an additional, autonomous ego more capable than his own of resisting the distorting influence both of the defenses and of the drives. The analyst himself works with relatively intact autonomous functions, provided they are not impaired by countertransference (Loewenstein 1952; Hartmann, Kris, and Loewenstein 1946, 1949, 1953).

Essentially, the task of the psychoanalytic treatment has been defined as enabling the patient to find a new solution to the pathogenic conflicts which formerly had led to neurotic symptoms. This is achieved by submitting the patient's conflict between his drives and defenses to the scrutiny of his autonomous ego. By this means, and with the aid of the analyst's autonomous ego, the patient attains a better tolerance for the pressures of his id, which before had been warded off by unconscious defense. Both the instinctual drives and the defense must be brought to consciousness; that is to say, subjected to the scrutiny of the autonomous ego.

2. *Relationship between Defense Mechanisms and Resistances*

Although the ego defenses might be said to represent the bulk of resistance to psychoanalytic treatment (A. Freud 1937), two considerations should be kept in mind. Resistances may also be due to instinctual drives. I need only mention, for example, the patient's intolerance to libidinal frustration, or illness as a source of masochistic or of aggressive gratification, etc.[1] On the other hand, it is an essential condition for the treatment that a certain degree of defense be maintained in the

---

1. In *The Problem of Anxiety*, Freud (1926) distinguished resistances due to the ego, to the id, and the superego.

analytic situation. The patient is able to overcome his defenses, to gain insight and to give verbal expression to warded-off drives, provided that defense is maintained against action, that is, against actual sexual or aggressive gratifications in the analytic situation. It is the patient's awareness that such transgression into action will not take place which permits the partial lifting of defenses that is aimed at in analysis.

3. The Influence of Ego Psychology on Psychoanalytic Technique

The study of defense mechanisms has been an essential part of the much wider field of ego-psychological investigation. These studies have had a very significant influence on psychoanalytic technique, and in discussing them we cannot limit ourselves to the defensive aspect of the ego alone. Ego psychology has greatly increased our understanding of the analytic procedure itself; it has enabled us to proceed with greater ease and assurance in that part of our work which we place under the heading of analysis of resistances; it has improved our therapeutic results in many instances; it has made accessible to analysis cases and symptoms where otherwise no results could be obtained. The better understanding we have thus gained of the analytic procedure and method has, in its turn, enriched our knowledge in the realm of pathological and normal psychology (Bergler 1937; Bibring 1937; Fenichel 1937; A. Freud 1937; Freud 1923; Gero 1951; Hartmann 1951; Kris 1951a; Loewenstein 1951a, 1951b; Nunberg 1937).

Important though this influence of ego psychology has been, it has brought about no fundamental change in psychoanalytic technique, but rather a shift of emphasis which, however, has had significant consequences. This shift of emphasis has manifested itself notably in three directions:

(1) As compared to the past, we now pay increased attention not only to early childhood but also to events and conflicts occurring in our patients in later life and in the present.

(2) We dwell nowadays, more deliberately and more persistently than we might have done in the past, on the resistance and on the ego aspect of the patient's productions.

(3) We accord greater attention to the patient's autonomous ego functions and the role they exert on conflict solution, on the choice of pathways of gratification, and, possibly, on choice of defense (Hartmann 1950; Hartmann, Kris, and Loewenstein 1953; Kris 1951b).

This shift of emphasis is but the systematic elaboration of Freud's advice that analysis of resistances should take precedence over analysis of id derivatives. We might suggest that what we call analysis of resistances inevitably ties in with analysis of the patient's way of reacting to his treatment in general as well as to specific interventions and interpretations (Glover 1931; Loewenstein 1930–31).

The understanding of ego psychology permits a more adequate assessment and comprehension of the rationale for a number of rules which guide our interventions and interpretations.

The interest of analysis does not, as is sometimes erroneously thought, focus on the past alone, but on the interrelationship between past and present: the influence of the past upon the present and, paradoxical though it may sound, of the present upon the past. The paramount role which the analysis of transference plays in psychoanalytic technique is based on this particular interconnection we find between the past and the present in human life.

In this context, we may also be reminded of Freud's general advice that the analysis should proceed from the so-called "surface" to the so-called "depth" (Freud 1912, 1913). The term "surface" can mean several things (Loewenstein 1951a). One of them, obviously, is the patient's present reality situation and his present interest. Another meaning refers to what is known to the patient, encompassing both the conscious and the preconscious accessible to his awareness, which might in turn provide a gauge for the degree of his tolerance or the intensity of his defense against certain drives. The surface also comprises the state and the nature of conflicts between drives and defenses at a given moment of the analysis. We know that the efficiency of interpretations is bound up with what might be called an optimal distance from the surface.

The term surface applies, likewise, to all the aspects of the patient's mental life which are at the disposal of his autonomous ego functions. By interpreting the defenses first, we submit the defensive functions to the scrutiny of the autonomous ego, thereby enabling the patient to deal better with previously warded-off id derivatives.

As a counterpart of this technical rule to give precedence to interpretations of resistance and defense, I should like to cite Freud's warning against so-called "deep" interpretations at the beginning of an analysis. Again, this term may have various connotations. It may refer to reconstructions of the remote past, including two alternatives. One is the reconstruction of dormant conflicts (Freud 1937), which will

either have no effect at all or will serve the patient as a welcome means
of flight from much more disturbing, currently dominant conflicts. The
other alternative is the reconstruction of the past involving nondor-
mant conflicts. The latter interventions are comparable to the other
variety of so-called deep interpretations, those which aim at strongly
warded-off id derivatives. We are all aware of the adverse effects such
interventions may entail when they reactivate drives with which the
patient is not yet prepared to deal. To enumerate but a few:

There are patients who respond to such untoward or untimely
interpretations by interrupting the analysis or who, as a result of highly
intensified defenses, experience needless suffering or a serious aggravation of their illness. Or there may be a severe increase of guilt
feelings, particularly in persons who have a tendency to moral masochism, with the same unfortunate consequences. Some patients react to
predominantly deep interpretations with acting out (Greenacre 1950).

It is believed that in child analysis incautious id interpretations
may possibly endanger existing sublimations, and we know that this
danger might also arise in the analytic treatment of adolescents and of
some adults.

Interpretations in depth are usually achieved by means of bringing
to the fore the patient's thought processes in terms of the primary
process. In certain cases, mostly of the borderline type, this may cause
the primary process to exert such influence upon the patient that his
reality testing may become seriously impaired.

It is well known that a particular affinity exists between passive
homosexual tendencies and paranoid symptoms. Many patients, it is
true, can tolerate a reactivation of such tendencies without psychotic
reactions. But others, especially latent psychotics or prepsychotics,
respond to interpretations aiming at their homosexual tendencies with
an ego regression that manifests itself in paranoid symptoms.

Generally speaking, consistent id interpretation without analysis
on the ego level risks bringing about an impasse in the treatment,
which may well become interminable.

An impasse may equally result from the use of analytic terms as
intellectual defense or, in certain obsessionals, as magic formulae designed to ward off anxiety. Nowadays, we frequently encounter this
intellectual defense in cultured and well-read persons who start their
analysis well provided with a knowledge of analytic terminology or
procedure. In speaking of themselves, these patients use such terms as

Oedipus complex, frustration, anxiety, homosexuality, etc., thereby evading the actual thoughts and emotions they experience. One of my patients tried to misuse his knowledge of analysis for what might be called a "flight into the past." His visits to me required some traveling. Before he came to one of his preliminary sessions, he dreamed that I had asked him to do me the favor of coming twice a week, to which he replied in the dream: "I'll be very glad to come even three times." In reality the necessity of coming more frequently, together with some disappointment on his part concerning the fee, produced the following reactions in the first few weeks of the analysis. On the one hand, he very soon manifested an exaggerated admiration for the analyst. On the other hand, his dreams expressing ambivalent feelings towards a man were consistently attributed by him to hostility towards his dead father, of which there was, however, no trace in his conscious memories. It was not an easy task to convince this obsessional patient that his hostility at this stage was aimed at the analyst who had started out by disappointing him.

Although interpretations of this kind have always been used in psychoanalysis, they had not been specifically discussed. I therefore suggested designating them by the term "reconstruction upwards" (Loewenstein 1951a). You will remember that Freud in his case history of the Rat Man (Freud 1909) relates how he used his knowledge of the patient's childhood conflicts, gained through the usual reconstructions of the past (Freud 1937), as a basis for such reconstruction upwards of the exact, recent events which had precipitated a relapse of the obsessional neurosis.

Reconstructions upwards have to be used in dealing with regressive behavior or material of the patient; for instance, when anal-sadistic fantasies are interpreted as the result of a regression from oedipal conflicts at the phallic level. Sometimes the reconstruction upwards aims at an emotion, in order to undo resistances achieved by means of regressive wording. A patient of mine, describing how he would hide from his wife the books he bought for himself, said about her: "My wife is castrating me." I interpreted this by saying that he must doubt whether his wife loved him. Although the patient's remark about being castrated by his wife was not without symbolic validity, it was not in its right place and served as an escape from his emotions.

The importance we attach to interpretations on an ego level is reflected also in the attention we bring in our work to wording, tact, working through, etc. (Fenichel 1939; Loewenstein 1951a). Unfortunately, lack of time forces me to omit these manifold facets of our technique in which the influence of ego psychology is clearly exemplified.

III. THE MECHANISMS OF DEFENSE

The study of defense mechanisms can be and has been undertaken from various points of view. Long ago, Freud stressed the predominant role of repression in neuroses of the hysterical type, whereas in compulsive neuroses he described, beside the repression, the frequency of regression and of isolation and reaction formation. He likewise pointed out the predominant role of projection in paranoid symptoms. However, it has not been possible as yet to base a classification of neuroses entirely upon types of defense mechanisms (Freud 1926).

On the other hand, Anna Freud has emphasized the consistency of certain types of these mechanisms in the history and throughout the analysis of some individual patients. There is also the problem of the chronology in the appearance of defense mechanisms, which might have an important impact on the development of the individual (A. Freud 1937). It may very well be that the study of certain defense patterns against specific drive patterns might prove fruitful.[2] Yet another aspect is what Waelder (1936) has called the multiple function, which will serve to remind us of the intimate interconnections between all psychic functions.

Thus, the complex relationship between defense mechanisms and instinctual drives offers a worthwhile area of research. It appears that repression does away with the warded-off drive, whereas regression and reversal into the opposite result in a substitution of one form of drive for another. Turning against the self and some forms of introjection change the direction or the object, but not the drive and its aim. Isolation, in turn, seems to deal not so much with the drives themselves as with the emotions related to them. It has been pointed out that projection may result in a gratification of masochistic tendencies (Bak 1946; Waelder 1936). On the other hand, projection in itself may imply an aggressive act. A further example of the intimate interrelation between defense and drives can be seen in the so-called "sour grapes

2. Ernst Kris, personal communication.

reaction," which in devaluating the object serves as a defense or protection against disappointment and frustration by means of turning
passivity into activity, and which, by the same token, gratifies vengeful
tendencies.

Of great promise, also, is the point of view which scrutinizes the
defense mechanisms in relation to the autonomous ego functions of
integration, organization, and adaptation (French 1938; Hartmann
1939, 1950; Nunberg 1931).

To conclude this enumeration of our various avenues of study, I
should like to focus on two areas in which but little is known so far.

One is the vicissitudes of defense mechanisms under the impact of
psychoanalytic treatment. We know that repression is partly replaced
by conscious suppression or by sublimation;[3] we also know that defense
mechanisms are not caused to vanish by the treatment, since they are
essential parts of a normal personality; but we do not know enough
about their modifications as a result of psychoanalytic treatment.

The second problem refers to the nature and development of
defense mechanisms against superego demands.[4] Denial of guilt, displacement and projection seem to be among the very early and primitive forms of this type of defense. Identification with the aggressor, as
described by Anna Freud, is apparently a more highly elaborated version of these primitive mechanisms. (There still remains to be examined the relationship between primitive mechanisms of defense against
the superego, on the one hand, and primitive forms of superego
functioning on the other.)

Most ego mechanisms of defense against superego demands will
center around the way in which an individual deals with the conscious
manifestations of the superego; I mean remorse and guilt feeling. Thus,
guilt feeling might itself become a form of self-punishment; but this
punishment, paradoxically, might also be achieved by the compulsive
repetition of the forbidden act. This relationship would emerge more
clearly if psychoanalytic theory were using demonological language,
since the devil represents the instinctual drives as well as the punishment for them (Loewenstein 1945). The complex, dynamic connections

---

3. If sublimation is to be considered a defense mechanism at all (Hartmann, Kris,
and Loewenstein 1949).

4. Dr. Hoffer has drawn my attention to a similar idea expressed by Fenichel in *The
Psychoanalytic Theory of Neurosis* (p. 132): "the ego develops a double countercathexis,
one against the instincts and another against the superego."

in the relationship between ego and superego are manifested in the consequences, for pathology, of what one might term disregard of superego demands. I allude here to neurotic symptoms, psychosomatic disorders, and self-inflicted accidents.

Of particular importance and interest, for both practical and theoretical reasons, are those defenses against superego demands which lead to a partial or complete disappearance of guilt feelings in certain patients. We are dealing here with mechanisms that may in some respects be akin to a real repression with consecutive regressive phenomena. In persons who rebel violently against a moral code without replacing it by another, the warding off of superego demands may well lead to symptomatology based on moral masochism with absence of conscious guilt feeling. That this state of affairs is very intimately connected with the vicissitudes of the Oedipus complex seems certain. It obviously also has to do with the very mechanisms which lead to the formation of the superego and determine its relations to the id and the ego.

To say that the subject of defenses, autonomous ego and psychoanalytic technique cannot be surveyed completely in a brief report is merely to state the obvious. I shall be content if these remarks have but succeeded in their limited objective: to highlight some of the knowledge we have gained and some of the problems challenging our further study.

REFERENCES

Alexander, F. (1930). *Psychoanalysis of the Total Personality.* New York and Washington: Nervous and Mental Disease Publ. Co.

Bak, R. C. (1946). Masochism in paranoia. *Psychoanal. Q.*, 15.

Bergler, E. (1937). On the theory of the therapeutic results of psychoanalysis. *Int. J. Psychoanal.*, 18.

Bibring, E. (1937). On the theory of the therapeutic results of psychoanalysis. *Int. J. Psychoanal.*, 18.

Fenichel, O. (1937). On the theory of the therapeutic results of psychoanalysis. *Int. J. Psychoanal.*, 18.

——— (1939). *Problems of Psychoanalytic Technique*, Albany: Psychoanal. Q.

French, T. M. (1938). Defense and synthesis in the function of the ego. *Psychoanal. Q.*, 7.

Freud, A. (1937). *The Ego and the Mechanisms of Defense.* London: Hogarth Press.

Freud, S. (1909). Notes upon a case of obsessional neurosis. *Coll. Papers* 4.

———— (1912). Recommendations for physicians on the psychoanalytic method of treatment. *Coll. Papers* 2.

———— (1913). Further recommendations on the technique of psychoanalysis. *Coll. Papers* 2.

———— (1915). Repression. *Coll. Papers* 4.

———— (1917). *Introductory Lectures on Psychoanalysis.* New York: Boni and Liveright, 1920; London: Allen & Unwin, 1920.

———— (1921). *Group Psychology and the Analysis of the Ego.* London: Hogarth Press, 1922.

———— (1923). *The Ego and the Id.* London: Hogarth Press, 1927.

———— (1926). *The Problem of Anxiety.* New York: Norton, 1936.

———— (1937). Analysis terminable and interminable. *Coll. Papers* 5.

———— (1937). Constructions in analysis. *Coll. Papers* 5.

Gero, G. (1951). The concept of defense. *Psychoanal. Q.*, 20.

Glover, E. (1931). The therapeutic effect of inexact interpretation. *Int. J. Psychoanal.*, 12.

Greenacre, P. (1950). General problems of acting out. *Psychoanal. Q.*, 19.

Hartmann, H. (1939). Ich-Psychologie und Anpassungsproblem. *Int. Ztschr. Psa. und Imago*, 25.

———— (1950). Comments on the psychoanalytic theory of the ego. *Psychoanal. Study Child*, 5.

———— (1951). Technical implications of ego psychology. *Psychoanal. Q.*, 20.

Hartmann, H., Kris, E. & Loewenstein, R. M. (1946). Comments on the formation of psychic structure. *Psychoanal. Study Child*, 2.

———— (1949). Notes on the theory of aggression. *Psychoanal. Study Child*, 3/4.

———— (1953). The function of theory in psychoanalysis. In *Drives, Affects, Behavior*, ed. R. M. Loewenstein. New York: Int. Univ. Press.

Kris, E. (1951a). Ego psychology and interpretation in psychoanalytic theory. *Psychoanal. Q.*, 20.

———— (1951b). Opening remarks on psychoanalytic child psychology. *Psychoanal. Study Child*, 6.

———— (1951c). The development of ego psychology. *Samiksa.*

Loewenstein, R. M. (1930–31). Le tact dans la technique psychanalytique. *Rev. Franç. Psychanal.*, 4.

———— (1945). A special form of self-punishment. *Psychoanal. Q.*, 14.

———— (1951a). The problem of interpretation. *Psychoanal. Q.*, 20.

———— (1951b). Ego development and psychoanalytic technique. *Amer. J. Psychiat.*, 107.

———— (1952). Some remarks on the role of language in psychoanalytic theory. Presented at the Annual Meeting of the American Psychoanalytic Association, Atlantic City, May.

Nunberg, H. (1931). The synthetic function of the ego. *Int. J. Psychoanal.*, 12.

———— (1937). On the theory of the therapeutic results of psychoanalysis. *Int. J. Psychoanal,* 18.

Reich, W. (1927). Zur technik der deutung und der widerstandsanalyse. *Int. Ztschr. Psa.*, 13.

———— (1928). Über charakteranalyse. *Int. Ztschr. Psa.*, 14. (Translated in *The Psychoanalytic Reader, I.* New York: Int. Univ. Press, 1948.)

Sterba, R. F. (1934). The fate of the ego in psychoanalytic therapy. *Int. J. Psychoanal.*, 15.

Waelder, R. (1936). The principle of multiple function. *Psychoanal. Q.*, 5.

4

Some Remarks on the Role of Speech in Psychoanalytic Technique

The discovery of the dynamic character of the unconscious, and the realization that most of the psychic processes usually observed in consciousness could be found also to exist preconsciously, led Freud to rely but little upon the presence or absence of conscious awareness in mental phenomena. Indeed, the factor of consciousness or its absence is elusive and deceptive, and the delimitation of the System Cs from the System Pcs cannot always be carried out unambiguously. Thus a conception of the psychic apparatus devised so as to include consciousness among its essential elements could not prove entirely satisfactory.

To these difficulties one might perhaps attribute the fact that Freud, as Ernest Jones reports in the second volume of his biography (Jones 1955), destroyed his manuscripts devoted to problems of consciousness. At any event, Freud cut through these complications by his fundamental change of the framework on which he proceeded to base the functioning of the mental apparatus. We know that the introduction of the structural approach to psychic phenomena became tremendously fruitful for the development of psychoanalysis. We also know that it permitted an understanding and a description of our technical procedure which before would have been impossible. The concept of the ego, in particular, had the advantage of encompassing conscious as well as preconscious and unconscious phenomena, and of uniting them within a common functional organization. However, it did not dispose

Based on a paper presented at a meeting of the New York Psychoanalytic Society, March 11, 1952, and at the Annual Meeting of the American Psychoanalytic Association, Atlantic City, May 11, 1952. An abbreviated version of the present text was read in the symposium on "The Theory of Technique" held at the Centenary Scientific Meetings of the British Psychoanalytical Society, London, May 5, 1956.

of the existence of conscious as opposed to preconscious and unconscious processes, and of problems related to the functional differences between them.

Freud never thought that conscious mental processes should be considered mere epiphenomena of unconscious and preconscious ones (Freud 1900), and he never relinquished his interest in problems connected with them. In his posthumous *Outline of Psychoanalysis* (Freud 1939) he wrote: "Conscious processes on the (perceptual) periphery of the ego[1] and everything else in the ego unconscious—such would be the simplest state of affairs that we might picture. And such may in fact be the conditions prevailing in animals. But in man there is an added complication owing to which internal processes in the ego may also acquire the quality of consciousness. This complication is produced by the function of speech, which brings the material in the ego into a firm connection with the memory-traces of visual and more particularly of auditory perceptions. Henceforth the perceptual periphery of the cortex of the ego can be stimulated to a much greater extent from inside as well; internal events such as consequences of ideas and intellective processes can become conscious; and a special apparatus becomes necessary in order to distinguish between the two possibilities—that is, what is known as *reality-testing*."[2]

Although less acute, the problem of the curative effect on neuroses being achieved by bringing unconscious phenomena to consciousness still remains. I shall try to contribute to its understanding by approaching it from a limited viewpoint; namely, that of the role of verbalization in the analytic procedure. But first I should like to make a few preliminary remarks about the term "bringing to consciousness."

Freud's original formulation of the aim of psychoanalytic therapy—to lift amnesias—was sufficient as long as only the undoing of the effects of repression was considered. But since psychoanalysis came to consider the results of other defensive mechanisms as well, the need has also arisen to encompass such processes as the reestablishment of connections, for instance, and the correction of distortions produced by various mechanisms of defense. We refer here to the important role of

1. Poetzl's work and the recent experimental studies by Charles Fisher (1954, 1956) indicate the existence of perception without consciousness.

2. Freud had discussed these problems previously in "The Interpretation of Dreams" (1900), "The Unconscious" (1915) and *Moses and Monotheism* (1937).

the synthetic and organizing function in the therapeutic process. Under these circumstances we are justified, I believe, in supplementing the term "bringing to consciousness" by the more comprehensive one "gaining of insight" when we wish to designate the results of changes in the ego which make warded-off mental functions available to the conflictless sphere of the ego. This term comprises both the bringing to consciousness and the reestablishment of connection (Bibring 1937; Fenichel 1937; Nunberg 1937; Kris 1950; Loewenstein 1951).

It is true that the term "gaining insight" has been submitted to critical scrutiny, and the objection advanced that it is used also in other contexts and thus might lead to confusion or misunderstandings. We know how frequently patients nowadays use a so-called "insight" to form resistances by intellectualization (A. Freud 1936; Kris 1956). But we also know that a wallowing in emotions may likewise, and at least as frequently, be used as resistance; yet this fact does not lead us to deny the importance of affects in psychoanalytic therapy. Therefore I believe that for lack of a better expression we are entitled to continue our use of the term "analytic insight" to designate, not only the increase in awareness, but also the dynamic changes encompassed by it. For we know that such insight is gained only after certain dynamic changes have occurred, and that gaining of insight, in its turn, leads to other dynamic changes (Kris 1950; Loewenstein 1951).

This terminological digression will, I hope, prove useful for our discussion of verbalization. Psychoanalysis is both an investigative and a therapeutic procedure, a long-drawn-out experiment and process taking place entirely in the realm of speech. It is an exchange of particular communications between two people, a kind of dialogue, very different from all other dialogues. The analytic set-up, the fundamental rule and the role of the analyst make it unique. The patient is expected in fact to relinquish, to some extent, the exercise of an essential function of conscious phenomena: the aim-directed character of conscious thinking; the ability of the System Cs to select deliberately, from among all preconscious memories, only those which at the moment suit its aim. In exchange, this controlled regression of the ego (Kris 1950) ultimately brings to the System Cs elements from the preconscious which otherwise would have remained outside the sphere of consciousness. These latter processes are facilitated, to a certain extent, by the protective role of the analyst and also by the fact that in the transference he happens to draw certain affects of the patient on to himself; but mainly by the role he plays in lending the help of his own ego functions to the weakened and restricted autonomous ego of the patient. He supplies the knowledge of mental phenomena, the understanding and objectivity which help the patient to face them.

In this peculiar dialogue the analyst is supposed to devote his entire attention to the mental phenomena of his patient, limiting his thoughts and words exclusively to the understanding of his interlocutor. One can say that in the person of the analyst the patient acquires an additional autonomous ego tending to enlarge the area of his System Cs over his unconscious.

Before going further into some details of the analytic procedure, let us dwell for a moment on the various functions of language.

Ferdinand de Saussure (1916) advanced the basic distinction between the two aspects which he designated, in French, by the terms *langue* and *parole*. Translated into English this is the differentiation between "language," defined as a system of distinctive signs corresponding to distinct ideas, on the one hand, and "speech," referring to utterances or spoken language, on the other. These two aspects of language are inseparable from one another, each being impossible without the other.

Following de Saussure's formulations, the Viennese psychologist Karl Buehler (1934) devised a general classification of the various functions of speech. According to him, speech encompasses three functions between addressor and addressee: they may speak of objects and their relationships; or the addressor may express (i.e., communicate) what is in himself; or he may appeal to the addressee. The act of speech therefore comprises: (1) what Buehler called the *Darstellungsfunktion*, which could be translated as *function of representation* or, according to Roman Jakobson[3] as *cognitive function*, since it refers to the knowledge and description of things or objects and the connections between them; (2) the *function of expression*, by which the speaker expresses something about himself; (3) the *function of appeal*, encompassing all those speech acts which appeal to the addressee to do something or to respond in some way; e.g., imploring, commanding, forbidding, seducing, etc.

In the analytic situation we might expect the patient's speech to be

3. Personal communication.

mainly confined to the expressive function and to that facet of the function of representation which deals mostly with the description of events. But experience shows that very soon the patient's thoughts lead him to exercise the third function, too, when his interest begins to center on the analyst. The latter, in accordance with the rules of analytic technique, has two tasks. He refrains from responding to the appeal function which manifests itself as transference reactions. Furthermore, he aims at transforming the appeal function of the patient's speech into the expressive function by showing him, through interpretations, how he expresses or describes something about himself when he speaks of persons or things outside himself. In his own speech the analyst will exclude both the function of appeal and the expressive function, limiting himself specifically to the cognitive function in relation to facts concerning his present addressee: the patient. He will thus, in turn, promote the expressive function of the latter, since the interpretation will communicate to the patient knowledge about himself that will favor his recall and expression of hitherto unavailable facts about himself.

But at the same time the patient's knowledge about himself will enhance that aspect of the cognitive function to which we wish to ascribe a particular importance in the curative effect of analysis, the one on which working through is based and which leads to insight.

Indeed, there may exist a difference between the cognitive function in its application to the nonself and to the self. In the latter case, the cognitive and expressive functions might be intertwined in a very significant way.

These three main functions of speech, then, encompass its various secondary ones as they are known to analysts.

The concept of catharsis was based upon the idea that by recounting some hitherto uncommunicated events of one's past one, as it were, gets rid of them. The phrase "to let off steam" is a colloquial expression of the same idea. In this connection, the various modalities in which a given patient utters or withholds information might be influenced by trends from the anal and urethral functions, leading to the retention or expulsion of words as though they were matter. A patient's way of talking may reveal that at times he uses speech for either seduction or aggression towards the analyst (Abraham 1927; Fliess 1949; Sharpe 1950).

Nunberg (1932) has pointed at two important functions of speech in analysis. First, the magic one (which, by the way, to a certain extent enters into the cathartic function of speech). He stresses that, with words, human beings try to influence the fate of others: they bless or curse them; some try to cling to other persons by means of speech. "Thus," he states, "under the influence of libido, speech is used to perform positive as well as negative magic." We may say that there is actually no more powerful magic than that of words. This is perhaps the one realm where so-called magic is really operative. The communication of guilty acts or thoughts, confession, has a real psychological effect. It frequently makes an accomplice of the listener, thus determining his future behavior in an important way.[4] From the consequences of so much knowledge about the hidden wishes and acts of others, from this role of an accomplice, perhaps only confessors and analysts can remain immune.

The second point emphasized by Nunberg is that speech is a substitute for action. Indeed, speaking involves motor discharge by means of the vocal organs and in this respect plays a role in the therapeutic action of psychoanalysis. Even if one stresses the discharge value of affects in analysis, they have this property only while the memory-contents are remembered, and this only inasmuch as they are being told to the analyst.

Superego, id and ego do not equally partake of the action of speech. As far as the superego is concerned, the confession of guilty acts or intentions may lead to actual change in the person. The sharing of experience and feelings, which is achieved through communication, might be in the service of the id. Although speech is but a poor substitute for sexual gratification, it plays an important role in the expression of love and in the conquest of a love object. It is most powerful, however, in the service of aggression. Here, words are not merely a substitute for action. Insults and expressions of irony or contempt are often more adequate than deeds, and sometimes hurt more than physi-

---

4. This is one of the most striking examples showing that it is human language, the communicability of human experience and its psychological consequences for the speaker and the listener, which makes it even more difficult to create a scientific psychology based exclusively on concepts used by the learning theory which describes man in terms of drive—stimulus—response.

cal blows. But it is in its function for the ego, which mainly concerns us here, that speech seems to play the most interesting and significant role.

In psychoanalytic practice, we often encounter considerable resistances in our patients to verbalizing certain thoughts and emotions of which they have always been perfectly aware. Some of them, we find, delay for a long time before telling the analyst about some conscious thought or memory, and at times will experience highly painful physical sensations when they finally do so. We all know that this resistance against reporting things which are entirely conscious reappears, time and again, throughout the analytic treatment. Thus we must conclude that a barrier exists not only between the unconscious and preconscious and between the latter and the conscious, but also between conscious thoughts or emotions and their verbalization.

Every analyst knows that this resistance to verbalizing conscious phenomena manifests itself in all kinds of areas. Some patients are reluctant to reveal specific facts of their lives; others, to divulge certain details of their past or present sex life; still others are ashamed of their emotions.[5] For most of them the telling of their daydreams is a particularly difficult task, and we all know how strong is the resistance in patients to expressing their conscious feelings and thoughts about the analyst. Undoubtedly one reason for the existence of this barrier between conscious experiences and their verbalization is the fear of letting another know one's most intimate secrets, the fear of loss of love and esteem from the analyst, fear of punishment in its various forms.[6]

Indeed, the analyst is a kind of superego to the patient. But he is also a witness. He is like an additional memory acting to remind the patient of certain facts when he may want, in periods of increased resistance, to forget or disregard what he had revealed before. At such moments a reluctant patient can sometimes be heard to say: "I know I told it to you, so it must be true." This role of a witness and a memory is, in fact, a part of the analyst's functions which we defined as being the patient's additional autonomous ego. But this very fact leads us to

    5. In some emotionally charged states, such as grief, awe, or communion with a love object, talking is experienced as a desecration. The same may be true of the reluctance to reveal highly valued beliefs or ideals: a refusal "to cast pearls before swine."
    6. The role of warded-off exhibitionistic tendencies in these resistances is obvious.

consider the resistance against verbalization from yet another point of view. It is not uncommon in analysis that, after reluctantly talking about certain consciously remembered events of his life, the patient will add that now, since he has told them, these events have become more real.

I should like to add here that often the mere fact of communicating such conscious thoughts or memories to the analyst makes hitherto hidden material (or important missing details of other material) easily available to the analysand, so that the latter either reaches some additional insight by himself or becomes ripe to grasp an interpretation.

What makes a memory more real when it is recounted than while it was kept secret? We might think of several explanations. That speech is a substitute for action has already been mentioned; this substitute action may render an experience more real, when it is verbalized, than one that is merely remembered. Another explanation is that the inner experience may, while being told, acquire an additional reality value through its auditive perception.

Furthermore, spoken words are products of the speech act. The function of objectivation, which Cassirer (1944, 1946) stressed in language, plays an important part in the analytic process itself, in the assimilation by the ego of hitherto warded-off elements, as pointed out by Bibring (1937) and Hartmann (1951). But this is not all. It is true that "unspoken words are our slaves, and spoken ones enslave us." The mere conscious awareness of psychological realities still keeps them in the realm of privacy; communicated, they become an objective and social reality.

A particular problem in analytic therapy centers around the verbalization of emotions and affects in the transference situation. Warded-off affects may emerge spontaneously in the transference or as a result of previous interpretation. But the mere experiencing of affects in analysis must be followed by their verbal expression. Moreover, although in the analytic process such verbal expression may be a necessary step, this process is not completed until the connections of the affects with specific contents have been reestablished. Only thus can the affects be reintegrated as a part of defenses as well as of instinctual drives; in other words, in their place within the structural framework of id, ego, and superego. The establishment of these connections is likewise achieved with the help of verbalization. (The difficulty of deal-

ing analytically with the impact of experiences stemming from preverbal stages in the patient's life is well known.)[7]

Affects expressed in words are henceforth external as well as
internal realities. The words denoting these affects are now being perceived by both patient and analyst; they have become realities of the
outside world in a factual and in a social sense.

Moreover, by analyzing the patient's transference phenomena or
acting out, we endeavor to transform his repetitive behavior in the
transference into thinking, into the achievement of insight into his
intentions and motivations through their verbalization. This may lead
the patient ultimately to remember the conflicts, situations, and
traumatic events of his past, which thus far he had been unconsciously
repeating.

Resistance against the analysis of the transference situation may
manifest itself at each of the points just mentioned. Moreover, resistance against the verbalization of affect can be traced to two types
of motivation. One is based on the fear of being carried away too far by
such expression of emotions, a fear that the affect might thus reach too
much intensity and also have an effect on the analyst. The other motive
seems to be of an opposite kind; some patients can indulge in their
emotional states as long as they do not talk about them, but to put these
emotions into words interrupts their silent gratification; it "breaks the
spell," one might say. To the discharge function through verbalization
we must therefore add another, equally important one: the *binding*, as
it were, of affects by speech. To a purely expressive function a reflec-
tive, cognitive function is added which may have an inhibiting influence on the discharge of affects. Both the discharge function and the
binding function[8] of verbalization underlie the curative effect of insight
in psychoanalysis. In turn both may at times be used by the forces of
resistance for defensive purposes.

Summarizing our remarks about resistance to verbalization, we
can say that at the point of verbal expression a last struggle is put up by
the ego's defenses against bringing the unconscious to consciousness.

---

7. Human beings learn to speak from their mothers. In the transference, the analytic
situation with all its emotional over- and undertones might well at times reawaken this
remote period of a patient's life.

8. This binding of the affect by words may be a factor in the neutralization of drive
energies to which Kris (1956) ascribes the therapeutic function of insight.

We must conclude that in the formation of analytic insight, verbalization is an essential step.

Man has the ability, either by concealment or lies or by communicating the truth, to influence or to create social realities through the spoken word. Language plays a decisive role in the formation and the development of thought processes (Sapir 1921, 1949). The thought processes that particularly interest us here are those which deal with understanding or knowing oneself. Every analyst has had occasion to observe that a patient may express some idea or affect and then suddenly realize that such thought or feeling was hitherto completely unknown to him. The fact of having expressed it in words makes him recognize its existence. Let me give a recent example of such an incident. One of my patients, a man in his forties, conspicuously presented the consequences of the mechanisms of isolation and repression of affect. It was not until the beginning of his analysis, for instance, that he became aware of ever in his life having been jealous. He was equally unaware that he might ever have wanted to be loved by his mother. All his life he lived, to use his own words, in the illusion of being the preferred child of his parents. When once, in a situation where he imagined that I might take sides with an adversary of his, he brought up the "illusion of communion" with the analyst and hesitantly spoke of feelings of jealousy, I remarked that his sentence was not complete. Reluctantly, and with a disbelieving chuckle, he finished the sentence which expressed that he wanted to be loved by his analyst. This wish had never occurred to him before uttering these words. (Needless to add that when the patient was reminded of this incident a week later, it had been forgotten by him.) Here, one might say, words carried to the surface of conscious awareness a thought and an affect which had been unconscious before. In these instances, language performs the function of a kind of scaffolding that permits conscious thought to be built inside.

Another category of the phenomena based on verbalization, with which we are familiar in psychoanalysis, consists in interpretations given by the analyst. These, too, might to some extent be compared to a kind of scaffolding which the patient's thought can gradually fill. They then play the role stressed by Kris (1950), when he spoke of recognition as an important step in the recall of repressed memories.

Not infrequently the interpretations are misused by the patient in the service of resistance. Thus intellectualization may use mere words, instead of insights; the empty scaffolding alone, without a building. This kind of resistance can sometimes be avoided by a judicious attention to tact, timing, and wording of interpretations. When the analyst believes, on the basis of preparatory work, that the time has come, that the patient is ready for it, he lends him the words, so to speak, which will meet the patient's thoughts and emotions halfway. In the peculiar dialogue going on between patient and analyst, their mutual understanding is based on the general property of human speech to create states of mind in the interlocutor akin to those expressed by the spoken words. The function of representation in speech elicits images and representations in the addressee which are similar to those used by the addressor. The expressive function tends to arouse emotions or states similar to those expressed. The function of appeal potentially creates the reactions corresponding to the appeal. As far as the analyst is concerned, we expect that the patient's speech shall elicit in him only those potential responses which may act as signals[9] for his understanding of the patient, and which ultimately may be used by him in interpreting the latter's utterances.

Freud advised listening to the patient's words while trying, at the same time, also to understand a second, a kind of coded message conveyed by them. The fundamental rule, since it requires the patient to relinquish the aim-directed character of his thought to some extent, brings this "coded message" closer into the foreground. This is another way of saying that we observe that the patient's utterances become more obviously influenced by the primary process. We know that in the psychic phenomena which are under the sway of the primary process, the relationship between word representation and object representation—or, to use Ferdinand de Saussure's terms, between the signifying and the signified—is altered as compared to thoughts within the framework of the secondary process. To put it still differently: one might say that next to the usual vocabulary of any human language—i.e., to a definite set of meaningful relations between signs and ideas, "signifying" and "signified"—there exists another which is limited in scope, less definite, usually unconscious, and unintelligible, and which gains a partial hold upon the human mind on certain conditions; e.g., in dreams, in neurotic and psychotic thought processes.

9. A similar idea was expressed by Kris (1956).

However, the use of the same kind of vocabulary in wit, jokes, and in actual love life often is conscious, intentional, and perfectly understandable to others.[10]

I do not intend to go into a detailed discussion of the various types of altered relations between "signifying" and "signified." Let me give just two examples, out of a countless number common in analytic experience. An airplane phobia results from emotional reactions to the fact that, to a given patient, an airplane means not only a flying machine, but also a symbolic representation of a penis. In a case of compulsive neurosis, the anxiety created by sitting down in a taxicab was based upon the unconscious meaning of the act for this patient, which centered around the French colloquial connotation of "sitting on somebody": an expression of contemptuous indifference.

In respect to the primary and secondary processes, the analytic process has a twofold effect. On the one hand, analysis elicits expressions of the unconscious vocabulary. On the other hand, it causes these thoughts to be translated into words of the ordinary language. Being confronted with them, as it were, by means of the speech act, the patient during the analysis is led to a gradual gaining of insight into phenomena that are under the sway of the primary process. By putting them into words, he subjects them to the influence of the secondary process.

In the passage quoted above, Freud (1939) ascribed to the function of speech the very fact that "processes in the ego may . . . acquire the quality of consciousness," since it "brings the material in the ego into a firm connection with the memory-traces of visual and more particularly of auditory perceptions"; adding that, as a consequence, "a special apparatus becomes necessary in order to distinguish between [stimulations from inside and from outside]—that is, what is known as *reality-testing*."

The analytic set-up "creates for the patient a situation where attention and reality-testing are withdrawn from the outside world [the analyst] and shifted on to the inner experience of the patient" (Loewenstein 1951).[11] Insight which a patient may gain during analysis widens

10. Benveniste (1956) attempts to describe these phenomena in terms of well-known figures of style.

11. Hartmann recently expressed similar ideas in a discussion on *Defense Mechanisms* at the Midwinter Meeting of the American Psychoanalytic Association in 1953.

his capacity for reality-testing in the area of his mental processes and permits a far more differentiated use of it. He may learn to distinguish the role of his own unconscious drives or thoughts in the evaluation of situations involving other people; he may learn to discern the complexity of his motivations where only rationalization was used before; he may learn to understand the mental states of other persons; and he may acquire the ability to differentiate between the past and present of his own experience as well as of outside reality. The latter point is crucial in the therapeutic effects of psychoanalysis. All these acquisitions of reality-testing in the area of the patient's mental processes are acquisitions of the System Cs, and are gained with the help of and by means of speech as it is used in the analytic procedure. Indeed, the use of language permits human beings to give actuality even to events that are remote in time and space, and yet to distinguish them from those which exist here and now.

Why is it that certain psychic phenomena may have a pathogenic effect so long as they remain unconscious, but become harmless after having been brought to consciousness?

Freud attempted to account for this peculiar state of affairs when he used the comparison with archaeology to explain the effect of analytic therapy. He compared it with the perennialness of the remnants of antiquity buried in Pompeii, and their speedy disintegration when brought out into the light (Freud 1933). Their apparent timelessness was due to their being removed from the effects of the outside world; and their disintegration, once brought to the surface, was caused by various physical and chemical factors, by the influences of air and humidity from which they had so long been removed. What is it, then, that corresponds to these physical and chemical influences upon the unearthed Roman relics? What causes our psychic antiquities to disintegrate when they become conscious? In their unconscious state they have a pathogenic effect because, unlike the buried Roman remains, they continue to exert an action in the present: namely, on the personality of the patient. Brought to consciousness, they become harmless because insight and verbalization subject them to reality-testing and thus unravel the effects of the pathogenic intertwinement between past and present.

We know the therapeutic effect of analysis to be a lasting one, even though the insights and recollections achieved during treatment may apparently be forgotten once more. By undergoing conscious experience they have acquired a resistivity to repression, whether or not they remain available to conscious awareness. This resistivity of hitherto pathogenic memories to repression is ascribed by Kris (1950) to the fact that, as a result of analytic insight, they have become part of a context. Freud (1915) advanced a hypothesis according to which there are two types of memory traces: those deposited by unconscious and those deposited by conscious-preconscious processes. One might then presume that the latter contain elements of having been part of a context, of having undergone insight and reality-testing, which may account for an increased resistivity to both repression and regression.

Before concluding, I should like to discuss certain limitations and qualifications that must be attached to my presentation.

We know that various modes of communication and understanding, other than verbal ones, exist between human beings. Certainly we do not underestimate the importance of the immediate understanding of the unconscious between two people, of the intuitive grasping of nonverbal forms of emotional expressions; and these important ways of communication might lie quite outside the realm of verbalization. They even may play a part in the analyst's understanding of his patient. However, the essential factor in the investigative and therapeutic function of psychoanalysis is based upon the use of speech between patient and analyst. To be sure, not all relevant processes during an analysis occur on the level of consciousness; nor are all of them ever verbalized. And yet, without verbalization on the part of the patient, without interpretations, without gaining of insight, there would be no analysis and thus no such processes.

Communication may have a considerable and enriching influence on the development of the human personality (Rapaport 1951). However, the importance of verbalization in the therapeutic procedure of analysis should not lead us to assume that communication per se has a title to therapeutic efficiency. First of all, communication is not the whole of either language or speech (Sapir 1921, 1949; Piaget 1948). Moreover, people do not change just because they communicate with others. What counts in analysis is, not communication by itself, but *what is being communicated* on the part of both patient and analyst, what leads to communication, and what psychic processes and changes occur as a result of this communication as such and of its contents.

A most pertinent consideration arises, however, with regard to the therapeutic effects of self-analysis. Most psychoanalysts, I presume, experience its effectiveness only in the form of a continuation of a previ-ous analysis with an actual analyst. As far as I know, it is then usually a solitary continuation of dialogue with the latter or with an imaginary analyst. In this respect it might be viewed as an imaginary dialogue in which the subject is able to play both parts, that of a patient and that of an analyst, and thus to some extent involving inner speech.

Nevertheless, the possibility of a therapeutic self-analysis serves to confirm what we would suspect in any case: that if verbalization and speech play an essential role in the therapeutic effects of the gaining of insight, they are not the only factors to do so.

REFERENCES

Abraham, K. (1927). The influence of oral erotism on character formation. In *Selected Papers*. London: Hogarth Press, pp. 393–406.

Benveniste, E. (1956). Remarques sur la fonction du langage dans la dé-couverte freudienne. In *Sur la Parole et le Langage*, ed. J. Lacan, *La Psychanalyse* 1:3–16.

Bibring, E. (1937). On the theory of the therapeutic results of psychoanalysis. *Int. J. Psychoanal.*, 18:170–89.

Buehler, K. (1934). *Sprachtheorie. Die Darstellungsfunktion der Sprache.* Jena: Fischer.

Cassirer, E. (1944). *An Essay on Man.* New Haven: Yale Univ. Press.

———— (1946). *Language and Myth.* New York: Harper.

Fenichel, O. (1937). On the theory of the therapeutic results of psychoanalysis. *Int. J. Psychoanal.*, 18:133–38.

Fisher, C. (1954). Dreams and perception: the role of preconscious and pri-mary modes of perception in dream formation. *J. Amer. Psychoanal. Assn.*, 2:389–445.

———— (1956). Dreams, images, and perception: a study of unconscious-preconscious relationships. *J. Amer. Psychoanal. Assn.*, 4:5–48.

Fliess, R. (1949). Silence and verbalization: a supplement to the theory of the "analytic rule." *Int. J. Psychoanal.*, 30:21–30.

Freud, A. (1936). *The Ego and the Mechanisms of Defense.* London: Hogarth Press.

Freud, S. (1900). The interpretation of dreams. *S.E.*, 4/5.

———— (1915). The unconscious. *Coll. Papers* 4.

———— (1933). *New Introductory Lectures on Psychoanalysis.* New York: Nor-ton.

———— (1937). *Moses and Monotheism.* New York: Knopf, 1949.

———— (1939). *An Outline of Psychoanalysis.* New York: Norton, 1949.

Hartmann, H. (1951). Technical implications of ego psychology. *Psychoanal. Q.*, 20:31–43.

Jones, E. (1955). *The Life and Work of Sigmund Freud, 2: Years of Maturity.* New York: Basic Books.

Kris, E. (1950). On preconscious mental processes. *Psychoanal. Q.*, 19:540–60.

———— (1951). Ego psychology and interpretation in psychoanalytic therapy. *Psychoanal. Q.*, 20:15–30.

———— (1956). On some vicissitudes of insight. Contribution to the symposium on "The Theory of Technique" held at the Centenary Scientific Meeting of the British Psychoanalytical Society, London, May 5.

Loewenstein, R. M. (1951). The problem of interpretation. *Psychoanal. Q.*, 20:1–14.

Nunberg, H. (1932). *Principles of Psychoanalysis. Their Application to the Neuroses.* New York: Int. Univ. Press, 1955.

———— (1937). On the theory of the therapeutic results of psychoanalysis. *Int. J. Psychoanal.*, 18:161–69.

Piaget, J. (1948). *Le Langage et la Pensée chez l'enfant.* Neuchâtel and Paris: Delachaux et Niestlé.

Rapaport, D. (1951). *Organization and Pathology of Thought.* New York: Columbia Univ. Press.

Sapir, E. (1921). *Language. An Introduction to the Study of Speech.* New York: Harcourt, Brace.

———— (1949). *Selected Writings*, ed. D. G. Mandelbaum. Berkeley and Los Angeles: Univ. of California Press.

Saussure, F. de (1916). *Cours de Linguistique Générale*, ed. C. Bally & A. Sechehaye. Lausanne and Paris: Payot.

Sharpe, E. F. (1950). Psycho-physical problems revealed in language: an examination of metaphor. In *Collected Papers on Psychoanalysis.* London: Hogarth Press, pp. 155–69.

5

A *Contribution* *to* *the* *Psychoanalytic* *Theory* *of* *Masochism*

I

When we speak of masochism we refer to a tendency to seek physical or mental suffering in order to achieve, be it consciously or not, sexual gratification in the widest sense. Quite apart from their clinical importance, these phenomena are so challenging because they seem to contradict a basic characteristic of the human mind: the trend to avoid pain and unpleasure, i.e., the pleasure principle. Indeed, to some masochists "physical or mental suffering at the hands of the sexual object is a condition" for sexual gratification (Freud 1905). Because of this paradox, one might expect that the study of masochism should also lead to interesting considerations dealing with the problems of the human mind when faced with some painful realities of the external and internal world.

In "The Economic Principle in Masochism" Freud (1924) noted that masochism "comes under our observation in three shapes: as a condition under which sexual excitation may be roused; as an expression of feminine nature; and as a norm of behavior."

Theoretical considerations on masochism thus can deal with several types of problems. The first and the comparatively best known of these are the cases of masochistic perversion. They have been most widely studied clinically; they were well described already in pre-Freudian psychiatric literature, and psychoanalytic research has con-

A brief version of this paper was presented at the Midwinter Meeting of the American Psychoanalytic Association, December 3, 1955.

tributed substantially to their elucidation. Numerous authors, in addition to Freud, have examined these problems from various points of view.

Freud stressed the prevalence of pregenital features in the sexuality of masochists. He pointed out that in masochistic fantasies or actual gratifications men unconsciously identify themselves with a woman in her role in intercourse or childbirth, and that in these cases the pain or punishment which arouses them is a regressive expression of their passive genital desires; that, in these cases, the punishing or cruel woman possesses phallic attributes which thus indirectly indicate that a woman here stands for a man. However, it must be added that these phallic characteristics of the female sexual partner also point to another very essential feature of the masochist, namely, to his stress on denial of the absence of a penis in the woman, and thus on denial of the castration danger. We shall come back to this point later on.

Still another essential feature is the connection between passivity and masochism. Absence of activity is sometimes called passivity. In such cases it might be more precise to use the term inactivity. Another form of behavior referred to as passivity is the readiness to comply with the will of other people. In connection with drives and their derivatives, we understand passivity in a twofold way: (1) passivity as opposed to activity can be used in reference to opposite aims of the instinctual drive; (2) passively being loved can be distinguished from actively loving (Hartmann, Kris, and Loewenstein 1949).

In both these latter meanings passivity is an essential feature of early infancy and childhood. The passive gratification of his vital and erotic needs is a prerequisite for the infant's survival. Even in the normal development of the phallic phase we can, I believe, distinguish two stages: an earlier one in which passive aims, e.g., being looked at, being touched or manipulated, are more prevalent than in the later one where wishes of active penetration appear. It is the transition toward this latter stage, of active phallic strivings and wishes, that most often meets with particularly strong inhibiting forces centering around the castration fear (Loewenstein 1935). A reversion or fixation to passive phallic aims is one of the characteristics of masochism, but not of masochism alone; indeed, we can find it at the base of numerous perversions and neurotic potency disturbances. In all these cases it seems that the active penetration of the woman remains either taboo or, at least, less gratifying than passively experienced genital gratification

(Loewenstein 1935). Thus we assume that passivity is not a result of masochism but, on the contrary, the prerequisite for it.

In certain female patients, in whom masochism is not even very pronounced, the erotic fantasies culminate in the wish to be a thing, a completely helpless infant taken care of by the beloved man. Indeed, it seems that the longing to revert to a stage of entire helplessness and of being completely taken care of by an all-powerful parent can frequently be observed both in men and in women, without necessarily entailing masochistic tendencies. We believe it is only when this wish is experienced as humiliating, and yet the latter feeling is being enjoyed too, that we are in the presence of real masochism. The distinction, it is true, is not always easy to make. Passivity is obviously not sufficient to explain the essential character of the masochistic perversion; namely, that unpleasure is so intimately bound up with sexual gratification.

Various mechanisms underlying masochistic perversions have been discovered and described in the psychoanalytic literature. They all center around the crucial problems with which human sexuality has to deal during its development; namely, fear of loss of the object and fear of loss of its love, castration fear and superego anxiety. Thus, for instance, the tendency to passivity and helplessness may have the implicit aim of appealing to the mercy of the threatening and protective parental figure (Horney 1935). By the same token, it permits sexual gratification by apparently eliminating all responsibility for it. Suffering may become a prerequisite for sexual pleasure, as a price that must be paid to appease guilt feelings (W. Reich 1949); or as a "lesser evil" (Rado 1933), a form of self-castration, to avoid actual castration. Or there may be a turning against the self of active genital and aggressive impulses directed at incestuous objects.

It has also been stressed that the masochist uses a mechanism generally designed to deal with anxiety (Freud 1926); namely, to anticipate actively what might be feared to occur to one passively (Waelder 1933; Fenichel 1945). By imagining or producing scenes of torture or punishment which he himself devises, the masochist excludes the possibility of being tortured or punished in an unexpected and uncontrollable way (Eidelberg 1933a, 1933b, 1934). This is particularly evident in the cases that have been described as "erotization of anxiety" (Laforgue 1930), and which lie somewhere between a neurosis and a perversion. Gruesome fairy tales, thrillers, mystery plays and horror films seem to be an institutionalized means of gratifying the same need (Freud 1905).

We have already referred to Freud's view that some masochistic fantasies cover up and represent a flight from a much more intense and dreaded desire; namely, from feminine wishes toward the father. In such cases the fear of castration is alleviated by the substitution of a female figure for the father, and of beatings and threats for the passive genital penetration.

These mechanisms may explain those cases of masochism where a man must first undergo a certain amount of suffering before he is able to behave in a sexually normal way. But this is not characteristic for those masochists who derive pleasure through suffering rather than after suffering (Fenichel 1945).

Freud insists on the role of pleasure in pain as being due to a regressive reinforcement of the erotogenic masochism. Indeed, fixation to pregenital and particularly to anal, muscular, and cutaneous erotism plays an essential part in the genesis of masochism.

A very well-known clinical fact common to many cases of perversion has not been sufficiently taken into account in psychoanalytic writings; namely, that the patients themselves describe the origin of their perversion as being linked to a particular, specific scene in childhood. We have learned in analysis to take such a remark by the patient seriously and to look for an explanation. One might explain it by referring to the fact that all sexual development proceeds silently or unconsciously for a while, until it becomes conscious as a finished product. But while this unquestionably is so, it would not explain why these specific memories of sexual scenes should be so much more frequent among perverts than among neurotics. We know, moreover, that they most often are screen memories standing for more significant events. It must be assumed that these remembered scenes allude to traumatic events. Greenacre (1953) has recently brought this to our attention by stressing the importance of traumatic overstimulation in certain cases of fetishism or severe neuroses. In masochism one must think, more specifically, of traumatic events which involve a mixture of prohibition, seduction and reassurance (Loewenstein 1938; Fenichel 1945; Bornstein 1949).

We come closer to a satisfactory understanding of the masochistic perversion by taking into account some of its peculiarities. Freud pointed out that the sufferings desired and instituted by masochists never go as far as those of sadists. He also mentioned that in masochism the genitals and eyes are never directly involved in the actual threat.[1]

Masochists seek only certain specific and individually variable forms of suffering and humiliation. As soon as these reach a greater intensity or take a different form, they are reacted to with the habitual fear and pain. We shall go into this problem again when discussing the relation of masochism with Freud's theory of the death instinct. In addition, what is characteristic for the masochist's enjoyment of suffering and humiliation is a tacit but essential prerequisite: namely, that the sexual partner participate in the sexual scene or in masturbatory fantasy. Thus, the partner's threats and punishments amount to something akin to play or make-believe (Loewenstein 1938; Fenichel 1945).[2]

We also know that the type of threat and suffering which the masochist strives for is invariably a more or less veiled threat of castration. The problem is how it comes about that the very threat of castration becomes the actual source of sexual gratification. One is led to the following conclusion:

The masochistic perversions are modified repetitions of childhood situations and scenes in which sexual fantasies, erotic games, direct or indirect attempts at sexual rapprochement toward forbidden objects, particularly the mother, have met with disapproval or rebuff coupled with actual or imaginary ridicule, threat or punishment. In perversion the object (i.e., parent) participates instead of rejecting; threat and punishment are only limited. The essential mechanism underlying the masochistic perversion is that, by inducing the sexual partner to enact a scene of castration threat or punishment, the masochist forces the prohibiting, threatening parent to annul and undo the rebuff and the castration threat through its simulated repetition while actually participating in the veiled incestuous gratification. The masochistic scene is thus a means of gratifying the forbidden, repressed incestuous fantasies, but with the castration threat undone (Loewenstein 1938).

1. This may not always be correct. We have seen cases of women as well as men in whom light and playful beatings of the genital organs produce a highly arousing effect.

2. If we assume that a similar erotogenic effect attaches even to intensely painful feelings, especially when the pain is toned down or kept at a distance by some accompanying condition, we should here have one of the main roots of the masochistic-sadistic instinct, into whose numerous complexities we are very gradually gaining some insight" (Freud 1905).

II

A few clinical examples may illustrate this point.

A young male patient suffered from a neurotic depression after a disappointing love affair. The girl preferred a slightly younger and sexually more aggressive friend of his. The situation revived his old problems centering around rivalry with a younger, more aggressive, and more precocious brother who had been preferred by the mother. Following his disappointment in love, my patient, who was a highly idealistic and even ascetically inclined young man and had never before had any sexual experience, started roaming through streets where he was certain of meeting prostitutes. Beset with guilt and doubts, he would resist temptation, even when accosted, until he happened to find a prostitute who intuitively knew the way to overcome his resistance: she ordered him peremptorily to follow her. He would do so and comply with her command to have intercourse with her. The meaning of this masochistic behavior became clear only when he described that at the very moment of orgasm he would freeze into anxious immobility. In analysis he remembered childhood scenes which he connected with this freezing-up during orgasm. There were memories of bed wetting in the morning, and of his mother leaving the preferred younger brother in order to come over to his bed and scold him for having wet the bed. He remembered the bed wetting as being similar to the orgasm with the prostitute; both willful and frightening, anticipating mother's threat and anger. These screen memories stood for much earlier fantasies of passive sexual rapprochement toward the mother.

Thus the scenes with the prostitute revive and at the same time undo both his recent disappointment and his childhood castration fear. He revenges himself on the unfaithful sweetheart and mother by going to a prostitute, thereby unconsciously debasing them in his mind. In childhood his bed wetting led the mother to proffer castration threats, but was also an unconscious appeal to her which, by the same token, forced her to take care of him. In the scene with the prostitute the lowered image of the mother aggressively induces him to seek sexual gratification with her, by being the strict and "angry" mother. But instead of forbidding sex, she incites him to it and participates in it.

In another case, where jealousy of a younger brother likewise played an essential role in the genesis of the patient's masochism, the masochistic desires would overwhelm the patient as soon as he began to imagine that his sexual partner preferred another man. He traced his masochistic wishes to a screen memory in which his mother took care of the preferred, one-year-old brother while he himself was lying very tightly swaddled in a crib, simultaneously enjoying this situation and suffering from it (screen memory for passive and masochistic fantasies).

The patient during his analysis was able to have an affair without any need for masochistic gratification, but this need reemerged violently when his girl friend decided to leave him. He begged her to beat and to tie him, as though hoping in this way to seduce her into the mother's sadistic role and thus to undo the desertion. He made use here of a mechanism, "seduction of the aggressor," which we shall discuss in some detail later. Incompleteness of the analysis in this instance did not permit a sufficient elucidation of the screen memory of being swaddled, but merely the guess that it alluded to the time when violent aggressive outbreaks against his mother for preferring the brother were squelched in him in order to regain the mother's love.

My third and last example refers to a case of beating fantasies in a female patient. The fantasies in this instance had the typical and well-known dual, sadomasochistic character.

It will be helpful, first, to recall the general kind of development which Freud discovered in this type of case. He described that the beating fantasies start out, at an early age, with a fantasy of a sibling being beaten. The motive for this fantasy is not yet clearly sexual; rather, it is the wish to make sure that the sibling is not loved by the parents. This phase then is followed by a second, usually unconscious one, in which the little boy's fantasies center around being beaten by the father. The shift, as Freud explained, occurs for two reasons. First, it is due to the guilt about the aggressive thoughts, which turns the aggression against the self. The second motive for this turning against the self are feminine-passive genital wishes toward the father, regressively expressed as being beaten. The actual beating fantasies as the patients remember them, which represent the third phase of this development, commonly occur at a later period, often in early latency. Their general content is that a child, usually a boy, is beaten by some unidentified man, frequently a teacher. At this stage the fantasy has a conscious, sexual character and continues with many variations for a more or less extended time. The unconscious motivation underlying the conscious beating fantasies of the latency period has to do with the repression of the oedipal wishes as well as with the conflict arising from penis envy and castration fear (Freud 1919).

In the case of my patient, the beating fantasies persisted into adult life and constituted the only condition under which she was able to experience any orgastic gratification. There were particular features in her childhood history which, on the one hand, made her beating fantasies more understandable and which, on the other hand, made them much more difficult to unravel. One was the fact that she was the only girl and between two brothers of whom the first, five years older than the patient, displayed a genuinely sadistic attitude toward her, whereas the younger one was born when she was five, shortly before the onset of her conscious beating fantasy. The main complications, however, were due to an actual, severe beating administered by the father when the patient was seven. This was a traumatic event of extraordinary intensity to which the patient consistently, and probably correctly, attributed the tenacity and power of her beating fantasies.

I do not intend here to describe the various types of beating fantasies which this patient had elaborated over the years, but will mention only one out of many fantasies of a type she had, on and off, all through her life. During most, though not all, of these fantasies she identified herself consciously with the powerful, cruel, sadistic figures in the imagined scenes. Unconsciously, however, the identification with a slave, who was being denied sexual gratification and aroused by this denial, had a particularly strong effect upon her.

The typical fantasy I want to describe dealt with two middle-aged women conversing in the presence of two girls, daughters or servants, who were completely at their mercy. The high point of the scene was that these women would tell one or both of the girls that it would be good for them to refrain from any sexual activity for some time, and that the girls would humbly acquiesce in this, being at the same time aroused by it. The sexual arousal at that very moment extended also to the patient herself and implicitly, therefore, to the older women with whom she consciously identified herself. There was a particular note of hypocrisy, which seemed to pervade many of the patient's imagined scenes. In this instance it was that the pseudo-moralistic reasons advanced by the older woman for imposing abstinence on the younger were very transparently given in order to arouse herself as well as the victim. The cruel woman of the fantasy to a certain extent seems to represent the opposite of the patient's real mother, who never actually forbade her daughter any sexual gratification but bashfully avoided any mention of the girl's sexuality. Yet for the daughter she was the strongest deterrent to any gratifying love life. The patient, who was then in her forties, once said: "I'd rather kill myself than tell my mother that I might love a man or might want to get married." Indeed, she never did.

To return to the fantasy and its connection with the theory of masochism: we see here what Freud called a regressive resexualization of morality. Morality is upheld, but with a transparent and unmistakable hypocrisy which invariably is the hallmark of this sexualization and aggressivization of morality.[3] In the fantasies the prohibitive role of the mother is continually repeated in a disguise, and thus annulled; therefore this repetition amounts to an incestuous—in this case, homosexual—reunion with the mother. As a matter of fact, the patient in her fantasies frequently imagined two punishing figures; herself as a woman punishing girls, and a parallel figure of a man punishing boys. In other fantasies, where only a woman or only a man was the main punishing character, we must assume a condensation of both parental figures.

III

I believe that our explanation of the masochistic perversion contributes to its understanding. It does not, however, exhaust the problem of masochism, not even of the sexual manifestations of masochism, of the frequency of masochistic elements in the normal life of women, the frequency of masochistic traits in the sexual development of childhood and puberty and even of adult men who do not present any actual perversion.

Before continuing our discussion of masochism, let us for a moment recall what we know about the role of repetition of early events. Repetition exists in the transference, as an archaic form of remembrance due to a displacement onto the analyst of unconscious strivings. The repetition compulsion exists as a way of surmounting or mastering painful, past traumatic events (Freud 1920). A slightly modified form of

---

3. More correctly one would say that either neutralization may never have been completely achieved or morality may have regressively deneutralized.

repetition of formerly gratifying situations or fantasies exists, sometimes, as a form of self-punishment for wishes underlying them
(Loewenstein 1945).

It happens that young men are initiated into normal sex life by
women somewhat older than themselves and that such sexual affairs
alone permit these men to overcome strong sexual inhibitions. It seems
that in these real situations the conditions of some fairy tale come true.
Punishment meted out by a bad witch can be undone only by another
witch, a good fairy this time. We see here a parallel to what is going on
in masochistic perversions.

Before going further, it might be useful to discuss the explanations
of masochism proposed by some authors, and to compare them with
the one suggested above. Eidelberg (1954) pointed out that the
masochist overcomes his anxiety by exercising control over the threats
and sufferings he undergoes. Fenichel (1945) makes reference to the
presence in masochistic behavior of mechanisms similar to those in the
signal function of anxiety as described by Freud. Neither of these views
is at variance with the ideas here presented; both deal with processes
aiming at active mastery of a passively experienced danger. However,
as we have seen, the mechanisms operative in masochism involve
much more than defense mechanisms of the ego alone: they involve id
changes and actions on outside objects that permit instinctual
gratifications. I shall have occasion to discuss this further on in connection with some early precursors of masochism.

On the other hand, the theory which sees in masochism a kind of
self-castration appears to be in striking contrast with the observable
behavior of masochists. To be sure, their masturbatory fantasies and
perverse devices abound in allusions to castration threats, and these
patients wallow in them. But the physiological reactions to these
threats reveal that castration is invoked here precisely in order to
annul it (Fenichel 1945). Self-castration does not result in erection or
orgasm, whereas the masochist's actual sexual gratification represents a
triumph over the danger of castration (in the man) or an overcoming of
it (in the woman).

Another point that has to be considered here is the role of bisexuality and of femininity in masochism. There is no doubt that bisexuality
plays a very important role in the masochism of men. But bisexuality
and identification with a woman is not specific for masochism. Indeed,
it plays an even more important and even a specific role in certain

forms of homosexuality. In masochistic men feminine wishes toward the father exist, but they manifest themselves in a form in which genital gratification is bound up with suffering. The latter point is decisive and specific for this perversion. Furthermore, femininity and female sexuality are not identical with masochism. Masochistically tinged sexuality is very much more frequent in women than in men, but there are also women whose sexuality is practically devoid of masochism. Moreover, there are women who present actual masochistic perversions. It does not seem adequate to consider the latter cases as typical representatives of female sexuality. Freud (1932) advised against equating any particular psychological trait, even such opposites as activity and passivity, with either masculinity or femininity. To equate masochism with femininity would not solve the problems presented by masochism. For all these reasons it seems preferable not to follow the classification of masochism, as proposed by Freud (1924) in 1924, which placed masochistic perversions under the heading of feminine masochism.

The time of appearance of the masochistic perversion, never before the oedipal period and frequently in early latency, also contributes to our understanding that they are, as Freud put it, "scars" formed by the passing of the Oedipus complex. Although one can observe occasional masochistic activities and fantasies earlier in children, they do not yet possess all the characteristics of later perversions and, particularly, lack the involvement of genital excitation. Yet they all hinge on the existence of erotogenic masochism and on the ability of the human being to act occasionally counter to the pleasure principle, to deceive the "guardian of our life," to derive pleasure from bodily or mental unpleasure.

In developing his ideas, Freud elaborated three distinct theories to account for the masochistic component drive. He first pointed out that, like all human sensations, pain also could be giving rise to sexual excitation. Later on he expressed his opinion in the following manner, which can best be conveyed by quoting him: "There seems to be a confirmation of the view that masochism is not the manifestation of a primary instinct, but originates from sadism which has been turned round and directed upon the self, that is to say, by means of regression from an object to the ego.... The transformation of sadism into masochism appears to be due to the influence of the sense of guilt..." (Freud 1919).

We know that he later modified this view and conceived the masochism due to transformation of sadism as being a secondary one, derived from what he then termed primary masochism. "A section of this [death] instinct is placed directly in the service of the sexual function, where it has an important part to play: this is true sadism. Another part is not included in this displacement outwards; it remains within the organism and is 'bound' there libidinally with the help of the accompanying sexual excitation mentioned above: this we must recognize as the original erotogenic masochism" (Freud 1924).

This conception thus hinges entirely on whether the speculation on the existence of a death instinct is a valid one or not. We believe that this question may only be decided, some day, through biological research and not by psychoanalysts. However, we assume the existence of two independent instinctual drives: the sexual and the aggressive (Hartmann, Kris, and Loewenstein 1949).

As to its application to erotogenic masochism, the theory of the death instinct does not seem to be satisfactory. We remember that the suffering which is sought after in masochistic perversions hardly ever really endangers the individual's life; it usually has only a limited character. As soon as the unpleasure reaches a certain limit of intensity, it loses its erotogenic quality and the masochist reacts, like anybody else, with genuine fear and displeasure. Dr. Maxwell Gitelson told me about a masochistic patient of his who remarked that there was "a compact in the sadomasochistic partnership, which forbade real injury or pain, and that on one occasion he knew that the breaking of this compact dissolved the partnership." Indeed, it is not the sexual element in masochism which prevents the supposed primary self-destructive tendency from exercising itself. Rather, to the contrary, the vigilance of the guardian of our life, the pleasure principle, is deceived, and this only within certain limits, in order to achieve sexual pleasure. Thus even if biological research were to confirm the validity of the concept of a death instinct, it is not certain that this would decisively add to the explanation of masochism.

Let us consider under what conditions, other than masochism, human behavior may be bound up with suffering or unpleasure. We must first of all remember that we regard pain, unpleasure and anxiety as signals of danger, which however may be used, in masochism, for unconscious gratifications of the id. We consequently find unpleasure bound up with human behavior whenever one group of strivings for gratification entails unpleasure of another group of forces. When males fight one another for the possession of a female, they take suffering and even death in their stride in order to achieve gratification of their sexual drives. Here the pleasure principle has placed itself entirely at the service of sexuality, deserting its function as the guardian of the individual's life. When men risk their lives and sometimes lose them to make money or to gain fame, one part of the ego functions takes over at the expense of the pleasure principle and of those other ego functions which aim at survival. Or when human beings face death to protect their loved ones, their country, or when they face unpopularity and suffering for some moral or intellectual ideal, it would be a mistake to believe that moral masochism is the driving force of such actions. Superego demands on the ego are generally based upon neutralized energy. It is only in case of deneutralization and more specifically of sexualization that one can speak of a sadism of the superego or a masochism of the ego.[4] The essential peculiarity of the human mind, consisting in an early division of functions into those of an id and of an ego, and in the later addition of a superego, accounts for the fact that what is pleasurable for the one part may be painful for the other.

Moreover, the function of safeguarding the individual's life is divided in man between the pleasure principle and the reality principle. The latter's functioning is a concomitant of the development of the ego (Hartmann 1939). The ego uses the reality principle in taking over a great number of the functions of self-preservation (Freud 1932; Hartmann 1939). However, some of the functions safeguarding the individual's life remain subordinated to the pleasure principle; the existence of pain or unpleasure as a reaction to threats to the individual's integrity is a case in point. We must assume that the pleasure principle is the main guardian of life at the earliest stages of development.[5] Later on it can serve the aims of either the ego or the id and can disregard the warnings of the self-preserving signals of the ego. This latter state of affairs as well as the one previously mentioned, i.e., the ability of the reality principle to override the signals given by the

4. R. de Monchy (1950) proposes to attribute acts of self-sacrifice for a cause or for "King and country" to a "sublimated masochism." Inasmuch as sublimation is based upon neutralization of drive energies (Hartmann 1955; Kris 1955), de Monchy's point of view is not far removed from the one presented here.

5. At the undifferentiated stage.

pleasure principle, account for the fact that masochism is not the only instance where the pleasure principle relinquishes its function of safeguarding life.

In discussing these complicated relationships between the pleasure principle and reality principle, Hartmann (1939) refers to the fact, stressed by Freud, that early libidinal manifestations follow the development of functions vital for the survival of the individual. Thus he suggests the possibility of both the pleasure and the reality principles being subordinated to a reality principle in a wider sense. Discussing their connection with problems of human adjustment, Hartmann refutes the theory advanced by Ferenczi (1950) and taken over by Nunberg (1955), according to which all adjustment to reality is based on masochism. He thinks the latter may be found in cases of psychoses (Nunberg), or may exist when reality is painful, but certainly not in adjustment to any kind of reality.

Not even when there is adaptation to a painful reality should we necessarily assume masochism as its motive power. I believe we should speak of masochism only when suffering is sought in order to gratify libidinal demands. True, the distinction between the two—whether suffering is taken in one's stride at the behest of the ego, or is sought after for the sake of libidinal gratification—is not an easy one when deprivation and suffering are caused by reality. Although it was an important discovery of psychoanalysis that masochism may lead an individual unconsciously to seek suffering and failure, this does not justify us to attribute every suffering or failure to masochistic strivings. External reality is not a mere projection of the individual's instinctual drives (Loewenstein 1938, 1940).

The existence of self-destructive tendencies in man was well known before the introduction of the concept of a death instinct. While we do not know whether the biological considerations on which this concept is based hold true, and while we may doubt its value for the explanation of masochism, we should not underestimate the importance of self-destructive forces, the tragic trends in human destiny and life's inexorable course, yet without seeing in all this manifestations of a death instinct, of a "primary masochism." The longing for death is understandable in many an older person for whom life holds more suffering than enjoyment. With the gradual disappearance of genital gratification there occurs a regression to earlier, pregenital stages of libidinal development. In old age this reversion to childhood may bring with it the wish for complete reunion with the mother, for eternal sleep. Suicide sometimes may be the result of such a wish to return to the mother. More frequently, however, it gratifies aggressive tendencies toward a hated object or fulfills the demands of the superego. It can be assumed that suicide often serves both these ends and that masochism is not the driving force in all such cases. I am thinking particularly of situations such as that of a captain going down with his sinking ship, where self-destruction occurs at the behest of the superego and possibly without any admixture of masochism. Indeed, severity of the superego should be distinguished from moral masochism of the ego and from sadism of the superego. In the latter, there occurs a resexualization of moral forces which degrades the morality represented by a severe superego (Freud 1924).

Freud distinguishes two types of moral masochism. In the one, the sadism of the superego is conscious and might periodically alternate with equally violent, unbridled, actual sexual and sadistic gratification. The other type, the moral masochist proper, does not usally present consciously exaggerated manifestations of guilt feeling or remorse; his need for punishment can only be indirectly inferred from his self-destructive behavior.[6]

Of special interest here is the relation of self-destruction to masochistic perversion. While masochists in their fantasies go very far in imagined self-destruction, their safety is assured by the fact that the damage to themselves is merely fantasied. As to perverse practices with real partners, the psychoanalytic literature, as far as I know, does not record any case where such practices actually led to deliberate self-mutilation or self-destruction. The perpetration of self-castration by psychotics or by adherents of some religious sects does not belong under the heading of sexual perversion, but of moral masochism; the religious fanatic, for example, acts out ascetic tendencies at the behest

6. Moral masochism and hypocrisy have in common that a kind of morality is being used in them for the gratification of deneutralized drives. The difference between the two is clear, however. In moral masochism proper, the masochistic gratification is unconscious and the moral motivation may be conscious or not. In hypocrisy the moralistic motivation is consciously stressed in order to hide more or less preconscious gratifications of ego interests or of sadism. Thus to some extent sadism of the superego is close to hypocrisy. The difference between them is that in sadism of the superego and in masochism of the ego, the self is the victim; in hypocrisy, the gratification is derived at the expense of others.

of a sadistic superego. However, there exist persons who inflict pain on themselves to squelch their sexual pleasures or desires. As a result of such "mortification of the flesh," sexual enjoyment of the suffering itself may occur.

Dr. Harry E. August, in a discussion of these problems, mentioned the case of a man who used complicated, masochistic devices for masturbation and eventually was found dead by hanging. Other such cases probably may be found in medicolegal records and police files. I believe that in some of these cases death may be the result of an unconscious wish. In others it may occur not intentionally but accidentally.

When I spoke of the playful or make-believe character underlying the masochistic devices, I did not mean to underestimate the intensity of suffering and anxiety with which the masochist has to deal. On the contrary, this playfulness is his means of reassuring himself that despite his fears and guilt, no real rejection or real castration is forthcoming.

IV

Psychoanalytic experience invariably confirms Freud's view that masochistic perversions in men, as well as the moral masochism, result from a turning of sadism against the self under the influence of guilt feelings. The latter seem less decisive in the masochistic component in the sexuality of women, although here, too, the yielding to superior power adds the relief from guilt feelings which is so important in sexual enjoyment. However, in a more general way the theory of masochism must take into account the vicissitudes of the aggressive drive in its relations to the libido as well as to the ego. Both from analytic work and from direct observation of young children one gains the impression that in childhood a seeking of pleasure in unpleasure exists, which is not based on this turning of aggression against the self; moreover, that the turning of aggression against the self has precursors in which guilt feelings do not yet play a role.

Let us turn, now, to the early manifestations pertinent to the development of what will in the course of time be recognizable as masochism. It might be advisable, in this respect, to distinguish between pleasurable reactions to two types of unpleasure: the physical and the mental. It seems that pleasure bound up with mental unpleasure appears at the end of the first year of life, very closely on the footsteps of the earliest forms of object relation. An example will describe what I mean.

Many years ago I witnessed a little girl of eleven months being jokingly scolded by her grandmother for putting her thumb in her mouth. The baby would, with visible fright, observe the stern face of her grandmother; but as soon as she saw the grandmother smile, she would start to laugh and put her thumb back into her mouth, with a naughty and provoking expression. And so the game would go on. When the prohibition became serious, however, i.e., when the grandmother's face remained serious, the child burst into tears. Needless to say that she would try to transform every prohibition into a game of this sort, to elicit the smile of the grownup, to create that affectionate complicity which undoes the prohibition and eliminates the danger of not being loved (Loewenstein 1938).

In other varieties of these playful activities between adults and children, both the threat and its pleasurable removal almost coincide in one and the same act, such as playfully attacking and frightening the child. It is well known how eagerly children ask for endless repetition of these games.

This type of behavior, this *seduction of the aggressor* which one can find in all children, already contains elements of future, actually masochistic behavior: the seeking for situations that entail danger, fear and unpleasure, and their attenuation through a loving, erotic complicity of the threatening person. It is true, the pleasure in these situations at first is not yet derived from the pain itself but from its removal, from cessation of the threat through a loving reunion with the parent. But one can observe that soon the two, i.e., the unpleasure of the threat and the pleasure of its removal, become intimately tied together. For instance, one can very well see how the child's unpleasure at being thrown into the air or being made to lose his equilibrium, or at being threatened with pain or really hurt slightly, becomes actually pleasurable in itself, provided the parents participate with a loving complicity. These games thus come even more closely to resemble the patterns we have described in masochistic perversion.

Although this normal behavior pattern in children obviously does not always lead to masochism, it contains the essential elements to serve as a prototype for an eventual masochistic perversion. The readiness with which some children pass from enjoying removal of the threat to enjoying the unpleasure itself may serve as a measure of their predisposition for future masochism. While such a predisposition may be constitutionally variable, there is no doubt that it can be reinforced or fixated through excessive stimulation, serving as actual seduction of the child, by a parent who overindulges in these games. But whenever one speaks of fixations which may become pathogenic, it might be wise to consider that they also may occur as a result of insufficient gratification of some libidinal needs in childhood.

This is not the place to attempt a comparative study of "seduction of the aggressor" with other behavior patterns representing defensive ego mechanisms. But it can be pointed out that the latter are mainly endopsychic mechanisms aimed to ward off undesirable instinctual demands or external danger, although they, too, may be much more than that. While the seduction of the aggressor likewise endeavors to ward off threats of loss of love, or of bodily injury, and while it unquestionably also uses an ego mechanism of the type known to us from anxiety formation, essentially it is very different from a defensive ego mechanism. Seduction of the aggressor consists of behavior which seeks and frequently achieves to change an unloving to a loving attitude in the parent. And while thus mobilizing libido in both, it wards off anxiety in the child and aggression in the parent. Although it occurs as a particular form of childhood play, it is different from other games inasmuch as it actually changes the behavior of another person and thus comes close to actions successfully adjusting reality to the needs of the child. However, eventually, it can also be modified and put to use by fantasy and play in ways similar to those described by Freud (1920) and Waelder (1933).[7]

7. Seduction of the aggressor hinges on the infant's very early ability to "perceive" the emotions of the mother. The child acquires this essential function for every object relation and for survival in the social world very soon (Loewenstein 1954). This is made possible by the fact that the infant, while nursing at the breast, looks at the mother's face, a phenomenon that has recently been stressed by Spitz (1955) in another context. Whatever may be the mechanisms through which this perception of the mother's emotion can be achieved, an introjection of her feelings becomes possible at all only after they have been "perceived." As to the mechanism of projection, one may conjecture that it is used concomitantly with introjection so as to distinguish or compare the child's own emotions and those being perceived in her, as a kind of trial-and-error procedure in the gradual acquisition of this knowledge about the mother's emotions. From the example of the little girl "seducing the aggressor," we must conclude that children are able quite early to "perceive the meaning" of an adult's facial expression and to distinguish between the disapproving or angry and the loving expression, the erotic component in the adult's

Should one call this normal behavior of children masochistic, inasmuch as it reveals mechanisms which later on will underlie masochistic perversions? It is more appropriate to term it *proto-* or *pre-masochistic,* as long as any involvement of the genital apparatus is absent. If it is permissible to consider these prototypes of future masochistic behavior from a point of view of survival, one might say that their function is to prepare the child to deal with frustrations and dangers imposed by one human being on another. In these games the roles of the protagonists are always the same; the child is in the "protomasochistic," the parent in the aggressive role. In the complicity of the adult there looms the shadow of erotic response which gives it a sadistic tinge. For the child these games thus have the function, aside from mastering the threat (Freud 1920; Waelder 1933), to seduce the parent, to soften his potential aggressions that might be really threatening the child (Loewenstein 1938).

The gradual development of sexuality, of aggression and of the ego leads the child to deal with new types of gratification and new forms of danger. The behavior of infants, as it was described above, does not stop there. Children evolve ways of enjoying imaginary danger in the form of fairy tales and later on, when they grow older, enjoy terrifying mystery stories. A source of gratification in these childhood activities is the same: the underlying reassurance that the parents love them in spite of punishments, that their threats should not be taken too seriously and would not really endanger the child.

Freud pointed out that all sensations and feelings, even painful ones, might give rise to pleasure when they reach a certain intensity. It is correct to assume that they are pleasurable merely within certain limits,[8] beyond which they are only painful. But it is difficult to determine where the threshold is in each case. There can be no doubt that this fundamental peculiarity underlies all masochistic phenomena. There certainly exist variations as to the extent to which individuals are

---

behavior (Kaplan 1916; Schilder 1950; Burlingham 1935; Greenson 1954). Thus it is not surprising that even when faced with severe bodily punishment by a sadistic mother (as in a case of E. Kris, discussed in connection with this paper), the child does maintain an object relation with her. The sadism of the mother is a form of loving which the child perceives in spite of the punishment.

8. Dr. Elisabeth R. Geleerd suggested this point of view.

predisposed to react in this way, and as to the nature of the painful sensations capable of eliciting pleasure in them.

It is well known that in sadomasochism the erogeneity both of musculature and skin plays a great role. Since we assume the existence of an aggressive drive concomitant to a sexual one, we must suppose that in all autoerotic as well as object-directed erotic activities both libido and aggression are being discharged (Hartmann, Kris, and Loewenstein 1949; Kris 1951). The musculature and skin can thus give rise to aggressive as well as libidinal gratifications which may be both active and passive in form; moreover, these gratifications may be bound up in various ways with the object. Active double gratification (aggressive and libidinal) may be elicited from an attack on an outside object or on the self;[9] a passive double gratification can be produced by an action from an object as well as from oneself.

In all these mixed autoaggressive and autoerotic activities, pain might be bound up with pleasure. There are some phenomena in which the order is inverted; i.e., in which the pain is present first, and the reaction to it has an autoerotic and autoaggressive character. I refer to a painful sensation, such as itching or the sensations produced by swelling of the mucosae of the gums, eliciting reflex responses in the individual that are simultaneously pain-relieving, painful, and pleasurable: scratching, clamping the jaws, teeth-grinding and biting.[10] These phenomena might serve as prototypes for some sadomasochistic reactions to actual or anticipated pain at the hands of the aggressor.

The essential mechanism to which Freud attributed the formation of masochism, namely the turning of sadism against the self, has precursors in which guilt feelings do not seem to be involved. Speaking of adults, for instance, to hit oneself in powerless rage when the object of hate is absent does not, in our opinion, necessarily presuppose an interference of guilt feelings in this turning against the self. In childhood the absence of a suitable object relationship may lead to self-aggressive activity (Kris 1951). One might say that what counts in these cases is the discharge of aggression, irrespective of its source, and that

9. We were accustomed to describe the transformation of the libidinal object relation into autoerotic activity as a narcissistic phenomenon, as a turning of the libido upon the ego. It is more correct to define it as a libidinal investment of the self (Loewenstein 1940a; Hartmann 1950; Kris 1951).

10. Clamping of the jaws is an expression of anger; "one's hands itch" to hit someone.

the recipient of the aggression is secondary, be it an outside object or the self.

There exists a mechanism of dealing with aggression, which can sometimes be observed, that is somehow different from the usual turning around against the self due to guilt. I mean instances where violent aggression is desired from the object in order to squelch one's own aggression against this same object. In patients who presented these reactions the role of guilt over their own aggressive wishes was obvious. But we believe that similar mechanisms may exist without a significant intervention by the superego, as for instance in the behavior of some adolescent girls during courtship. They display obvious aggressive behavior against the wooer, which changes to loving surrender only if the boy succeeds in taming the girl, in being the stronger or more aggressive one. The mechanisms involved in these cases must be of importance for the understanding of the masochism of women.

We may schematically distinguish two opposite forms of expressing aggression: one is the direct attack upon the hated person; the other is a complete ignoring of that person (Hartmann, Kris, and Loewenstein 1949). Some individuals display an extraordinary proclivity, ability and power to hurt by means of this type of "passive aggression." When it exists in childhood, as sulking, it predisposes to later masochistic character formation.[11]

Certain masochistic fantasies are based upon a bending inward[12] of the child's aggressive responses to narcissistic injury, which results when these aggressions cannot be adequately discharged on the outside (Lampl-de Groot 1937). The little child's difficulty in finding ways for aggressive discharge outside might be due to his evaluation of the adult's "power." This power may reside in the latter's size, but also, as in the case of all who are endowed with attributes of power, in those "signs of potential aggression" to which human beings may react with a tendency to bend their own aggression inward.[13] The young child's difficulty of discharging aggression on the outside in threatening situa-

11. It might be interesting to investigate whether a proclivity to passive aggression can be correlated with a condition manifested by some patients when they are in a state of rage; namely, a tonic, immobile contraction of their musculature.

12. I use the term "bending inward" as an English equivalent of the French "*inflexion de l'agression*" (Nacht 1938).

13. One might see in these phenomena a counterpart of what in animal psychology is referred to as dominance.

tions is enhanced by his own helplessness; the counterpart of this helplessness is the absence of a bodily apparatus permitting adequate active mastery of the outside world. Thus there is a tendency in the young child to react to potential threats on the part of the adult with a bending inward of his own aggressive response, and with a heightening of passive wishes that may ensure safety and possibly transform a painful into a pleasurable situation. This can be achieved by means of the same mechanism of "seduction of the aggressor" which we described before in the child's dealing with mental unpleasure.

Bending of the aggression against the self, as a result of the object's overwhelming strength, could be observed by me in two male patients. In one of these, the powerless rage provoked in the child by frequent enemas administered by the mother led him, several years later, to develop masochistic fantasies connected with enemas.[14] There can be no doubt that in his case the libidinal excitation of the rectum paved the way for this change, but it was not the only factor. The ineffectiveness of his rebellion against the enemas, i.e., the mother's actual power, made a discharge of his aggression impossible. Eventually the aggression turned inward, and through masochistic fantasies the incestuous gratification was made possible.

In the other patient, masturbation with sadistic fantasies prevailed over masochistic ones, and both were clearly based on the need to overcome castration fears. The shift from the sadistic to the masochistic fantasy, with the same girl as object, could be understood as follows. It occurred when the girl, whom my patient knew to be attracted to him, suddenly became unfriendly and aloof. Instead of imagining her as being his slave, he now imagined himself in this role toward her. He hoped thus to retain her, as he had succeeded in being loved by his mother after giving up his aggressive behavior toward her. That in his case the superego played a great role in this shift was very obvious, and yet it seems to rest on an earlier mechanism in which the anxiety over losing a powerful object is responsible for turning the aggression inward.[15] This, however, is not the only result which the masochistic

14. As a matter of fact, a mixture of masochistic fantasies and of fetishism of rubber objects.

15. Similar early mechanisms may be responsible for the particular type of homosexuality described by Freud (1922) in "Certain Neurotic Mechanisms in Jealousy, Paranoia, and Homosexuality." In these men, hopeless and powerless rivalry suddenly turns into a homosexual attachment to the very man who had been the rival.

fantasy achieves. It undoes the threat of losing the woman; it attenuates her anger into a domination precluding desertion. In both cases the seduction of the aggressor through masochism has the aim of assuring the love of the object.

We spoke of situations in childhood in which mental unpleasure is due to threats of loss of love, punishment, castration fear. A much earlier danger, the loss of the object, might be dealt with by the mechanism of the "peek-a-boo" game which Freud described as being "related to the child's great cultural achievement—the instinctual renunciation which he had made in allowing his mother to go away without protesting" (Freud 1920). Reacting to the loss of the object with throwing things away and finding them again, the child used a mechanism comparable to the later "seduction of the aggressor" in a child faced with another danger: that of loss of love. In a personal communication, Dr. Ernst Kris expressed the opinion that it ought to be possible already at this stage to discern a potential proclivity to masochism if during the "peek-a-boo" game the child's anxious expectation itself becomes pleasurable.

V

Guilt feeling as the motive for the turning of the aggression against the self, so essential in masochistic perversions and in moral masochism, appears later in childhood. We have dwelt in detail upon mechanisms of an earlier period, which may be made use of in the course of the later development of both the ego and the superego.[16]

Though we do not intend here to elaborate on the origin, development and function of guilt feelings, we can say that they may arise early in consequence of expectation of punishment; they may be the outcome of a conflict of love and hate for the same object; but mainly they are the result of the gradual development of superego functions. As important for the formation of guilt feeling and of masochism, however, must be stressed one point in the child's development; namely, when identification with the parents enables him to behave in various ways at the same time. He can be the threatening parent or the

---

16. These points will be discussed by Hartmann, Kris, and myself in a paper devoted to the study of superego functions.

punished child; he can employ seduction of the aggressor and also be the (internalized) seduced aggressor. The child then is able to use this identification for the undoing of punishment as well as for self-punishment or for provocation of punishment. Later on the identification with the parents becomes involved in the oedipal conflicts and in superego formation. The superego eventually brings permanence and continuity to the turning of the aggressive drives against the self.

The Oedipus complex adds new intensity and new dimensions to the conflicts between the aggressive and libidinal drives as well as between these drives and the ego and superego. In the normal development of men, the castration fear puts an end to the incestuous genital desires. In masochism this process does not succeed. Instead of a passing of the oedipal wishes, a regression occurs to earlier strivings, to pregenital stages of development where to suffer or to inflict suffering, to be humiliated or to humiliate, stands for feminine or masculine, for being castrated or possessing a penis (Freud 1919). In this regression the genital involvement stems from the oedipal phase, the form and condition of the genital excitation—inflicting or undergoing suffering—from the earlier stage whose various modes of interrelation between pleasure and unpleasure were described above.

We know that in boys the oedipal strivings may take a negative form, of a passive feminine attachment to the father. Most frequently and perhaps regularly this homosexual attachment to the dangerous rival-father has the function of giving up the incestuous wishes for the mother, in order to appease him and thus to avoid the danger of castration. The identification with the woman is a utilization, on the phallic level, of a pregenital mechanism existing irrespectively of sex differences since infancy: the seduction of the aggressor. Viewed from this angle, masochism represents one form, although not the only one, of this attempt at solving the conflicts of the oedipal phase.

As for masochism in women, it is essential to bear in mind that the early instinctual development of the female child, as opposed to that of the male, reflects the anatomical and developmental differences between them. In contrast to the boy, the normal girl enters the oedipal phase by giving up both the original love object (the mother) and the sexual organ (the clitoris). Her masculine, phallic attachment to her mother is being replaced by a feminine attachment to her father, in which the primacy of the clitoris yields to the preeminence of the vagina. For the girl, therefore, the entering into a feminine,

heterosexual attachment presupposes an acceptance of "being castrated" (Freud 1925, 1931, 1932; Deutsch 1925; Lampl-de Groot 1928;
Brunswick 1940). And this acceptance may become bound up with the
pregenitally preformed pleasure in unpleasure.

The little girl seems to present a greater tendency to suppress
aggressive strivings than does the boy, which might well be due to her
congenital equipment as well as to social pressure (Freud 1932). The
absence of an organ for sexual aggression may reinforce this tendency
(Deutsch 1925) and may, moreover, favor the bending inward of her
aggression (Lampl-de Groot 1937).

Indeed, the importance of a masochistic component in the sexuality of women was related by H. Deutsch (1944) to women's greater
passivity as well as to the fact that suffering is bound up with their
sexual organs and functions. Marie Bonaparte (1935) has pointed out
that the conformation of their genitalia, their concavity, demands a
penetration which their self-preservatory forces oppose. This danger to
their bodily integrity evokes aggressive reactions against the male
which are, furthermore, reinforced by their active phallic strivings.
Thus it seems that a stronger erotic "concave" striving, combined with
the bending inward of the woman's aggressive tendencies through
superior aggression and with the mechanism of "seduction of the aggressor," leads her to enjoy the unconsciously dreaded sexual aggression of the male. Through this mechanism women disarm the dangerous man by seducing him, and are themselves seduced by this
threatening situation.

VI

We must add to our discussion of masochism a few remarks about its
relations to object choice. Masochism may be involved in particular
ways in the choice of a love object. In the masochistically tinged sexuality of women pleasure in pain appears as a factor heightening sexual
gratification, but may also be a stimulus for the choice of a love object.
H. Deutsch (1944) describes several cases of women slavishly attached
to men who inflicted severe physical pain and humiliation on them.[17]

In the love life of both women and men, an exclusive attachment
to a single object is frequently regarded as a most highly integrated
form of emotional development. However, in some cases this exclusiv-

17. The greater role of object relation in the little girl, which is mentioned by Freud
(1932), thus may be an additional factor predisposing to future masochism.

ity is the result of a particular and limited balance of forces; such, for instance, that some men or women can be sexually gratified only by a certain partner whose own sexuality presents peculiarities without which they are unable to be potent or to reach an orgasm. Among these various peculiarities are those which gratify some perverse "conditions" for sexual gratification. Masochistic persons, for example, who find in some partners a corresponding form of sadism, might become exclusively attached to those partners. One gains the impression that masochism may be the prerequisite or the consequence of some extreme cases of infatuation built on the model of early incestuous attachments. Thus a certain lack of exclusivity in the choice of love objects may represent a "lower" form of integration and yet on the whole a less vulnerable form of sexuality, less limited by some particular balance of "ingredients" in the partner's emotional make-up.

On the other hand, the sexuality of individuals for whom the value of the love object as a person is unimportant and the partner merely counts as a means of sexual gratification, without other emotional tie, might certainly be considered limited or arrested in its development. In the case of certain perverts, very often indeed the partner counts only in terms of gratifying the specific perversion. One would hardly refer as a love object to the special shape of shoe or foot all-important to a fetishist. The same may apply, more or less, to some masochists for whom the sexual object is not a person, or is so only by virtue of behaving in a particular way which satisfies their condition for sexual gratification.

This pattern must be especially pronounced in the cases we mentioned before as appearing probably in police records but not in the consultation room of the psychoanalyst. Those may very well be the kinds of perversion in which some have seen a special affinity to psychoses. In such cases one might assume the existence of a severe ego disturbance pertaining to object relations, a disturbance which on the one hand leads to psychosis, and on the other hand precludes any integration of the partial drives under the aegis of genitality related to a real and stable object. However, there exists an unquestionable correlation between masochistic characters and paranoic conditions (Freud 1919; Waelder 1936; Nacht 1938; Bak 1946; Brenman 1952). But in our opinion these cases do not justify the belief in a general affinity between "perversion" and "psychosis." Because of their considerable variations in terms of relationship to objects, perversions encompass a heterogeneous group of disorders which cannot easily be pigeonholed under a single heading like "The Perversion" whose only common denominator would be a negative one: "deviation" from normal sexual behavior.

VII

Whatever the mechanisms and the motives for turning the aggression against the self, clinically and theoretically masochism and its counterpart, sadism, are intimately bound together. In both of them suffering, pain, unpleasure are the conditions for sexual excitation, and this is the very point about which we do not know enough. To be sure, we know that in sadism and masochism libido and aggression exist in a certain state of fusion. But we know them also to be observable in a state of fusion outside of sadism and masochism. What, then, is the difference between these two kinds of fusion? If we assume, as we do, two different drives, the sexual and the aggressive, the gratification of each of which is accompanied by a specific form of pleasure (Hartmann, Kris, and Loewenstein 1949), might the difference between the two types of fusion—or degrees of defusion—be found to reside in different types of mixtures of these specific, pleasurable experiences? Could it be that in sadomasochism the pleasure of aggressive gratification has retained a greater independence from the pleasures afforded by libidinal gratifications? We do not know it.

Whatever it may be, both sadism and masochism presuppose a rather evolved object relation (Hartmann, Kris, and Loewenstein 1949). In both, the enjoyment of causing or suffering pain is clearly perceived in the sexual partner and is an essential part of the perversion. One of the functions of sadism and masochism is thus to maintain object relations, however precarious, in the face of aggressions which threaten the object world or the individual himself.

VIII

Of the various factors we have described as entering into the formation of masochism, not all seem to be of equal importance in its various forms.

Erotogenic masochism expresses mainly the fundamental property of the human mind, of experiencing as pleasurable some painful processes. The very early mechanisms of turning aggression against the self or passively bending it inward, with or without intervention of guilt feelings, and the mechanism of seduction of the aggressor make use of this property. In its individual development the aggressive drive is very closely bound up with the libidinal development. During this development, both active and passive forms of these fused drives manifest themselves. Thus the passive forms, i.e., the erotogenic masochism, according to the stage of libidinal development, take on the shape of the wish (or fear): to be devoured, to be beaten, to be castrated, to play the role of a woman in intercourse (Freud 1924).

The importance of the *masochistic component in the normal sex life of women* has the same basis, with particular importance of the mechanism of seduction of the aggressor due to the additional factor of passivity and to the psychological consequences resulting from the conformation and functions of the female genital apparatus. These factors undoubtedly are reinforced by turning of aggressions against the self, due to guilt feelings derived from the girl's castrative as well as from her incestuous fantasies. However, guilt feelings here do not seem to have the paramount role which they play in masochistic perversions and in moral masochism.

We must assume that in the *masochistic perversions* the inherent proclivity to experience some painful sensations as pleasurable is particularly pronounced. This may be due to some congenital equipment or to environmental influences, such as early traumatic stimulations or seductions. In these perversions, the role of guilt feelings in the turning of the aggression against the self seems to be superimposed upon the erotogenic masochism. Masochistic perversion, be it in men or in women, is the result of a process in which the reinforced erotogenic masochism has undergone a particular development by having been "brought in relation with the Oedipus complex" (Freud 1919). It represents "the legacy of that complex" (Freud), inasmuch as the masochist's sexual gratification never severs its connection with it. The fixation to the incestuous object choice, and the guilt and anxiety connected with it, pervade the masochist's sex life. Indeed, the sexual partner is expected to behave like a threatening, punishing parental figure. Masochists unconsciously use the early mechanism of seduction of the aggressor toward the heterosexual as well as the homosexual parental object. And the very function of the perversion, which allows the masochist to have an erection and an orgasm, resides in the undoing of both guilt feeling and castration threat, and in the unconscious incestuous gratification.

There are instances of masochism where one of the factors, i.e., the reinforced erotogenic masochism, has greater importance, and others in which the role of the "legacy of the Oedipus complex" predominates. The former would obtain when enjoyment of physical pain is the essential point, the latter when enjoyment of threats and humiliation is the condition for gratification. In cases where the "legacy of the Oedipus complex" is of little importance, masochism or other perversions might also be due to a severe disorder of the ego in the area of object relations.

We can distinguish three forms of *masochistic behavior:* the masochistic character, the behavior caused by what is called the "mentality of a slave," and the moral masochism. In all three the connection with sexuality is loosened, though in an unequal degree. The connection with aggression, however, is not lost in all of them to the same extent.

In cases of *masochistic character*, suffering as a means of aggression is very obvious (W. Reich 1949; Berliner 1947). Genetically it can be traced to early forms of "passive aggression." Since these disorders are those of character formation, we must assume that they are based not only on particular forms of instinctual development, but to a great extent also on that of the ego (Berliner 1947).

In childhood, shutting the mouth to food and closing the anal sphincter as a refusal to defecate may be prototypes of this behavior (Bergler 1949). Guilt feelings inhibit active manifestations of aggression and, by turning them against the self, reinforce the passive forms of aggression. Since he himself suffers, the masochist feels justified in having his suffering cause pain to others. In childhood a normal form of this behavior is well known: sulking is a powerful means of aggression against the mother and frequently an effective one in forcing her into manifestations of love.[18] Feeling sorry for oneself and the "*délectation morose*" or being a "comic teasee" (Brenman 1952) usually entail far less aggression against the outside world. In adult life the behavior of the masochistic character is usually more effective in causing the subject himself to suffer than in swaying other adults into a behavior resembling that of a loving mother. Occasionally adults may, by delib-

18. For its role in psychopathology, see also Borel and Robin (1925).

erately using similar mechanisms, achieve effects on the outside world which no other method might afford; I am alluding here to hunger strikes, for instance.

In masochistic character disorders the interplay between the drives and the ego is a complex one. On the one hand, the warded-off masochistic tendencies, persisting unconsciously, influence the development of the ego in such a way that its functions lend themselves to an unconscious gratification of related instinctual demands. On the other hand, faced with actual or imagined human aggression or loss of love, the ego uses mechanisms which reactivate masochistic tendencies in order to find pleasure in suffering and to attenuate aggression. (The ego may thus, for instance, indirectly reactivate the mechanism of seduction of the aggressor.) We may assume that both these processes are always at work in such character structures. Their results manifest themselves as character neuroses, as behavior patterns bound up with considerable sensitivity to actual or potential aggression from without. The presumed aggressor is made to feel guilty and therefore often actually becomes aggressive. The teasee displays an uncanny skill in provoking actual teasing (Brenman 1952). Thus in such cases the unconscious masochism is being gratified by actual aggression from the outside, which perpetuates these neurotic mechanisms.

The behavior caused by the *"mentality of a slave"* occurs in people subserviently submitting to a victor and identifying themselves with him on the level of the superego without neutralization of the aggression and with libidinization of self-destructive tendencies (Hartmann, Kris, and Loewenstein 1949). Inmates of concentration camps were observed to take over the mannerisms of their S.S. tormentors and their sadistic behavior toward other captives as soon as they had the opportunity to do so (Bettelheim 1943). It is not unlikely that such behavior occurs when the submission to aggression initially elicited a masochistically tinged sexual attachment to the aggressor.

About the *moral masochism* we know (Freud 1922, 1924) that it exists in two forms: as sadism of the superego and as masochism of the ego. These two types of attitudes of the superego toward the ego reflect the two forms of gratification in aggressions against the self in early childhood. In the one, the discharge of libido and aggression is paramount, be it directed against an outside object or the self. In the other, unconscious libidinal gratification is effected by undergoing aggression, be it from outside or from oneself. The relationship of moral masochism to sexuality is quite remarkable and puzzling. The moral masochist does not derive any manifest sexual gratification from suffering, and there does not seem to exist any obvious correlation between masochistic perversion and its moral counterpart. In the perversion, both "crime and punishment" remain in the sexual sphere; not so, apparently, in moral masochism. Freud pointed out that even the condition that suffering be inflicted by a loved person seems to have disappeared. On the other hand, the relationship of superego and ego in moral masochism is more sexualized (Freud 1924) and aggressivized, i.e., less neutralized, than it is in people not afflicted by it. In its masochistic relationship toward the superego, the ego appears to have reactivated early passive homosexual wishes toward the father in their regressive form of suffering and punishment (Hartmann, Kris, and Loewenstein 1949). Thus, we must say, moral masochism is not completely devoid of connection with a love object; even when the masochist seeks suffering "caused by impersonal forces or circumstances" (Freud 1924), he longs for parental love in this disguise. Does not the religious person accept God's punishment as proof of His love? Fate, as Freud pointed out, is unconsciously conceived of as personal, as a remote representative of the parents. Underlying the self-destructive tendencies involved in moral masochism, one can see at work in it the desperate attempt to seduce the aggressor, the harsh conscience, to appease the gods or fate by suffering; i.e., to revert to childhood, to the state when threats and dangers could actually be averted or minimized by using the method which was effective then.

The masochistic perversion as well as the behavioral masochism originate in the early processes of sexualization of mental and physical unpleasure. But they derive from them on different pathways and perform different functions. In the perversion, conscious pain is sought in order to reach conscious sexual gratification. In the masochistic behavior we observe an unconscious libidinization of suffering caused by aggressions from without and within.

In discussing masochistic behavior we have been led to consider not only problems of drive development but also those of survival. Viewed from this angle, masochism seems to be the weapon of the weak—i.e., of every child—faced with danger of human aggression. The masochistic perversion does not deal with the survival of the individual, but one can say that it permits a limited and precarious survival of genitality. Female masochism is linked to survival, however, inasmuch as it permits the woman to overcome dangers to her bodily integrity that are inherent in her sexual functions. The mechanism of "seduction of the aggressor," which we have found to be operative in masochism and its forerunners since childhood, appears at that early age to ensure the existence of parental love, at a time when parental love is as necessary for the development of sexuality as it is for survival. It continues to be operative in both, even when they have parted ways and at times even oppose one another.

REFERENCES

Bak, R. C. (1946). Masochism in paranoia. *Psychoanal. Q.*, 15:285–301.
———— (1953). Fetishism. *J. Amer. Psychoanal. Assn.*, 1:285–98.
Bergler, E. (1949). *The Basic Neurosis*. New York: Grune & Stratton.
Berliner, B. (1940). Libido and reality in masochism. *Psychoanal. Q.*, 9:322–33.
———— (1947). On some psychodynamics of masochism. *Psychoanal. Q.*, 16:459–71.
Bettelheim, B. (1943). Individual and mass behavior in extreme situations. *J. Abn. & Soc. Psychol.*, 38:417–52.
Bonaparte, M. (1933). Des autoerotismes agressifs par la griffe et par la dent. *Rev. Franç. Psychanal.*, 6:192–216.
———— (1935). Passivité, masochisme et féminité. *Rev. Franç. Psychanal.*, 8:208–16.
———— (1953). *Female Sexuality*. New York: Int. Univ. Press.
Borel, A. & Robin, G. (1925). *Les Bouderies Morbides*. Paris: N.R.F.
Bornstein, B. (1949). The analysis of a phobic child. Some problems of theory and technique in child analysis. *Psychoanal. Study Child*, 3/4:181–226.
Brenman, M. (1952). On teasing and being teased: and the problem of "moral masochism." *Psychoanal. Study Child*, 7:264–85.
Bromberg, N. (1955). Maternal influences in the development of moral masochism. *Am. J. Orthopsychiat.*, 25:802–12.
Brunswick, R. M. (1940). The preoedipal phase of the libido development. *Psychoanal. Q.*, 9:293–319.
Burlingham, D. T. (1935). Die Einfühlung des Kleinkindes in die Mutter. *Imago*, 21:429–44.
Deutsch, H. (1925). The psychology of women in relation to the functions of reproduction. *Int. J. Psychoanal.*, 6:405–18.
———— (1930). The significance of masochism in the mental life of women. *Int. J. Psychoanal.*, 11:48–60.
———— (1944). *The Psychology of Women, I*. New York: Grune & Stratton.

Dooley, L. (1941). The relation of humor to masochism. *Psychoanal. Rev.*, 28:37–46.

Eidelberg, L. (1933a). Zur Metapsychologie des Masochismus. *Int. Ztschr. Psa.*, 19:615–16.

——— (1933b). Zur Theorie und Klinik der Perversion. *Int. Ztschr. Psa.*, 19:620–21.

——— (1934). Beiträge zum Studium des Masochismus. *Int. Ztschr. Psa.*, 20:336–53.

——— (1954). *A Comparative Pathology of the Neuroses.* New York: Int. Univ. Press.

Eissler, K. R. (1953). A clinical note on moral masochism: Eckermann's relationship to Goethe. In *Drives, Affects, Behavior*, ed. R. M. Loewenstein. New York: Int. Univ. Press, pp. 285–326.

Feldman, S. S. (1951). Anxiety and orgasm. *Psychoanal. Q.*, 20:528–49.

Fenichel, O. (1953a). The clinical aspect of the need for punishment. *Collected Papers*, 1:71–92. New York: Norton.

——— (1953b). A critique of the death instinct. *Collected Papers*, 1:363–72. New York: Norton.

——— (1945). *The Psychoanalytic Theory of Neurosis.* New York: Norton.

Ferenczi, S. (1950). Stages in the development of the sense of reality. In *Sex in Psychoanalysis.* New York: Basic Books, pp. 213–39.

Freud, A. (1922). Schlagephantasie und Tagtraum. *Imago*, 8:317–32.

——— (1946). *The Ego and the Mechanisms of Defense.* New York: Int. Univ. Press.

Freud, S. (1905). Three essays on the theory of sexuality. *S.E.*, 7.

——— (1919). "A child is being beaten." *Coll. Papers* 2.

——— (1920). Beyond the pleasure principle. *S.E.*, 18.

——— (1922). Certain neurotic mechanisms in jealousy, paranoia, and homosexuality. *S.E.*, 18.

——— (1924). The economic principle in masochism. *Coll. Papers* 2.

——— (1925). Some psychological consequences of the anatomical distinction between the sexes. *Coll. Papers* 5.

——— (1926). *The Problem of Anxiety.* New York: Norton, 1936.

——— (1931). Female sexuality. *Coll. Papers* 5.

——— (1932). *New Introductory Lectures on Psychoanalysis.* New York: Norton, 1933.

——— (1937). Analysis terminable and interminable. *Coll. Papers* 5.

Greenacre, P. (1952). *Trauma, Growth, and Personality.* New York: Norton.

——— (1953). Certain relationships between fetishism and faulty development of the body image. *Psychoanal. Study Child*, 8:79–98.

——— (1954). Contribution to the discussion on problems of infantile neurosis. *Psychoanal. Study Child*, 9:18–24.

_____ (1955). Further considerations regarding fetishism. *Psychoanal. Study Child*, 10:187–94.

Greenson, R. R. (1954). On empathy and sublimation. Presented at the Midwinter Meeting of the American Psychoanalytic Association.

Grunberger, S. (1954). Esquisse d'une théorie psychanalytique du masochisme. *Rev. Franç. Psychanal.*, 18:193–214.

Hartmann, H. (1939). Ich-Psychologie und Anpassungsproblem. *Int. Ztschr. Psa. und Imago*, 24:62–135.

_____ (1950). Comments on the psychoanalytic theory of the ego. *Psychoanal. Study Child*, 5:74–96.

_____ (1952). The mutual influences in the development of ego and id. *Psychoanal. Study Child*, 7:9–30.

_____ (1955). Notes on the theory of sublimation. *Psychoanal. Study Child*, 10:9–29.

_____ Kris, E. & Loewenstein, R. M. (1949). Notes on the theory of aggression. *Psychoanal. Study Child*, 3/4:9–36.

Horney, K. (1935). The problem of feminine masochism. *Psychoanal. Rev.*, 22:241–57.

Kaplan, L. (1916). *Psychoanalytische Probleme*. Vienna: Deuticke.

Keiser, S. (1949). The fear of sexual passivity in the masochist. *Int. J. Psychoanal.*, 30:162–71.

Kris, E. (1950). Notes on the development and on some current problems of psychoanalytic child psychology. *Psychoanal. Study Child*, 5:24–46.

_____ (1951). Some comments and observations on early autoerotic activities. *Psychoanal. Study Child*, 6:95–116.

_____ (1955). Neutralization and sublimation: observations on young children. *Psychoanal. Study Child*, 10:30–46.

Laforgue, R. (1930). On the erotization of anxiety. *Int. J. Psychoanal.*, 11:312–26.

Lampl-de Groot, J. (1928). The evolution of the Oedipus complex in women. *Int. J. Psychoanal.*, 9:332–45.

_____ (1933). Problems of femininity. *Psychoanal. Q.*, 2:489–518.

_____ (1937). Masochismus und Narzissmus. *Int. Ztschr. Psa.*, 23:479–89.

_____ (1953). Depression and aggression. In *Drives, Affects, Behavior*, ed. R. M. Loewenstein. New York: Int. Univ. Press, pp. 153–68.

Lewin, B. D. (1950). *The Psychoanalysis of Elation*. New York: Norton.

Loewenstein, R. M. (1932). D'un mécanisme auto-punitif. *Rev. Franç. Psychanal.*, 5:141–51.

_____ (1935). Phallic passivity in men. *Int. J. Psychoanal.*, 16:334–40.

_____ (1938). L'origine du masochisme et la théorie des pulsions. *Rev. Franç. Psychanal.*, 10:293–321.

_____ (1940). The vital and somatic instincts. *Int. J. Psychoanal.*, 21:377–400.

———— (1945). A special form of self-punishment. *Psychoanal. Q.*, 14:46–51.

———— (1954). Contribution to the discussion on problems of infantile neurosis. *Psychoanal. Study Child*, 9:47–48.

Menaker, E. (1953). Masochism—a defense reaction of the ego. *Psychoanal. Q.*, 22:205–20.

Menninger, K. A. (1938). *Man Against Himself.* New York: Harcourt, Brace.

———— (1942). *Love Against Hate.* New York: Harcourt, Brace.

Monchy, R. de. (1950). Masochism as a pathological and as a normal phenomenon in the human mind. *Int. J. Psychoanal.*, 31:95–97.

Nacht, S. (1938). Le masochisme. *Rev. Franç. Psychanal.*, 10:173–291.

Nunberg, H. (1955). *Principles of Psychoanalysis. Their Application to the Neuroses.* New York: Int. Univ. Press.

Rado, S. (1933). Fear of castration in women. *Psychoanal. Q.*, 2:425–75.

Reich, A. (1949). The structure of the grotesque-comic sublimation. *Bull. Menninger Clin.*, 13:160–71.

Reich, W. (1949). The masochistic character. In *Character Analysis*, 3rd ed. New York: Orgone Institute, pp. 208–47.

Reik, T. (1924). Psychoanalysis of the unconscious sense of guilt. *Int. J. Psychoanal.*, 5:439–50.

———— (1925). *Geständniszwang und Strafbedürfnis.* Wien: Internationaler Psychoanalytischer Verlag.

———— (1940). The characteristics of masochism. *Am. Imago*, 1:26–59.

———— (1941). *Masochism in Modern Man.* New York: Farrar & Rhinehart.

Schilder, P. (1950). *The Image and Appearance of the Human Body.* New York: Int. Univ. Press.

Spitz, R. A. (1953). Aggression: its role in the establishment of object relations. In *Drives, Affects, Behavior*, ed. R. M. Loewenstein. New York: Int. Univ. Press, pp. 126–38.

———— (1955). The primal cavity. *Psychoanal. Study Child*, 10:215–40.

———— & Wolf, K. M. (1946). Anaclitic depression. *Psychoanal. Study Child*, 2:313–42.

———— (1949). Autoerotism. Some empirical findings and hypotheses on three of its manifestations in the first year of life. *Psychoanal. Study Child*, 3/4:85–120.

Waelder, R. (1933). The psychoanalytic theory of play. *Psychoanal. Q.*, 2:208–24.

———— (1936). The principle of multiple function: observations on overdetermination. *Psychoanal. Q.*, 5:45–62.

Wittels, F. (1937). The mystery of masochism. *Psychoanal. Rev.*, 24:139–49.

Zilboorg, G. (1937). Considerations on suicide, with particular reference to that of the young. *Am. J. Orthopsychiat.*, 7:15–31.

6

Reflections on the Treatment of a Case of Obsessional Neurosis

Over twenty-five years ago an analyst living abroad asked me if I would take care of one of her patients during the latter's visit to her sister in Paris.

Some time later the patient in question came to see me. She was a married woman of about thirty, with symptoms of a serious obsessive-compulsive neurosis. She had such a dread of having perhaps "touched the old woman" that she could not get along without seeing her analyst every day. She would not let me question her in any detail on the history of her life and illness because she said, "It upset her too much and made her anxiety unbearable." Knowing that my role during the few weeks I would be seeing her should be that of a temporary crutch, and that the responsibility for her treatment was in the hands of her regular analyst, I decided to accept the passive role the patient imposed on me, and to observe and help her as much as I could.

The patient began each session by relating a dream of the preceding night and followed it up with "associations." Mainly through these "associations" I discovered that she had been in treatment for a considerable number of years without much result. But I will give the biographical data further on in my description of the case, since it was only later that I learned many more details about her history.

Some months after the patient had returned to her country I received another letter from her analyst, this time asking me if I would be willing to take over her patient, who was showing no improvement

From *Revue Française de Psychanalyse* (Freud Centenary Issue), Vol. 20, No. 3 (July-September 1956), 384-404, "Réflexions sur le traitement d'un cas de névrose compulsionnelle." English translation by Vera Dammann, 1958.

at all. I wrote for details of the case and in reply received a letter from the analyst in which she enumerated a number of the patient's "complexes." It was a fairly comprehensive list containing, among others, the unconscious need for punishment—then a comparative newcomer in the categories of pathogenic factors described in the psychoanalytic literature of the period. The reason I am stressing this letter is because it made rather an unfavorable impression on me at the time, but it was not until much later that I realized why: the list of "complexes" she had sent me could have applied equally well to a large number of patients and did not read like the description of a particular case. There was nothing in the letter that referred to the specific problems of this patient and made her recognizable as an individual or distinguished her from the general group of people suffering from the same "complexes." I had a premonition that this lack of attention to the personal peculiarities of the patient might be partly responsible for the lack of success in the treatment. However, I was cautious about passing judgment in view of the seriousness of the patient's symptoms which had persisted for many years: continuous and excessive anxiety; an extreme degree of *folie du doute;* endless compulsive ablutions; total absorption in her "touchings" and her treatment to the exclusion of all other activities. Therefore, when her husband came to see me, I offered to analyze his wife for a period of six to eight months and then tell him whether I felt myself capable of continuing with any chance of success. It is hardly necessary to mention that all the medical examinations the patient had undergone, both in her own country and in France, had failed to discover any somatic disorder. However, I did keep in mind the possibility that she might be suffering either from one of those neuroses which are inaccessible to psychoanalysis or from a latent psychosis in the guise of obsessional neurosis: hence my reservations in making a prognosis. Such possibilities had to be contemplated in the presence of symptoms which had been growing steadily worse over the years. Fortunately, my fears were to prove unfounded.

I have already mentioned the patient's fears and her obsessive dread of having "touched the old woman." I also mentioned her ablutions, or to use her own expression, "washings." It became clear to me later that the fears were not lest she had touched some real old woman, but lest she had touched someone or something that might have been in contact with an old servant, a maid she had had six years previously. It made no difference whether the object in question was a man or a young woman or a table, nor whether the person or object was quite close to her or several yards away. What mattered was that she had the idea, the obsession, that she might somehow have been in contact with this person or thing that had been touched by the "old woman," the maid in question. To avoid being "contaminated" by such "touches," she isolated herself from all sorts of objects—including the psychoanalytic couch—by spreading out innumerable pieces of tissue paper. Every morning following an established ritual, she scrubbed herself for hours with soap and water. And if during these "washings" she had the obsessive thought that she might somehow have touched "the old woman," she was compelled to start all over again. The result was that she walked around with her red, chapped hands held away from her body, avoiding contact with any of the furniture, in a state of continual panic anxiety. One of her constant preoccupations was the problem of getting herself new clothes. Although she had a great many dresses hanging in her closets, each one carefully separated from the others by layers of tissue paper, she was unable to touch them because they had been contaminated by "the old woman's touch." She was continually faced therefore with the terrifying task of buying a new dress. Curiously enough, but typical of the ambivalence in this type of obsessional patient, side by side with this exaggerated cleanliness in her clothes and her person, she only washed her hair once or twice a year, and wore the same underwear for several months without a change. "It is clean," she used to say, "because I wash myself so often." Her life was completely taken up with her neurosis; she had no time left for recreation, rest, or occupation.

II

At about this time I learned a few details about the patient's history, and although the complete story only came out during the course of her treatment, I propose for the sake of clarity to give a consecutive summary here, and will come back to certain facts in more detail later.

Mme. N was the second youngest of four children. There was a considerable gap in age between the older brother and sister and herself, and she had always been closest to the younger sister, with whom she was now living in Paris. She herself had been her father's favorite and used to protect her younger sister from his injustices. The two sisters had remained extremely close. The parents had been a united couple; they had managed to impose their way of life on their children, although not their small-town bourgeois opinions. Later, after the patient's marriage, the father's authoritarian attitude was greatly modified as the result of financial reverses, a fact which was to have considerable influence on the patient's neurosis.

The first signs of neurosis appeared when the patient was sixteen.[1] She was studying the piano and planning to make a career in music. Her father objected violently to her plans; "he was not going to allow a daughter of his to become an artist; she must marry and have children." The patient did not relinquish her plans, but from that time on she had "concentration difficulties" and this effectively prevented her doing as good work on the piano as before. She was treated by a well-known psychotherapist and her condition improved. Some years later her parents decided to marry her to a young man they had selected, the son of family friends. He was an amiable, pleasant young man, but the patient neither respected nor admired him. She rebelled and refused to consider the marriage. She left with her sister to spend a weekend in the mountains and there had an affair with a young man she had never met before and never met again. When she returned home, tearful and conscience-stricken, she told her mother all about the episode as proof that she could not possibly marry the young man her parents had picked out for her. Her father remained adamant and threatened to make her knuckle under. She gave in.

During the honeymoon her neurosis erupted definitively in the form of continuous states of anxiety and depression. For two years she was under the care of Dr. X, who used a kind of "cathartic" technique. When there was still no improvement after two years of treatment, Dr. X told her husband about his wife's premarital affair, which he considered responsible for her anxiety state. Fortunately, the patient had already related the whole episode to her husband a few weeks previously so that he did not show too much resentment. She then went into treatment with Dr. Y. The patient related—whether accurately or not I had no means of knowing—that after about two years of treatment, when she began to express suicidal thoughts, Dr. Y abruptly broke off the analysis without giving her any other suggestions or ad-

1. There was no way of ascertaining the existence of a childhood neurosis and the patient never mentioned recollections of neurotic symptoms in childhood.

vice. Her anxiety grew worse. She then went to Dr. Z, with whom she remained in analysis for eleven years prior to coming to me. During the first five years of treatment her life was a succession of anxiety crises, depressions, and phobias. Among other things, she was afraid to enter any street or public square if the name contained an allusion to rust or red. During the course of analysis it came out that this color was contained in the name of the boy she had the weekend affair with.

After five years her condition suddenly worsened and the neurosis took the acute form described earlier. Immediately preceding the aggravation of her symptoms some important life events had occurred. Her father, who had been having business difficulties, lost all his money with the result that the whole family was now in serious financial straits. Perhaps as a result of his financial misfortunes, Mme. N's father permitted her younger sister to marry the man she was in love with, an artist with neither money nor position. This had a profoundly disturbing effect on the patient. And while the financial situation of her own family was growing more and more critical, her husband inherited a fortune from his father. Thus the patient became the only member of her family in easy circumstances, a situation which she found very distressing. Her humiliation was complete when her father, whom she had always admired and feared, borrowed money from her husband and failed to pay it back. Mme. N's condition suddenly deteriorated. She had recently engaged a maid whom she hated and feared. She only kept her for four weeks but by the time she dismissed her the damage had been done, and she was already in the grip of the obsessional neurosis in which, as we have seen, this maid becomes the old woman who haunted her. Mme. N could not bear to touch anything in the house—furniture, clothes, etc.—that this woman might have touched. Henceforward her clothes remained hanging in their closets. She could not even bear to sleep in the same bed as her husband unless she was separated from him by layers of tissue paper, so that intercourse between them occurred even less frequently than before. Her anxiety was intolerable, and in order to rid herself of any trace of contact with the old maidservant, she started the ritual of daily ablutions described earlier. In all fairness to Dr. Z it should be stated that the latter tried several times to get her to go to another doctor but the patient refused. And Mr. N told me later in confidence that, unknown to his wife, Dr. Z had not charged any fees for the last six years.

III

As I mentioned in the beginning, the patient's behavior during her analytic sessions followed a fairly regular pattern. She avoided coming into contact with any furniture, covered the couch with pieces of tissue paper, stretched out on it, and then began by beseeching me tearfully to reassure her that she had not "touched the old woman." Then she would relate a dream and follow it with "associations." The "associations" were of a very special nature. They resembled fantasies based on symbolic interpretations of the dream, interspersed with wisps of memories from her life. It was obvious that she was continuing a routine pattern she had grown accustomed to with Dr. Z. At first I had no inkling of what this way of behaving represented. After a few weeks my interpretation of one of her dreams seemed indirectly to impress the patient; the next day she brought a new dream and associations which seemed to confirm my interpretation of the previous day exactly. I was very pleased about this. But when a few weeks later the same thing occurred again with the interpretation of another dream, my satisfaction became tinged with uncertainty. There was something strange about this: it was not usual to see one's interpretations so readily confirmed, without struggle or resistances on the part of the patient, and particularly such a seriously sick patient. When soon the same thing happened a third time I was sure I was on the wrong track. Subsequently these initial interpretations were shown to be more or less irrelevant. It then became clear to me that everything concerned with the treatment, the sessions themselves, her "associations," my interpretations, had been absorbed into her obsessional neurosis and had become part of a sort of magic ritual which, like her ablutions, she used to help ward off the "old woman's touch." The treatment had lost all character of psychoanalytic cure and had become an integral part of her neurosis.

The patient had a peculiar habit which gave me the first clue to the enigma. At the end of every session she would insist on my repeating my last interpretation several times, on the pretext either that she had not understood a word of it, or that she did not get the full meaning, or because she could not remember the exact phrasing. She claimed that she had to get my interpretation by heart so that she could remember and use it to help her cope with her doubts and fears until the next session. I then recalled how Freud had interpreted this type of obsessive symptom in his patient known as the "Rat Man." Freud explained that this type of obsessive doubt expresses an unconscious lack of confidence in the interlocutor—a sort of derisive doubt. Only much later did I realize that my patient's mockery and unconscious distrust were directed against her last analyst, Dr. Z, and that she had had good reason to question the latter's interpretations and to deride her counsels. When I suggested to her—with great circumspection in view of her extreme anxiety—the possibility that she had such feelings, she was seized with panic. I concluded that I had guessed right, but also that I would have to exercise extreme caution in probing further in that direction. I then chose another line of approach. I decided to use the "rule of abstinence" and in future not to repeat my interpretations so many times. At first I repeated them five times instead of six, then four times instead of five, and so on. It was hard for the patient to tolerate this frustration.

I shall not go into all the details of this analysis; but I should like to mention that this progressive breaking up of her ritual, through deprivation, brought some aggressive reactions closer to the surface. The first two valid and relevant interpretations of her obsessions had similar results. On her way to my office the patient had to pass the window of a pastry shop. She was often tempted to go in and buy some candy, both for herself and to take home to her mother, but she always resisted the impulse for fear of "touching the old woman." One day she plucked up sufficient courage to get as far as the door, but there she recoiled in horror; someone had passed near her, whether man or woman she did not know, but she was seized with a horrible dread that perhaps it was the "old woman." I told her quite simply that she did not really want to buy candy for her mother. She refused to believe this, but the interpretation bore fruit; the patient gradually became able to express hostile thoughts toward her family and her analysts. Another of Mme. N's obsessions, as we have mentioned, was to buy herself new dresses because she could never wear again any dress that she had once put in a closet, where it would hang along with all her other dresses of the past six years, separately wrapped in tissue paper. The purchasing of material for a new dress was preceded by weeks of preparation during the analytic sessions. She had to "associate" and obtain assurance through magic interpretations that she was justified in buying a new dress that would not be contaminated by contact with the old woman. After a few months of analysis she found the courage to buy some silk for a new dress. Just as she was passing the cashier's desk with her parcel under her arm, she was suddenly obsessed with the idea that the cashier had stretched out a long arm and touched the parcel. Once again she was seized with panic and resolved not to touch the silk for a long time. She added that on leaving the shop she found herself humming over and over the melody of a children's song. I insisted that she tell me the words. It was the nursery rhyme, "J'ai du bon tabac dans ma tabatière... Tu n'en auras pas." (I have good tobacco in my pouch. ... You shan't have any.) This, then, was the meaning of her symptom. She, the only wealthy member of her family, wants to buy a new dress; the old maidservant, her mother, her sister—all jealous, all poor—want to take it away from her. Overcome with guilt and anxiety she has to renounce the dress, just as she has to deprive herself of candy, because she ought, but does not want to, share it with her mother and sister and feels too guilty to eat it alone. Once I had understood this, I could tell Mr. N when he came to see me again that I would undertake to treat his wife.

Here I should like to leave the analysis for a moment in order to complete the account of the events which preceded the appearance of the obsessional neurosis in the middle of her treatment with Dr. Z. I was gradually able to reconstruct these during the three and a half years that she was in analysis with me. At the end of that period her analysis was, with my approval, interrupted for extremely important external reasons. However, there had already been very considerable improvement in her condition.

After the death of her father-in-law, when the question of dividing the inheritance came up, the mother-in-law came to live with them and the patient had to spend a great deal of time with the old lady. The patient disliked her intensely but had to appear outwardly civil and amiable. All this took place soon after her own family's financial ruin, and after her father had permitted her younger sister to marry the poor man she was in love with. Dr. Z, who had been kept informed of all matters pertaining to the inheritance, at this point suggested that the patient and her husband get the help of a lawyer. This they did, with the result that her husband's share of the inheritance was considerably increased.

Mme. N, who had never found sexual satisfaction in her marriage, was always tempted to take a lover, but fear of guilt feelings prevented her from succumbing to the temptation. She always felt that if she had a satisfactory love life she might perhaps be cured of all her ills. With the thought that she might one day have a lover, she surrounded herself with young, attractive, flirtatious maids. She would imagine their love affairs and think that they would not blame her if she had an extramarital love life of her own. The "old woman"—ugly, forbidding, straitlaced—was the first "old maid" she had ever hired. She wanted to dismiss her at once, but Dr. Z advised her to keep her, we have seen with what result: a few weeks later Mme. N was seized with such intolerable anxiety that she was unable to touch anything in the house and her husband finally had to dismiss the old maidservant. Thus the patient, while not actually disobeying Dr. Z, obtained her ends through her neurosis.

About that time Dr. Z intervened in still another matter. My patient told me about it quite casually, without realizing its significance, when she was well on in her analysis. She had made the acquaintance of an attractive young man who courted her assiduously. She decided to go to a masked ball where she knew she would meet him, in the hope that a liaison would develop. Dr. Z advised her to give up the idea. She went even further; when Mme. N later reproached her and said she would never stop regretting having given him up, Dr. Z suggested that she tell herself that she might have caught a venereal disease from him if she had become his mistress. Here then was the source of the patient's obsessive fear of being "contaminated by the old maid's touch." But in her obsession it was no longer a man who might contaminate her, but a woman—an old woman. The maid in fact was a substitute for her analyst: both had red hair and both were spinsters— "old maids." Now her horror of the "old woman's touch" and the latter's domination over her both become understandable as violent, affective conflicts with the analyst as object. All the patient's rage against her, all her distrust and unconscious derision had been displaced onto the old servant, seemingly sparing her analyst. I say seemingly because in actual fact the patient took her revenge by unconsciously making a mockery out of the treatment, and punished the analyst by burdening her with her pitiable and incurable presence.

IV

Before continuing discussion of the technical problems involved in Mme. N's case, I should like to say a few words about the structure of her neurosis. I shall not go into details about her childhood history, but concentrate rather on the relation between her neurosis and the events described above.

We have seen that during the first five years of analysis her anxiety hysteria centered around the conflict between her sexual desires on the one hand, and her obedience and attachment to her father on the other. Her symptoms represented guilt on account of her sexual escapade and a constant effort to avoid the temptation of being unfaithful to her husband and thus to her father. But with the episode of the old maid and the resulting symptoms, a very different picture emerges. True, the horror of red hair continues the old phobia, but it has now become displaced to the "old woman." The difference is striking: the fear refers no longer to contact with a man, but with a woman; and it is no longer a fear of sexual contact but of some horrible contamination or pollution. Moreover, the analysis revealed that during the period of the obsessional neurosis the "touches" invariably expressed two things: on the one hand a hostile contact, or assault, by the "old woman," and on the other it represented touching money. As we saw earlier, her obsessive fears represented the impossibility of deriving satisfaction from the money she had come to possess in spite of herself. During a considerable part of her analysis the material centered around the secondary gains from her neurosis, which consisted in depriving her mother and sister of reaping any benefit from her wealth. She often promised to give her sister discarded dresses or other possessions of hers; but the "old woman's touch" prevented her making the gift. On such occasions her obsession took the following form: "If I give these dresses to my sister she will be contaminated by the 'old woman's touch'; she will become the 'old woman.'" This can be interpreted in the following way: "If I give her my dresses she will not only have a husband whom she loves but also beautiful clothes to please him; I would hate her so much that I would be afraid what she might do to me." She deprived her sister of looking attractive and pretty without being to blame: it was the fault of her neurosis which she could not help; moreover she also deprived herself and suffered terribly from anxiety. The incident of the candy is a good illustration of this mechanism. After her neurosis took the obsessive-compulsive form, she was no longer tempted to have a love affair. One might say that the old conflict centering around sexual temptation had regressed into a conflict centering around money, aggression, defilement, and guilt connected with a woman. This change clearly confirms the distinction Freud made between anxiety hysteria (phobia) and obsessional neurosis. Her former neurosis, a phobia, had been based predominantly on conflicts of the phallic stage, but it had regressed into a neurosis based on the anal-sadistic stage of libidinal development. One can also observe her regression from the oedipal to the pre-oedipal stage: from interest focused on the man in the phobic phase of the patient's neurosis to absorption in the woman in the obsessional phase. It is this latter element that contains the explanation of some otherwise puzzling aspects of her symptoms, namely that it could be either a man or a woman who reminded her of the "old woman" in her "touch" obsessions: sometimes even her husband. She would reveal this by telling me, "I loathe his physique." In her derogatory fantasies about her husband she saw him as the son of the "old woman"; hence she had to make a barrier between them, in bed, with layers of tissue paper.

The strength of her aggressive tendencies during the obsessional period can be gauged by her inability to tolerate the slightest aggressive impulse or hostile feeling in herself. At first my slightest hint that she might have such feelings stirred up intolerable anxiety and guilt which only gradually became bearable. As for the anal component in the structure of her neurosis, we have seen it at work in her ablutions and in her constant concern with pollution and contamination. We have seen how Dr. Z precipitated this symptom by suggesting that the patient tell herself that genital contact might result in venereal disease. The intensity of ambivalence toward money is particularly striking in this case.

From her adolescence on, her father had opposed the idea of her marrying for love; she must have an arranged marriage with a man who was comfortably off. Through attachment to her father she submitted outwardly to his will. But in actual fact the neurosis which broke out during her honeymoon was a blow at her father and represented a sort of unconscious revenge, which she in turn paid for dearly in terms of anxiety and guilt. Later, after the loss of his fortune, this father for whom she had sacrificed her love life was to betray her by allowing her younger sister to marry the man she loved. Everything then conspired to depreciate love in favor of money: she had to go about in the company of her mother-in-law—another "old woman"—instead of a lover; her father borrowed money from her husband and did not pay it back. Dr. Z added the finishing stroke by advising her to take a lawyer, who increased her husband's inheritance, while at the same time she advised her to reject a lover but to retain a disagreeable, ugly old maid in her service. As with her father, the patient outwardly submitted, and her revolt took the form of the obsessive-compulsive neurosis.

The question arises to what extent Dr. Z's suggestion that she imagine herself contaminated as a result of sexual intercourse is enough in itself to explain the patient's fear of "touches." We know of course that there are many cases with similar obsessive symptoms which cannot be traced back to a similar source. It is true also that fear of venereal disease is often a component in the pathogenesis of such cases, but not always; and it is often only a rationalization of other underlying anxieties. The fear of touching or being touched has extremely complex connotations. Generally speaking, contact with the hand can represent the whole gamut of human behavior extending from affection to aggression. It may mean proximity, tenderness, sexual contact, taking possession, etc. So, too, in Mme. N's case the obsession was overdetermined. In the incident of the cashier, the cashier's long arm and hand which seemed to reach out and touch the parcel signified a sort of *mainmise* or seizing of the silk, forbidding the patient to use it. The obsession in this instance implied that the "old woman" exercised her power over the patient unscrupulously and forbade her to be an attractive woman; and that she was jealous and wanted to steal her silk. On other occasions touching had the meaning of "touching money" with similar underlying affects: she had no right to have money or to benefit by it; the old woman wanted to touch her money and take it away from her. It is interesting that in Mme. N's case the symbolic meaning of the act of touching that is usually so important—masturbation—played only a secondary role. What was important was the fantasy of being at the mercy of a sexual gesture on the part of a hated and feared woman. The patient's unconscious thought on hearing Dr. Z's advice might be translated as follows: "You want me to give up my life as a woman, to lie to myself by imagining I might have been contaminated by the man I love; at the same time you want me to submit to a forbidding, ugly old maid like yourself; I can just as easily imagine that you are the one who has contaminated everything I possess, you 'old woman.' So you want me to imagine contaminations? All right I am going to imagine some. If this is the kind of help you give me to get well, just you wait and see the results."

While Dr. Z's advice may not have been sufficient in itself to determine the form of the patient's neurosis, it was certainly an important factor in bringing it about.

V

There were a few special features about Mme. N's treatment that have a bearing on some important problems of psychoanalytic technique.

Her pattern of behavior when she first came into treatment with me, i.e., reporting a dream every day and following it up with associations that implicitly invited an interpretation of the dream, was clearly a continuation of a routine she had developed during her preceding treatments. We have seen how I was taken in at first by this insidious form of resistance. The interesting thing about her associations was that they more or less compelled interpretations in terms of childhood problems: attachment to her father; jealousy; sexual games with her sister; guilt feelings about masturbation, etc. We have seen, too, how my interpretations of this material stimulated further dreams and associations which appeared to confirm them, but without producing the slightest effect on the patient nor any modification in her symptoms. She neither denied nor confirmed the validity of my interpretations. Her one invariable reaction was to ask me to repeat them several times at the end of the session. She seemed to have no resistance: she was always punctual and talked freely; her outward manner betrayed none of the well-known little signs of resistance. It was precisely this apparent absence of all resistance that led me to discover that her defenses were camouflaged in a much subtler way. I gradually realized that her associations tended to prompt me to the interpretations she wanted or expected from me. Furthermore, in this first period my interpretations were centered almost exclusively around the patient's distant past, as I suppose Dr. Z's had been. She contributed little and gave only the scantiest information on events in the present or recent past. At first I was never able to explain to my own satisfaction why a certain dream had occurred on a certain night, or what it was in the present that had evoked or reactivated a particular childhood memory. And we know that to get at the true meaning of a dream it is essential to know this. All this helped to convince me that Mme. N was using the routine recital of her dreams as a resistance to the analysis. We have already seen how she had absorbed the analytic treatment into her obsessional rituals, so that it had become an integral part of a sort of transference neurosis. We also know that unconsciously she made a mockery out of her analysis, thereby unconsciously expressing her lack of confidence in her doctors and her treatment. She had had good reason not to have much confidence in them: Dr. X had betrayed her confidence; Dr. Y abruptly dismissed her when she started to talk about suicide; as for Dr. Z, the reasons for the patient's mistrust were more complex. Dr. Z had certainly stepped out of her role of analyst in some of her recommendations. I do not know if she had given the patient advice on other occasions besides the three already mentioned, but in the three we know about, although not of equal importance, there was one element in common: in all three instances Dr. Z had sided with money against sexuality. She was evidently not sufficiently aware of the meaning and impact this had for her patient, namely, that of definitely discouraging any aspirations toward a satisfactory love life and thereby reinforcing the regressive tendencies that were stimulated by outward events that occurred at that time. Dr. Z's recommendation to keep the old maid and to renounce the love affair certainly betray her own lack of confidence in the efficacy of analytic procedure, and there can be no doubt that this undermined the patient's own confidence in it. One of her recommendations had a quite special significance that is worth discussing in some detail: her advice to her patient to console herself for renouncing the lover by imagining she might have been contaminated by him. It is as if Dr. Z told the patient to lie to herself. Now intellectual dishonesty in an analyst is a fault that inevitably does irreparable damage. The patient, of whom total frankness and sincerity are asked, will never be able to give them to an analyst who has given proof of lack of intellectual integrity himself.

Dr. Z had also lent herself to another subtle deformation of the analytic technique, which the patient exploited every time that she wanted to buy a dress for example. For weeks beforehand Mme. N asked her doctor for reassurance through analyzing her dreams that she would be able to make the contemplated purchase without danger of the "old woman's touch." As a matter of fact when she did finally decide to buy a dress the transaction was almost always interrupted by the "old woman's touch," which was a way of giving the lie to her analyst's assurances. Thus Dr. Z had let herself be maneuvered into allowing the patient to use the analytic procedure as a sort of magic ritual to exorcize her obsessive fears. The patient faced me with the same problem. I told her frankly that I could give her no assurance that the sessions preceding the purchase of the dress would insure her against the "old woman's touch." I did however advise her to behave as much as possible as she would want to behave when she was cured; to judge for herself the risk of so doing, but not to be afraid to go counter to her apprehensions. This advice was based on Freud's recommendation in the analysis of phobic patients—to suggest to the patient, once the analysis is sufficiently advanced, to confront the object of the phobia little by little.

Mme. N also tried to gain the complicity of her analyst in extracting secondary benefits from her neurosis. One day she asked me to write to her husband to ask him to send her extra money so that she could come to analysis in a taxi, and thus avoid the "old woman's touch." I refused categorically, telling her that coming in a taxi could have no influence whatsoever on the progress of her treatment. From that day forward her analysis made great progress. On another occasion she tested me out in a different way: she suddenly started to mention suicidal thoughts. Her intention of scaring me was quite transparent and there was obviously no real danger; so I assured her that I was not going to interrupt the treatment as Dr. Y had done. Her suicidal thoughts disappeared immediately and never recurred.

I do not think I am mistaken in saying that one of the flaws in Dr. Z's method had been to concentrate her interest and effort exclusively on the analysis of the patient's childhood. That was why her interpretations of the dreams, and mine during the first months of treatment, were mainly centered on events or affects which had hardly any bearing on the patient's later life experiences. They might be said to hang in mid-air, unrelated to her present life. Dr. Z's habit, too, of analyzing the dreams for themselves and not her patient through the dreams had accentuated still further the divorce of the analysis from the patient's psychological reality. In fact Mme. N reacted as if the interpretations did not concern her; in other words, she did not react to them at all. We have seen how my first interpretations, which suffered from the same defect, also failed to reach her. By this mechanism she was following a pattern of behavior adopted toward her father at the time of her marriage: outward compliance coupled with stubborn inner resistance. Her passivity toward interpretations continued for so long, albeit in a somewhat attenuated form, that I later took the step of requiring her to tell me whether she agreed or disagreed with them and why.

Because of her excessive concentration on the patient's childhood,

Dr. Z failed to give enough attention to analysis of the transference, as is clearly shown by the fact that she had never made the connection between the old maid and herself. When toward the end of the third year of analysis I finally confronted the patient with this connection, she was quite shocked at first, as if such an idea had never occurred to her. During her treatment with me she also had numerous ambivalent transference reactions toward me. I was fortunate enough however to be able to analyze them correctly before they could endanger the treatment. It was then quite a common fault among some analysts to concentrate, as Dr. Z had done, exclusively on events in the patient's remote childhood. Generally this was due to a confusion between interest in scientific research and its application in the treatment of patients. Because a neurosis derives from early childhood conflicts it was thought that only these early conflicts were important in analyzing the patient's symptoms. Yet Freud had warned analysts long ago against just such a mistake. He had stressed the vital importance of the relation between the past and the present—the past being only important, in an analysis, insofar as it is carried into the present, and the present insofar as it reactivates the past. He also said that it is not enough to discover the source of the original conflicts, but it is also necessary to retrace all its subsequent vicissitudes in later life, in which the ego and the superego as well as the instinctual drives are involved. He used the following metaphor: when a building is damaged by a fire, it is not always at the seat of the fire that the worst damage is found; sometimes flames spreading from the first fire may start fires in other parts of the building that cause much more serious damage. There are times in therapy when it is more important to repair the damage from these later fires before turning our attention to the earlier damage.

In Mme. N's case the main conflicts were expressed in a compulsive-obsessive form which had developed while she was in analysis with Dr. Z. It was imperative to deal with these relatively recent conflicts first, and only through them could their origins in childhood be approached. It was not possible in the relatively short time at my disposal to elucidate this patient's early conflicts sufficiently, which accounts for the incomplete results of the analysis. We have seen that the only effective interpretations were those which included her ego reactions as well as her aggressive and libidinal drives. As a general rule interpretations are only effective when they are concrete and personal and apply specifically to the individual case.

Recently it has become more common to see patients with variations of Mme. N's type of resistance. I am referring to patients who use psychoanalytic jargon in their sessions, glibly making use of analytic terms that they have picked up in psychoanalytic books or that their analyst has rather rashly imparted to them. They unconsciously make use of these terms to disguise their real psychological experiences. Frequently it is not easy to overcome such paradoxical intellectualized resistances. It is of course essential in scientific work to describe problems of psychopathology in generalized terms and to use such concepts as, for instance, the Oedipus complex, etc. But it is equally essential in the treatment of an individual patient to retranslate these concepts into concrete terms of the patient's personal life. Dr. Z's original letter to me showed that she had failed to make such a retranslation, and her analysis of Mme. N suffered in consequence. Whenever a patient makes use of analytic terms as a means of resistance, the analyst should be particularly careful to express his patient's experiences in simple, nontechnical language, and the terms he uses should correspond exactly with the thoughts and affects of the patient. The following experience with Mme. N is an illustration. On the way home from my office, during the third year of analysis, she sometimes took a taxi from the subway station to her sister's apartment. Sometimes when she got into the taxi she was seized with the horrible dread that she was "sitting on the old woman." She invariably associated these obsessions with a sexual game she used to indulge in with her sister, when they took turns sitting on each other's knees in the bathroom. She had often reported these memories before, but neither the obsession nor its accompanying anxiety had lessened. Moreover, she had always retained conscious memory of these games and felt neither guilt nor anxiety about them. Therefore these episodes as such were not sufficient to determine her obsession. They had to be considered screen memories. Gradually I elicited more details about the little incidents that preceded the occurrence of the obsession. It was generally either the sight of a beggar to whom she had just refused money, or an old news vendor watching her get into the taxi; other incidents were connected with having to control her resentment against her mother, who was also living in her sister's apartment. It then became possible to reconstruct the repressed thought behind the obsession. The repressed thought centered round the meaning of the colloquial expression, *"Je m'asseois dessus"* (literally, "I sit on them," an expression of contemptuous indifference that might perhaps be conveyed by, "I don't care two hoots about them"). Thus it meant that she was not going to feel sorry for the old beggar, nor for her impoverished mother nor for her sister, but was going to indulge in the extravagance of a taxi. But her hostile impulse aroused such guilt that she immediately punished herself in the place where she had sinned: she sat down on the old woman whose contact disgusted her so much. It was only from that point that the thread led back to the sexual games with her sister, which indirectly represented scarcely disguised fantasies of sexual contact between the father or mother and the child sitting on their lap. The latter fantasies had been completely repressed and the patient was filled with horror when they were mentioned in the analysis. They also led back to the old jealousy of her sister which had been repressed and overcompensated. Nevertheless it was only very gradually that I learned to translate accurately the thoughts underlying the obsession about "sitting on the old woman." One day she greeted my interpretation with the comment, "It's almost that, but not quite." And after I changed the wording slightly she blushed, burst our laughing, and said, "That's it exactly." The obsession disappeared for a few days. But we had to work these conflicts through again and again before the symptom disappeared for good.

Mme. N's treatment took place more than twenty-five years ago. One may speculate how the analysis would have developed had it taken place today. There has been such a great advance in psychoanalytic technique with the acquisition of a deeper and more refined insight into the psychology of the ego.[2] Nowadays, of course, I am much quicker to recognize resistance that uses the technique which Mme. N managed to impose on me for several months. And while the technique that I later employed successfully in her case was along the lines of ego analysis, it seems certain to me now that had I then possessed a greater knowledge of ego psychology I would have avoided needless mistakes and loss of time. In particular one may ask whether, in the light of our present knowledge of the ego, it was necessary to apply the "rule of abstinence" in the way described. It is difficult to know for certain. But it seems to me probable that this rule should have been applied, but with more subtlety. Whenever a patient finds a way to act out his resistances within the analytic procedure itself by means of a transfer-

2. These advances are in a very large measure due to the work of Anna Freud.

ence neurosis, then almost inevitably the rule of abstinence has to be used. However, it is then necessary to give the patient plenty of time (as I in fact did in the case of Mme. N) and to conduct the analysis *lege artis*, with a great deal of tact and respect for the patient, so as to make it possible for the patient's ego to learn to tolerate the warded off drives, and to transform acting out into insight.

I treated Mme. N for three and a half years, at the end of which she showed very considerable improvement. She was able to wash and dress in a normal manner. Her anxieties and obsessions occurred less and less frequently and were tolerable. At the end of this period she received letters from her husband announcing his intention of getting a divorce in order to marry his mistress. I encouraged her to return to her country, where she remained about eight months until the divorce proceedings were finished. Mme. N was mainly upset by the hostility of her daughter, who sided against her violently. During the whole period of the divorce proceedings Mme. N had no psychiatric help, and when she returned to Paris her improvement appeared to be consolidated. It was not possible for me to take her back into analysis at that time; so I sent her to a colleague, under whose treatment she continued to improve. I saw her some time later when she had just spent some time with her daughter, with whom she was now on better terms. She was leading a normal, though lonely and not very happy, life and was thinking of returning to her own country. Her fears had diminished to the point where they hardly hampered her at all. Then the war broke out and I lost touch with Mme. N.

REFERENCES

Fenichel, O. (1939). Problems of psychoanalytic technique. *Psychoanal. Q.*, 8.
Freud, A. (1936). *The Ego and the Mechanisms of Defense.* New York: Int. Univ. Press, 1946.
Freud, S. (1909). Analysis of a phobia in a five-year-old boy. *Coll. Papers* 3.
_____ (1909). Notes upon a case of obsessional neurosis. *Coll. Papers* 3.
_____ (1912). The dynamics of the transference. *Coll. Papers* 2.
_____ (1913). The predisposition to obsessional neurosis. *Coll. Papers* 2.
_____ (1914). Recollection, repetition and working through. *Coll. Papers* 2.
_____ (1937). Analysis terminable and interminable. *Coll. Papers* 5.
Glover, E. (1953). *The Technique of Psychoanalysis.* New York: Int. Univ. Press.

Hartmann, H. (1951). Technical implications of ego psychology. *Psychoanal. Q.*, 20:31–43.

Kris, E. (1951). Ego psychology and interpretation in psychoanalytic therapy. *Psychoanal. Q.*, 20:15–30.

Loewenstein, R. M. (1951). The problem of interpretation. *Psychoanal. Q.*, 20:1–14.

———— (1951). Ego development and psychoanalytic technique. *Amer. J. Psychiat.*, 107:617–22.

———— (1954). Some remarks on defenses, autonomous ego, and psychoanalytic technique. *Int. J. Psychoanal.*, 35:188–93.

Nacht, S. (1950). *De la Pratique à la Théorie Psychanalytique*. Paris: P.U.F.

Reich, W. (1933). *Charakteranalyse*. Berlin: Selbstverlag des Verfassers.

7

Some Thoughts on Interpretation in the Theory and Practice of Psychoanalysis

If one compares the psychiatry before Freud and its development since Freud's discoveries, one is struck by an essential difference. The symptoms of neurosis were formerly accounted for in purely descriptive terms, and the terms were no more than labels. The essential change which Freud introduced in the approach toward neurotic symptoms was that one could consider them explainable. They acquired a meaning; they were no longer regarded as foreign bodies within the mind, but as an intelligible part of the personality.

But they can be understood as part of the personality only after having been correctly interpreted. The neurotic symptom stands for the patient's memories, conflicting tendencies, thoughts, impulses, fears, which instead of appearing as such are disguised as a neurotic symptom. These tendencies as well as the disguising forces must be interpreted in order to understand and explain the meaning of a symptom.

As we know, at a later stage Freud was able to establish that the neurotic symptoms are determined by typical pathogenic conflicts and that the forces underlying them, the libidinal and aggressive drives, as well as the forces of defense against these drives, present particular developmental characteristics and can be described in a scientific way. This is why in reports published on the results of analytic investigations of individual neuroses, the symptoms are usually interpreted in terms that strike psychoanalysts as well as their critics as being relatively monotonous. When we interpret the meaning of a neurotic symptom,

The Brill Memorial Lecture of the New York Psychoanalytic Society, delivered at the New York Academy of Medicine, March 26, 1957.

we explain it dynamically as an interplay of forces and genetically as a result of the interplay between developmental and environmental factors. Yet this apparent monotony stands in conspicuous contrast to the immense wealth of data and information about human beings which our interpretative work yields to us in each individual psychoanalysis.

Is the comparative monotony in our explanations of the neurotic symptoms due to an insufficiency of our knowledge? Indeed, we find that psychoanalytic explanations are more convincing when they constitute a tracing back of neurotic symptoms to particular pathogenic conflicts than when we attempt the reverse: a synthesis, trying to account for the particular development that ensued from a given conflict.

But perhaps this relative monotony of our scientific explanation of neurotic symptoms is not due only to these limitations of our knowledge. The contrast, I believe, rather reflects the difference in kind between interpretations we use when attempting to condense the result of an individual analysis and to express the meaning of a neurotic symptom in generalized scientific terms, and those we use within the individual analysis when we aim to explain the meaning of a dream, for instance, or to reconstruct a specific conflict that left its imprint on the patient at a certain age.[1]

In his book *Die Grundlagen der Psychoanalyse* (1927), which unfortunately has never been translated, Hartmann stressed a point which characterizes the scientific position of psychoanalysis as opposed to other approaches to psychology and psychopathology. Psychoanalysis offers explanatory concepts, theories and hypotheses, as well as a great wealth of observational data. As in other natural sciences, the concepts were derived to some extent from these observations; but they transcend them and, in their turn, permit organization of the data and often help to discover new facts.

Let me present a concrete example. A very severely obsessional neurotic, who was referred to me after many years of unsuccessful treatment with another analyst, puzzled me by the fact that at the end of the hour she would usually ask me to repeat my interpretations several times over. It occurred to me that Freud had described a similar behavior in an obsessional patient as expressing an unconscious

----

1. Devereux (1951) has rightly pointed out that one interprets something *to someone*, i.e., to the person whose material is being interpreted.

doubt, a disbelief in the words of the interlocutor. But the differences between the two cases were great. My patient's need to have interpretations repeated was limited to the analytic situations, whereas in Freud's patient the symptom was more generalized. Moreover, my patient's demand to hear the interpretation several times was consciously motivated by the need to get the greatest possible relief from it, which was not so in the case of Freud's patient. Phenomenologically, i.e., on the level of conscious thought, there were considerable divergencies. The analogy lay in the fact that both patients were obsessional neurotics and that I was entitled to suspect in mine the same type of unconscious ambivalence as Freud could infer in his. Thus my reason for applying the knowledge derived from Freud's case to mine was based upon the use of an explanatory concept; namely, that in both instances an underlying ambivalent attitude and a reaction formation against it might have determined comparable behavior: the need to have the interlocutor's words repeated. As is characteristic of concrete interpretative work, these interpretations led my patient ultimately to discover the very complicated, specific motives for this behavior. After prolonged analytic work she indeed became consciously aware of ironical and mocking feelings toward the analyst.

We see here that the more general, explanatory concept common to these cases was the unconscious ambivalence in the patients. A more specific, individual meaning was that of unconscious, mocking disbelief in the words of an analyst. This juxtaposition exemplifies types of what in analysis we call interpretation. Thus the various meanings attached to the term interpretation can be brought out by approaching it from various points of view: (1) interpretations as statements of general, explanatory concepts; (2) as statements about the results of psychological investigation of a given person; (3) as used in the individual therapeutic analysis. These three aspects overlap partly, but present sufficient divergent elements to be thus distinguished from each other.

To illustrate the differences one could say that my patient's wish to have interpretations repeated was the result of disguised ambivalence. More particularly, it was the expression of a mocking disbelief. The psychological investigation, which aimed to uncover the history and the motives of this disbelief, revealed that it referred to a former analyst, to the analytic treatment as such and to the reasons for these repressed doubts and resentments. In the therapeutic procedure, the interpretative work encompassed not only all the preceding steps, but also the various means needed to enable the analyst as well as the patient to gain insight into this state of affairs and, finally, to enable the patient to deal with her resentments in a different way than by obsessional symptoms.

A discussion of interpretations from a methodological point of view, or rather from the point of view of their scientific logic, was undertaken by Bernfeld in his paper "Der Begriff der 'Deutung' in der Psychoanalyse" (1932). Without going into the details of this valuable study, I may briefly say that he draws a distinction between the structure of interpretation as a tool of psychological investigation and that of interpretation as a therapeutic tool, but without discussing the latter. Interpretations as tools of psychological investigation are classified by Bernfeld in the following categories: interpretation of the unconscious intention;[2] functional interpretations, disclosing the function of a given psychological phenomenon within the framework of the personality or a part of it; diagnostic interpretations; symbolic interpretation; and finally, most important in psychoanalysis, the genetic interpretation by which the genesis of a phenomenon is being reconstructed: "It is always," he states, "aimed at the reconstruction of a concrete, completed, psychic process. This aim is contingent on two essential premises. (1) The process to be reconstructed must have left traces behind it. (2) Some regular, consistent relation must exist between specific psychic, personal experiences and the traces they leave, permitting the former to be determined, inferred, 'interpreted' from the latter."

Bernfeld thus throws into relief the existence in psychoanalysis of what he calls a *"Spurenwissenschaft"*: a "science of traces" left by past mental phenomena, which he compares to the analogous reconstructive processes in archaeology.

Most psychoanalytic literature concerns either the results of this science of tracing (i.e., the reconstructions) or the description of such traces of past phenomena, while writings on psychoanalytic technique deal more specifically with the methods of obtaining those traces and of putting them to use for ultimate reconstructive processes. The question logically arises as to the criteria on which our interpretative work is based, or the way by which we arrive at the meaning of the patient's material. Two authors have particularly dealt with this problem: Robert Waelder and Susan Isaacs.

---

2. *Finale Deutung.* He mentions, by the way, that this type of interpretation, however important it may be practically, is very often misused by analysts.

In his paper "Kriterien der Deutung" (1939), Waelder compares the work of psychoanalysis with that of other sciences: criminology, history and linguistics. According to him, it is based on inferences drawn from various clues.

Isaacs, in her paper "Criteria for Interpretation" (1939), not only mentions the inferences we draw from the patient's material, but also stresses the importance of what she terms "perception of the unconscious meaning of the patient's words and conduct as an objective process." Among examples used to explain analytic work to nonanalytic students, she cites the following: "a boy of five years of age, one day at a meal, addressing no one in particular, said in a very subdued voice, 'I don't like dreams: they are horrid things'; and then, after a pause, 'and another thing—I don't have any.'" She found "that every hearer, save the most obtuse, appreciates perceptually that in his denial the boy actually makes a positive statement, namely, that his dreams are so horrid that he wishes he did not have any, and cannot bear to remember them. The ordinary hearer does not set out his awareness of this in conceptual terms, as analysts have learnt to do, using it as a means of generalizing the mechanism of denial; but everybody perceives the immediate concrete meaning." She adds that the difference between the ordinary hearer and the analyst resides in the degree of the latter's education.

One might wonder whether the unqualified use of the term "perception" here is correct, or whether this immediate grasp of the meaning of the child's words does not presuppose the existence of innumerable, preconscious inferences. We might agree with Isaacs that the analyst's understanding of his patient is sometimes based upon such immediate comprehension (highly improved by specific training in which his own personal analysis is not a small factor). But however direct or immediate such understanding of other human beings may be, it is usually combined with the countless preconscious inferences which everyone draws from both verbal and nonverbal expressions of an interlocutor.[3]

We touch here upon the complex problem of the understanding of one human being by another. There can be no doubt that the very young child perceives and understands the facial expressions of his

3. Recently Dr. Leo A. Spiegel, in the New York Psychoanalytic Society, mentioned the work of Egon Brunswik on the role of cues in perception, which the latter also applied to the perception of social phenomena.

mother in a way that may be called immediate or direct, and unconscious understanding of emotional states of the mother may exist even
in older children (Burlingham 1935). But the problem becomes more
complicated as the child learns to understand and use speech, i.e.,
with the addition of verbal communication. From here on the understanding by way of clues and cues is superimposed on his direct perception of the mother's and other persons' emotional states, so that
these two modes of comprehension become combined.

However interesting it might be at this point to discuss the ways in
which human beings gain knowledge of the mental life of others, I am
afraid this would lead us too far afield. While we may assume that such
understanding can come about through inference, empathy or perception, it is important to add what Hartmann (1927) stressed; namely,
that an additional and much more reliable way of knowing about other
human beings is provided by the objective, scientific method of
psychoanalytic investigation. I do not intend here to attempt a presentation of the psychoanalytic investigative method, but shall touch upon
it only inasmuch as it directly concerns the problem of interpretation.
Briefly, we may say that the psychoanalyst's means of obtaining observational data include all the ways by which one human being understands another. The psychoanalytic method employs also two steps that
are unavailable to any other form of psychological investigation. The
first of these is the method of free association, which provides the
analyst with some additional data and prepares the way for the second
step, the interpretation.[4] By means of interpretations the analyst is
able to acquire further, otherwise inaccessible, data.

Freud originated the comparison between psychoanalytic investigations and those of archaeology. It was an analogy he liked to use, but
he also stressed the fundamental difference between archaeological
research and the uncovering of the remote past in an individual. In
"Constructions in Analysis" (1937), he pointed out that we are not
dealing with dead remains, but with living human beings. Save for a
few exceptional finds, archaeologists work with relics of objects destroyed once and for all, whose reconstruction at best can merely reach
a certain degree of probability. But in the psychoanalyst's objects of

---

4. For the sake of brevity, I neglect here all the intermediate or preparatory steps:
interventions (Loewenstein 1951a), confrontation (Devereux 1951), clarification (Bibring
1954), parameters (Eissler 1953).

research everything essential has somehow been preserved, although buried, and it is only a question of psychoanalytic technique whether it can be brought to light. He also emphasized other differences between them; namely, that the psychological object is incomparably more complex than the material one and also that we know so much less about it. And he adds that "our comparison between the two forms of work can go no further than this; for the main difference between them lies in the fact that for the archaeologist the reconstruction is the aim and end of his endeavours while for analysis the construction is only a preliminary labour."

If we apply the same comparison more specifically to our work of interpretation in psychoanalysis, we find other significant differences. First of all, even the best preserved relic of antiquity may remain unnoticed until the curiosity of some searcher uncovers it; only then can it become capable of influencing the present. By contrast, the buried remains of an individual's past may influence his present not only during but because of their concealment, and it is precisely due to this indirect influence they exert on the person's actual behavior that they become subject to investigation and thus can be uncovered at all. Another striking difference is that not only the buried psychic objects continue to live and to express themselves in the patient's present behavior, but also the agents of distortion, the defenses, persist and remain active as continuous, most stubborn obstacles to their unearthing. Every analyst knows that in the transference both the buried past and the repressive forces come singularly alive again and even may put an end to all investigation. But if properly dealt with, these transference phenomena become the analyst's and patient's best allies in uncovering the forgotten past.[5]

Bernfeld (1932) spoke of the difference between interpretation as an investigative procedure and as it is used in the therapeutic process. Indeed, in an investigation, any elements of the personality may become subject to scrutiny; in a therapeutic analysis, not all can be investigated but some must be.

---

5. In a personal communication, Heinz Hartmann mentioned still another difference between archaeological and psychoanalytic reconstruction. The latter makes use of the known existence of maturational and developmental stages in the individual human being. Archaeological research cannot avail itself of such scientifically established, regular historical processes.

An investigation may be satisfied with the psychoanalytic exploration of a dream, for instance, or a type of dream. But it is obvious that
for the analytic investigation of more complicated aspects of the human
personality an actual psychoanalysis is necessary, whether this process
leads to a therapeutic result or not. The therapeutic analysis, in its
turn, is essentially based upon a process of investigation, but of a very
particular type. Thus the therapeutic and investigative procedures,
although different as to intention, yet are identical inasmuch as the
former hinges on the latter. Furthermore, the analytic inquiry becomes a therapy if it is an investigation not alone for the investigator
but for the patient as well.

In archaeological research, the work of investigation culminates in
the achievement of reconstruction. The psychoanalyst's task is far more
complicated; whenever he has been able to reconstruct some part of his
patient's forgotten past, he must go on to the next essential step in his
work. For, as Freud (1917) put it: "The time and manner in which he
conveys his constructions to the person who is being analyzed, as well
as the explanations with which he accompanies them, constitute the
link between the two portions of the work of analysis, between his own
part and that of the patient."[6]

And both parts of this work are encompassed in what we call
interpretations in the therapeutic procedure. Indeed, the analyst's interpretations stand in a twofold relation to the part of the patient. (1)
The patient's material enables the analyst to make interpretations
which in turn bring new material to the fore. (2) In the patient these
interpretations must have their counterpart, the gradual gaining of
insight, which is decisive for the outcome of the psychoanalytic work.

Until now we have examined only one aspect of our interpretative
work in analysis. The analyst's concern with the counterpart of his work
in the patient leads to yet another set of considerations about interpretations, which frequently is viewed in the context of the psychoanalytic
technique proper. I do not intend, however, to discuss practical prob-

---

6. Freud distinguished interpretation of isolated parts of a patient's material, such as a
parapraxis or a dream, from the reconstruction of important events in the patient's past
for which he proposed to use the term construction. Thus most of what we call genetic
interpretations should, according to Freud, be called constructions or reconstructions.
However, we shall not here follow this rigid distinction, but rather use the term interpretation in the customary and more comprehensive sense.

lems arising in connection with the technique of interpretation, but want rather to highlight some questions of a more general nature.

The question raised by Freud's statement about the time and manner in which the analyst communicates his constructions to the analysand has in part been answered in various writings on technique, particularly by Freud himself. In more recent years the development of ego psychology has permitted us to sharpen and to refine our knowledge in this area, and indeed has helped considerably to improve the efficiency of our technical skill. On the other hand, as Hartmann (1951) pointed out several years ago, actually a large body of knowledge on matters of psychoanalytic technique is being transmitted by one generation of analysts to another without having been theoretically formulated.

It happens not infrequently that in the material of the patient presented by a younger analyst, the supervisor perceives a meaning or a trend which the candidate did not suspect but can confirm from material appearing in subsequent sessions. To the beginner such an achievement seems not only amazing but sometimes a result of uncanny intuition. It cannot be denied that the work of some analysts has a quality reminding us of the work of an intuitive artist. But as a rule one can say that this apparent intuition is based on experience which has taught the older analyst to grasp slight signs presented by the patient and not yet perceived by the younger colleague. It would seem desirable for us to be able to supplement this intuitive, often preconscious grasping of clues by a more systematic study of the latter and of the implicit method which leads the analyst to draw conclusions from them.

Such a study might be considered a special branch of what Bernfeld termed our science of traces. On the one hand, this science of traces hinges on the knowledge about the existence in every person's past of processes, developments, typical conflicts, their vicissitudes, derivatives, transformations and recombinations they undergo in the course of years. It thus hinges, on the other hand, upon the acquaintance with signs that permit us to infer their existence.[7] Information concerning these processes derives from reconstructions in other

---

7. This in turn hinges on the assumption, which may not always be justified, that all processes leave traces or that there is a regular relation between each process and the trace it leaves.

analyzed cases and from direct observation. In recent years the latter source of information has greatly gained in importance for our knowledge of very early instinctual and ego development. I should like here particularly to mention the work of Anna Freud and Dorothy Burlingham, of Ernst Kris and his co-workers at Yale, of René A. Spitz, of Margaret E. Fries, and of John Bowlby.

In a recent paper, "The Recovery of Childhood Memories in Psychoanalysis," Kris (1956b) gives an account of the way a little girl, "Dorothy," observed at the nursery school of the Child Study Center in Yale, reacted in her third year to a series of events important for her life: the birth of a sibling, the death of her grandfather and of her pet dog. Kris then proceeds to engage our interest in an "experiment in thought: let us imagine," he writes, "how after twenty years the recollection of the material here reported in considerable simplification may appear in Dorothy's analysis. The network of overdeterminations seems almost infinite: the wish for a child from father, the death wish against the mother, the fear about both sexual and destructive impulses, and finally the fear of castration which . . . age adequately added and superimposed, are likely to baffle the future analyst's imagination." He adds that reconstructive work in analysis might in one sense be "a hopeless task" if its aim were to reconstruct exactly "what had happened." "But," he continues, "reconstructive work in analysis cannot aim at such a goal: its purpose is more limited and yet much vaster. The material of actual occurrences, of things as they happen, is constantly subjected to the selective scrutiny of memory under the guide of the inner constellation. What we here call selection is itself a complex process. Not only were the events loaded with meaning when they occurred; each later stage of the conflict pattern may endow part of these events or of their elaboration with added meaning. But these processes are repeated throughout many years of childhood and adolescence and finally integrated into the structure of the personality. They are molded, as it were, into patterns, and it is with these patterns rather than with the events that the analyst deals."

This greater importance, in our work, of patterns rather than of exact events is the reason why unconscious fantasies were regarded by Freud as approximate equivalents of actual traumatic events. Yet we also know since Freud that in many cases we are not or should not be satisfied with this equivalence. Not only do we feel impelled to distinguish between them in our work of reconstruction of the past, but we also have indirect reasons for assuming that unconscious fantasies and real events are not to be treated as psychological equals in their present effects. I am alluding here, for instance, to the transference reactions of patients when faced with some correctly perceived peculiarities of their analyst's behavior. In most instances, these perceptions simply trigger off some fantasies and transference reactions that can be traced back to the past, i.e., analyzed. But there are some cases where it does not seem to work that way, where the patient feels his reactions to be so well justified by the analyst's actual behavior that such reactions may become unanalyzable (Bibring-Lehner 1936).

And yet, not until this year did we have any thorough study on the signs permitting us to distinguish, in analysis, the existence of actual traumatic events in the patient's past as opposed to unconscious fantasies. I refer here to Greenacre's (1956) important work on the subject. It was also she who drew our attention in recent years to the particular importance of actual traumatic events in the pathogenesis of severe neuroses (Greenacre 1952).

We must confess that notwithstanding the considerable amount of knowledge we have acquired, we are still far from possessing a satisfactory "science of traces" in Bernfeld's sense. Let me give an example from my recent experience.

A young man of twenty-six seeks help from psychoanalysis for his severe inhibition in work and social relations. He is the youngest of four children and the only one still living with his parents. From the beginning he complains about his inability to do any work, in spite of ambitious fantasies, and soon he illustrates his inhibition by stressing his inability to comply with the requirements of analysis: he can neither remember anything of his life, nor can he tell what occurs to him. After two months this difficulty becomes increasingly strong. One day, while begging me to tell him what to say, he violently and somehow provokingly rejects any help I offer and at the same time smilingly asks me to declare that I am not at all interested in his talking and would not even listen to him if he did. These latter words reminded me of the behavior of a mother driven to violent anger by the passive, stubborn refusal of a child to do what she has asked. I suggested that he must have been a bad eater as a child and must have had many fights with his mother when she tried to persuade him to eat. The patient laughingly acquiesced. And although he could remember no specific incidents, some details of more recent fights with his mother then came to the fore, where both would display an equal degree of stubborn, defiant sulkiness.

The interpretation I proposed to this patient thus seems to have been correct and to the point, and yet I would be hard put to it to explain on what grounds I made this inference. It must have been arrived at by way of many small signs which remained preconscious to me, until the conclusion suddenly was brought to my conscious awareness by the patient's invitation to declare that I would no longer be interested in his talking to me. What these little signs are, which in this case permitted me to draw a correct conclusion, but which in many other instances may be entirely lost, could be the subject matter of a highly rewarding research for the systematization of our "science of traces."

In two of his recent papers Ernst Kris contributed fundamentally to the theory of psychoanalytic technique by studying the effects of interpretation on two phenomena most essential and characteristic for the psychoanalytic process: recall and insight.

In his study on the recovery of childhood memories, which I mentioned above, Kris (1956b) takes up an idea he developed before (Kris 1950), on the relationship between recollection and the recognition of what has become familiar through an interpretation or reconstruction. He adds that "the communication with the patient is never exclusively regulated by the secondary process. Our interpretations may stimulate linkages between various strata of the mind which reawaken the flow of primary process connections." According to Kris, the process of recollection is set in motion by interpretations not because they directly produce recall, but rather because they establish conditions under which recall becomes possible: "conditions more similar to those which existed when the recalled scenes and events occurred."

We may say that these conditions are gradually achieved through the fact that interpretation effects a regrouping of the material available to the patient. We know that with the use of classical analytic technique the dramatic reappearance of forgotten memories, so conspicuous in Freud's early experience, is quite rare. Kris, discussing this point in his paper, mentions that a recall occurring in analysis is often accompanied by the experience of *déjà raconté*. Here I should like to bring an example which illustrates another variant of recall experience during analysis.

Many years ago I analyzed a young man suffering from severe premature ejaculations which caused him no end of humiliation and anxiety. In the fourth month of his analysis he told me of an experience at the age of nine. His father had taken him along to a swimming pool where only men were admitted and where it was customary to swim in the nude. The patient recalled how, while lying in the sun, he had felt terribly humiliated when one of the grownups looked at him. He attributed his embarrassment to the fact that he had a mole on the thigh. Shortly after this session, the analysis entered a period of intense transference resistances. This culminated after several months in the patient's becoming aware not only of his competitive reactions toward the analyst, but also of his unconscious fear of retaliation, the fear that the analyst might wish to keep him impotent. A calmer period then ensued in the analysis, during which he once more recounted the incident of his embarrassment at the swimming pool. This time he told it differently: his humiliation, he recalled, had been due to the comparison between the large penis of the grownup and his own penis which appeared so small to him. When I reminded him of having related this incident to me incompletely, he responded indignantly: he had always recalled it exactly as he just told it to me, and he was absolutely certain he had never before mentioned it in the analysis.

This example permits us to draw a number of conclusions. In one respect my patient was different from those described by Kris: his recall was accompanied not by the experience of *déjà raconté*, but of its opposite, *jamais raconté*, which is not very common. But in some respects, I believe, this patient resembled Kris's patient and many others. Indeed I think that recall of previously unavailable, warded-off memories or of some details occurs regularly in our cases; but much of it occurs in such an inconspicuous way that neither the patient nor the analyst can become aware of it. My patient was right in saying that he had always known all the details of the event recalled; except, we must add, that some of them were not conscious, not available to him when he first described it. The reappearance in his awareness of these previously unavailable details could be ascribed to the preceding analysis of transference resistances. This case is but one example of the well-known fact that interpretations rarely have an immediate and direct effect upon recall. Here one must even assume that the reemergence of memory traces was due to an interpretation which in its content had only indirectly and remotely to do with the scene involved. It was, I believe, the partial diminution of the patient's fears of competing with a man—the analyst—that permitted the reemergence of similar reactions toward a man in the childhood scene. Indeed, it is a remarkable fact that although our interpretations deal directly and explicitly with only some of the facets and aspects of the conflict involved, they implicitly encompass and indirectly affect a much larger number of them. This is the fact to which Hartmann (1951) referred when he spoke of the "multiple appeal" of interpretations.

Complex consequences indeed may ensue when, due to analytic work, some resistance of the patient is overcome. We are not dealing with isolated defenses or resistances, but with "defensive structures" (Hoffer 1954; Kris 1956). I believe that this is the state of affairs to which Freud (1917) alluded in his *Introductory Lectures* where he compared the psychoanalytic technique with the then raging First World War and spoke of the important consequences of winning a battle on a piece of territory that in itself is insignificant.

In his study "On Some Vicissitudes of Insight in Psychoanalysis," Kris (1956a) describes convincingly that what he calls a "good analytic hour," in which real insight is achieved, is the result of a long drawn-out process in which "energies attached to the repressed material have been set free," and he says: "The reorganization which takes place is the essence of the analytic process with its vicissitudes and changing facets. As part of this reorganization some of the energies set free are . . . at the disposal of the ego." We will add: at the disposal of the autonomous ego functions.

We know that this result is attained by way of a complicated preparatory work, a work which comprises many steps of various kinds. Some of them have to deal with immediate tasks of facilitating the patient's communication. Others involve a forming of provisional hunches which later may be corroborated or, on the contrary, modified or even discarded when confronted with additional material. Still other steps consist in communicating to the patient some observation derived from his associations, hoping that it may group or organize the material in such a way as to elicit additional material ultimately leading us to an understanding and thus to an interpretation of the patient's behavior. For a long time usually these interpretations are only of limited scope, until a more comprehensive one becomes assured.

This grouping of the material, as we are all aware, is being achieved in a number of ways; for instance, by bringing out similarities in the patient's reactions to various important events of his life, or similarities of mechanisms in dealing with situations, with people, with impulses or with the analyst. We know the importance this type of work assumes when the analyst can point to the similarity of such behavior patterns to the patient's mode of resistance (A. Freud 1936). Let me give an example of a less frequent, though also well-known type of preparation. The stressing of a time sequence of some reactions may bring a patient a considerable step forward in understanding his reactions. Thus to a college girl, say, who has always been preferred by her father, it may bring a sudden insight into the reasons for her wish to quit college when she is shown that the decision to abandon her studies and return home coincided with receiving a letter from the father telling her that his relation with her mother had improved.

By and large, the nature of the preparatory work we perform every day is incompletely defined and has not been described in sufficient detail. And yet it is on this gradual and painstaking work that the outcome of an analysis usually depends. It would be a worthwhile task to make a careful study of this preparatory work in analysis, as a counterpart to the one on traces which I mentioned before.

As my next illustration I have chosen an example that may serve as a link between preparation and interpretation proper.

A patient of mine, a girl in her twenties who had recently become acutely distressed by her boyfriend's unfaithfulness, spoke of the following matters within one session. She described at length her enjoyment at listening to Gluck's aria "I lost my Euridice," then talked about the special enjoyment she used to get in her childhood and adolescence from playing records of sad songs. She then shifted over to the painful events of her prepuberty when, after having been a tomboy among boys, one day she realized that these boys were running after a girl who was girlish and pretty, and that she herself could not run as fast as the boys; then she again related a painful incident of having been humiliated and threatened by a nurse in childhood, adding: "I feared I might lose the respect of my younger siblings." At the end of the hour I pointed to the importance of the notion of a "loss" in her associations. I thought, rightly or wrongly, that this word might help in grouping her memories and reactions. This word could form a bridge between several chains of memories and developments in her life: the enjoyment of a loss, leading toward her masochistic fantasies of prepuberty and centering around that precise childhood event in which she feared the loss of her siblings' "respect"; the loss of her illusion of masculinity as a tomboy, with feelings of inability to compete with a pretty girl, in its turn is a link to that of her boyfriend who prefers another girl. May I add that my choice of this common denominator of the session was not made arbitrarily; it derived from the material of the session and, moreover, must have been prepared in me by my thorough acquaintance with the patient.

We must realize that in speaking of preparatory work a distinction cannot always be clearly drawn between preparation (Loewenstein 1951a), confrontation (Devereux 1951), clarification (in E. Bibring's sense, 1954) and interpretation proper, and that interpretations themselves have various structures and functions.

From experience we know that the effectiveness of interpretations as well as of the various interventions which prepare them is contingent upon certain conditions, such as dosage, hierarchy, timing, and the wording of interpretations. These are sometimes classified under the more general and less precise heading of psychoanalytic tact (Loewenstein 1930–31, 1951a), a term which by its very vagueness, by its allusion to intuition, betrays our lack of well-established knowledge.

Since interpretation aims at helping the patient to uncover what he does not know by means of what he knows about himself, tact in interpretation often consists in choosing a wording that will permit the material to be regrouped in a significant way. Among the various ways in which the material is thus being reorganized during the analytic process, I should like to stress a particular one. Genetic interpretations essentially are reconstructions of psychological events considered to be the prototypes or the causes of later psychological manifestations whose significance or determinants are thus being explained. But genetic interpretations can also move in the opposite direction, as it were, when it is necessary to find the more recent derivatives of a known event or pattern in the past. In other words, genetic interpretations aim at the establishment of a reciprocal relationship between the present and the past. If the term reconstruction is used for the establishment of a forgotten childhood event from its more recent derivatives, one might use the term reconstruction *upward* to denote the type of interpretation we employ in reconstructing the more recent consequences of a former event (Loewenstein 1951a). Permit me to give an example of this not infrequent type of interpretation.

A medical student had a fear of dropping to the floor when looked

at by the professor in class. While relating this symptom he remembered that in his adolescence, when he was very religious and had to
lift the Torah in the synagogue, he was terrified lest he might drop it on
the floor. He added that he was so worried lest in the eyes of the
assembled religious community the dreaded accident might represent
a disgrace to his father. His next thought was that while afraid of
dropping to the floor during the lecture, he was preoccupied with what
his classmates might think, who knew that he was in analytic treatment. The conclusion is obvious to any analyst that the patient at this
time was under the impact of an ambivalence conflict toward his
analyst, resembling the one toward his father when he had feared to let
the Torah drop to the floor; that he was under the influence of his fear
and unconscious wish to disgrace the analyst, as in adolescence he had
been afraid of his unconscious wish to disgrace the father. A more
complete interpretation, in this case a reconstruction upward, would
have to take into account some differences between the two situations,
as for instance the change from an active dropping of a revered object,
the Torah, to a passive dropping to the floor under the gaze of a
teacher. Such reconstructions upward often have great importance in
the analysis of transference resistances.

The interpretation in this case was based upon the use of three key
ideas: dropping, being seen, and disgrace. In adolescence, the disgrace
would have ensued from being seen dropping the Torah; in the analytic
situation, the presence of idea of disgrace had to be inferred from the
fantasy of being seen dropping to the floor by those who knew the
patient to be in analysis. The use of key ideas in the wording of interpretations derives its importance from several reasons. They are
ideas used by the patients themselves and thus facilitate recognition.
They also are those which emerge as compromise formations into the
preconscious and therefore bear traces of the interplay of forces that
led to the compromise. Interpretations aim at reflecting the work not
only of the id, but also of the superego and the ego. Thus, when they
use key ideas in their wording they have the ability to promote that
regrouping of the patient's thoughts and emotions which leads to recall
and insight (Kris 1951; Loewenstein 1951a).

In many a case insight in the patient is made possible only if the
wording of interpretations contains words corresponding to some particular derivative of his conflicts.

I remember a case of a patient whose symptoms centered around obsessional fears about the health of her grown-up son. These anxieties had started shortly after the death of her mother, approximately twelve years before the patient came for analysis. They were actually a continuation of previous, similar anxieties about her mother's health. This continuity also was attested by frequently recurring dreams in which the mother was still alive but ill, and the patient had to worry lest something happen to her mother. After some time the analytic work, which then centered around the nature of her relationship with her mother and its influence on her present obsessional fears, bogged down. The analyst's emphasis on her love or attachment or submissiveness to her mother, which were all facts, seemed no longer to help the progress of the analysis. One day I picked up a word the patient herself had used; faithfulness to her mother. This term struck her as expressing the exact nature of what had remained after a period of violent and prolonged struggles between daughter and mother. And the term faithfulness helped the patient considerably in gaining insight into her complicated, ambivalent reactions to her dead mother and into their continued impact on her obsessional preoccupation with her son's health.

But there are other cases where it takes the patient a long time to accomplish the change in the wording of a thought. One patient, for instance, who suffered from the consequences of extended phenomena of isolation of affect, always spoke of his mother as a rather harsh, unbending, and sarcastic person. Yet when first confronted in his analysis with the idea that he might have wished for his mother's love, he remained completely incredulous. Such a thought was entirely foreign to him. It took several years of analytic work and a gradual reconstruction of his childhood history until the existence of this wish became conscious to the patient. He himself remarked, correctly, that it took so much work simply to turn the knowledge he always had a few degrees to the side.

The reason for the importance of the wording in an interpretation resides in the function of speech in the analytic procedure. Speech, in the communication between patient and analyst, is the main vehicle that permits the lifting of psychological processes out of their unconscious state into the preconscious and finally into consciousness.

While interpretations decisively influence the process of analysis and while, to be effective, they have to be timed and worded in certain ways, they are continuously influenced in their turn by the psychological processes taking place in the patient. It is not, as it may seem, that the analyst knows it all in advance and but judiciously chooses the moment and the way to impart this understanding to his patient. To be sure, frequently the analyst sees or knows something long before the patient is able to remember or to grasp it. But he acquires this knowledge gradually from his patient. If the analyst's interpretations enable the patient to gain insight, the latter's communications and interpretations, in their turn, create insight in the analyst. Moreover, an interpretation is meaningless as a one-sided act and acquires its full significance only through its counterpart, the effects it produces on the patient. This subtle interaction between patient and analyst is an essential feature of the analytic process.

Actually this interaction between analyst and analysand can exist only in the type of psychological process which we call a psychoanalysis, since to acquire its full significance an interpretation must be followed by its counterpart; namely, dynamic change leading to recall and insight in the patient. But this condition need not obtain in an analytic investigation in a narrow sense; and it is certainly absent in those explanatory interpretations which I mentioned earlier, in contrasting the scientific explanation of a symptom with its concrete interpretation in the analysis of an individual.

To underscore these differences somewhat more sharply, I should like to remind you of certain forms of resistance in analysis.

Analytic interpretations have always been opposed by the patients on rational or intellectual grounds. In the last decade a particular variation on this theme has appeared with increasing frequency. The patients who present this type of resistance seem overeager to accept analytic interpretation, and they express this by jumping to conclusions couched in psychoanalytic terms. These patients will immediately translate the meaning of their dreams into such terms as, for instance, Oedipus complex, homosexuality, castration, etc. The use of psychoanalytic jargon or of the cliché, as Martin Stein (1957) recently described it, is quite frequent nowadays.

I learned most about this form of resistance from a patient whom I analyzed some twenty-five years ago. This was the obsessive-compulsive patient already mentioned, who had been analyzed for many years before she was referred to me. She had entered that previous treatment as an agoraphobic and during its course had developed the symptoms of a severe obsessive-compulsive neurosis. From the start of her treatment with me she would bring daily dreams and would "associate" to them in a particular way which clearly indicated that she continued a style of analysis established by her former analyst. She did not use analytic terminology in the crude way, just described, but somehow more subtly spoke in her associations of fantasies and events that left the analyst no choice, at first sight, but to interpret them in terms of direct derivatives of typical early childhood conflicts. These were the interpretations which she would then ask me to repeat many times at the end of the hour.

I shall not go into the details which permitted me to understand the meaning of this patient's type of resistance. Suffice it to say that she used the analytic procedure and the analyst's interpretations, not as a means of understanding herself but as a magical conjuring away of her main obsession: the dread of having "touched the old woman." The repetition of the interpretations had the same meaning of a magical procedure. I mentioned before that underneath this magical function of her analysis there existed another one, that of a mocking parody of her previous treatment.

In this case, as in many another instance of the misuse of analytic concepts by the resistance, the patient's style of resistance was but a slight variation of the analyst's mode of interpreting. What strikes one in those pseudo interpretations so eagerly suggested by the patients is that they are not completely wrong; nor are they completely correct. And if one examines them as well as the somehow awkward interpretations of the analyst which may have led to this state of affairs, one is struck by the peculiar language of these statements; by a paucity in the choice of verbs, mostly limited to the verb "to be." However, and this is their most conspicuous distinction, these statements are characterized by the absence of an adverb of time; as for instance: "this is homosexuality," "this is a father figure," etc. While such statements fit very well into a scientific paper describing the general category of phenomena into which a dream might be placed, they are not adequate to describe any concrete psychological phenomenon which, in order to be placed into its genetic and dynamic context, requires qualification by a temporal adverb.

This peculiar state of affairs can be understood if one considers the function of speech in analysis.

Although nonverbal communication may flow from the patient toward his analyst and to some extent also from the analyst to the patient, the essential interchange of communication in psychoanalysis is by speech. This peculiar and protracted dialogue, which constitutes the analytic process, can also be characterized by its division of certain functions of speech between patient and analyst. I discussed these speech functions rather extensively in another paper (Loewenstein 1956), using the classifications proposed by Karl Buehler (1934). Here I may repeat, briefly: whereas the analyst is supposed not only to limit his speech to its so-called cognitive function, but to that part of it which refers to his understanding of the patient, we expect the patient in analysis to use the expressive function of speech and that part of its cognitive function which deals with the knowledge of one's own self.

Recall and insight in the patient use a kind of thought and speech function which combine the cognitive and expressive functions in a particular way. Of patients who present intellectualization of the type mentioned before, i.e., analytic jargon, one might say that they make use of the cognitive function devoid of its expressive counterpart. Thus their verbalized thoughts concern phenomena that are not theirs personally, but are impersonal and possibly valid for a large number of individuals whose symptoms or dreams fall under the same heading of, for instance, Oedipus complex, or sibling rivalry, or whatever it may be. The absence of the expressive function in the speech of these patients is the result of their resistance. The analyst's use of psychoanalytic jargon in interpretations reveals a shift of the cognitive function from the patient's individual problems to more general phenomena. As a matter of fact, while analyzing we always do, consciously or preconsciously, work with these concepts as a general framework. But when actually interpreting we retranslate them into the patient's concrete experiences.

This brings us back once more to the problem of the difference between interpretations of specific psychological phenomena in an individual case and those interpretations which present a more general, explanatory, scientific character. By using particular interpretations in the individual analysis, which enable us to uncover further data, we reach more generalized, explanatory interpretations of mental phenomena. But the obverse likewise is true and characteristic of psychoanalytic work: we use explanatory concepts in order to arrive at concrete interpretations and thus, in turn, are led to discover new data.

But should we assume that concrete interpretations in therapy do not have the character of an explanation? This assumption would certainly be wrong; some of them undoubtedly possess this quality, even though their validity is limited to a given patient. For instance, the reconstruction of a forgotten childhood event out of symptoms, dreams, etc., states that this event caused or codetermined the existence of such symptoms or dreams. A scientifically valid explanation need not make explicit the assumptions on which it is based, and the assumptions implied in such interpretations are contained in the psychoanalytic theory.

In each individual analysis there is an interplay between observation and the application of some theoretical assumption or hypothesis, without which the observational data would simply remain in a state of chaos (Hartmann, Kris, and Loewenstein 1953). And yet, every psychoanalysis can and perhaps ought to be conducted as though the theory were never completely taken for granted. This is a way to make new discoveries; it was the way Freud, in the past, discovered most of what we know now. It may also enable us in the future to effect possibly necessary realignments or modifications of our theoretical assumptions on the basis of new observations. The essence of psychoanalysis is that particular interplay between observational data, gathered from clean clinical work, and their interpretation within a scientifically valid conceptual framework—be it the one we have now or possibly a future, better one.

REFERENCES

Bernfeld, S. (1932). Der Begriff der "Deutung" in der Psychoanalyse. *Ztschr. f. ang. Psychol.*, 42.

Bibring, E. (1954). Psychoanalysis and the dynamic psychotherapies. *J. Amer. Psychoanal. Assn.*, 2.

Bibring-Lehner, G. (1936). A contribution to the subject of transference resistance. *Int. J. Psychoanal.*, 17.

Brenner, C. (1955). The validation of psychoanalytic interpretation. Summarized in panel report: Validation of psychoanalytic techniques. *J. Amer. Psychoanal. Assn.*, 3.

Buehler, K. (1934). *Sprachtheorie. Die Darstellungsfunktion der Sprache.* Jena: Fischer.

Burlingham, D. T. (1935). Die Einfühlung des Kleinkindes in die Mutter. *Imago*, 21.

Devereux, G. (1951). Some criteria for the timing of confrontations and interpretations. *Int. J. Psychoanal.*, 32.

Eissler, K. R. (1953). The effect of the structure of the ego on psychoanalytic technique. *J. Amer. Psychoanal. Assn.*, 1.

Ekstein, R. (1955). Discussion remarks in panel: Validation of psychoanalytic techniques. *J. Amer. Psychoanal. Assn.*, 3.

Fenichel, O. (1939). Problems of psychoanalytic technique. *Psychoanal. Q.*, 8.

Freud, A. (1936). *The Ego and the Mechanisms of Defense.* New York: Int. Univ. Press, 1946.

Freud, S. (1900). The interpretation of dreams. *S.E.*, 4/5.

_____ (1917). *Introductory Lectures on Psychoanalysis.* London: Allen & Unwin, 1922.

_____ (1937). Constructions in analysis. *Coll. Papers* 5.

Glover, E. (1955). *The Technique of Psychoanalysis.* New York: Int. Univ. Press.

Greenacre, P. (1952). *Trauma, Growth and Personality.* New York: Norton.

_____ (1956). Reevaluation of the process of working through. *Int. J. Psychoanal.*, 37.

Hartmann, H. (1927). *Die Grundlagen der Psychoanalyse.* Leipzig: Georg Thieme.

_____ (1951). Technical implications of ego psychology. *Psychoanal. Q.*, 20.

_____ & Kris, E. (1945). The genetic approach in psychoanalysis. *Psychoanal. Study Child*, 1.

_____ & Loewenstein, R. M. (1953). The function of theory in psychoanalysis. In *Drives, Affects, Behavior*, ed. R. M. Loewenstein. New York: Int. Univ. Press.

Hoffer, W. (1954). Defensive process and defensive organization: their place in psychoanalytic technique. *Int. J. Psychoanal.*, 35.

Isaacs, S. (1939). Criteria for interpretation. *Int. J. Psychoanal.*, 20.

Kris, E. (1950). On preconscious mental processes. *Psychoanal. Q.*, 19.

_____ (1951). Ego psychology and interpretation in psychoanalytic therapy. *Psychoanal. Q.*, 20.

_____ (1956a). On some vicissitudes of insight in psychoanalysis. *Int. J. Psychoanal.*, 37.

_____ (1956b). The recovery of childhood memories in psychoanalysis. *Psychoanal. Study Child*, 11.

Loewenstein, R. M. (1930–31). Le tact dans la technique psychanalytique. *Rev. Franç. Psychanal.*, 4.

_____ (1951a). The problem of interpretation. *Psychoanal. Q.*, 20.

_____ (1951b). Ego development and psychoanalytic technique. *Amer. J. Psychiat.*, 107.

————— (1956). Remarks on the role of speech in psychoanalytic technique. *Int. J. Psychoanal.*, 37.

Reich, W. (1945). *Character-Analysis.* New York: Orgone Institute.

Schmidl, F. (1955). The problem of scientific validation in psychoanalytic interpretation. *Int. J. Psychoanal.*, 36.

Stein, M. (1957). The cliché: a phenomenon of resistance. Summarized in panel report: Clinical and theoretical aspects of resistance. *J. Amer. Psychoanal. Assn.*, 5.

Sterba, E. (1945). Interpretation and education. *Psychoanal. Study Child*, 1.

Waelder, R. (1939). Kriterien der Deutung. *Int. Ztschr. Psa. und Imago*, 24.

8

Remarks on Some Variations in Psychoanalytic Technique

In recent years, problems connected with variations of technique have aroused a great deal of interest among analysts. This may partly be due to the appearance of interesting modifications of psychoanalytic technique that have created considerable controversy and thus led, in turn, to renewed study of the base of classical technique. (Of the many authors who have dealt with the subject, only a few will be specifically cited here.) Moreover, this revival of interest is influenced by the "widening scope" of the application of psychoanalysis, as well as by the increasing use of analytically oriented psychotherapy. Thus the need for a scrutiny of the rationale of all such techniques has become more acute.

However, my discussion does not concern different types of psychotherapy, nor will it deal with proposed modifications of our technique.[1] It will remain within the framework of what is usually called the classical or standard technique, as applied to psychoneuroses and related characterological disorders, to sexual perversions and to

Main presentation in the panel discussion "Variations in Classical Psychoanalytical Technique" read before the 20th Congress of the International Psychoanalytical Association, Paris, July–August 1957.

1. The distinction between modifications and variations is a necessary one, especially when questions of indication for either standard or modified technique are involved. As modifications, in contradistinction to variations, I would mainly describe changes in three areas of the analytic process: (1) Any tendency to curtail the spontaneous productions of the patient, with the resultant neglect of understanding his unconscious. (2) Minimization of the interpretative work in favor of manipulative interventions, i.e., procedures that diminish reliance on insight achieved in the patient by verbalization and working through, in favor e.g., of transference results or "corrective emotional experi-

conditions which, for want of a better term, may be described as disturbed reactions to complicated life situations.

At this point, I might be expected to define the classical analytic technique and to delimit it from related therapeutic procedures. I shall refrain from this because I do not know any foolproof definition of classical analysis. It would evidently have to be based on the importance we ascribe to the analytic way of dealing with resistance, transference, transference neuroses, and working through (A. Freud 1954; Greenacre 1956; Stone 1954). Such a definition is necessary at times, particularly for pedagogical and polemic purposes. However, I shall take the essentials of classical analytic technique for granted. I shall also take for granted that in some areas considerable disagreement may exist among analysts as to whether a technical procedure should be called classical or not.

A few years ago Anna Freud (1954), in a discussion dealing with the same area of problems, expressed the view that changes in the application of technical rules and procedures are necessary at times when they can be theoretically justified in relation to the structure of a given case. Among several examples of changes in the analytic procedure, she cited the case of a male homosexual patient whose first analyst had felt it impossible ever to recommend that he refrain from actual gratification of his homosexual impulses. When Anna Freud took over the case, she could not bring herself to impose this aspect of the rule of abstinence either. Only later did she understand why it would have been contraindicated; she recognized that in this patient, as in others of the same type, a renunciation of homosexual gratifications would have provoked intolerable castration anxiety.

Unfortunately, the variations in technique usually stop with the first stage, i.e., they remain on an intuitive basis. Let us hope that in the future we shall be able, as Anna Freud was in this case, to understand much more about the value of such changes in terms of the specific neurosis involved.

The above example may also illustrate the problem of choice of a conceptual framework when describing variations in technique. Anna

---

ence," etc. (3) Such modifications of the optimal conditions for an analysis as hamper the patient's analyzability, e.g., those jeopardizing the formation or analytic resolution of the transference neurosis.

Freud's description here dealt with but a single aspect of the analytic procedure: the applicability of the rule of abstinence in cases of homosexuality.[2] This rule as such cannot easily be compared with other requirements of analysis; e.g., with the timing or hierarchy of interpretations. Nor does the applicability of one part of the rule of abstinence even imply, necessarily, that other forms of it can or cannot apply, e.g., the imposition of abstinence on the patient by not gratifying his transference wishes. This very example shows that our notion about the analytic rules requires further and more precise scrutiny before we can comprehend in what cases and situations some variation of technique may be considered useful. Here we must note that the various interventions of the analyst, or the various empirical rules which he usually follows, do not all lie on the same psychological level. They have various meanings and values, and do not perform the same functions within an analysis. The significance of interpretations is not on the same level, for instance; as the practice of having the patient lie on the couch; nor can it be compared with the rule of abstinence or with the problems arising from the fee we ask the patients to pay. Not only do all these steps differ as to their rationale and function, but their meanings both for the analyst and a given patient may vary at diverse moments of the analysis.

K. R. Eissler (1953) recently attempted a study of variations in technique based on the state of the patient's ego. According to him, in the ideal case interpretations alone are used and suffice to perform the analyst's task; if specific ego disturbances do not allow the use of classical technique, the analyst deliberately introduces "parameters" in order to make the patient's ego amenable to analysis. However, it is a matter of fact that in all cases analyzed according to the classical technique we use not only interpretation, but also a number of interventions designed either "to make it possible for interpretations to have the desirable dynamic effect" or even "to create conditions without which the analytic procedure would be impossible" (Loewenstein 1951a). Eissler designates as a "parameter" any action of the analyst which is not an interpretation. I myself prefer the term "intervention" because it is more neutral and thus points more clearly to the need for

---

2. In former years it was frequent usage to advise patients afflicted with perversions to refrain from gratifying them during analytic treatment.

greater precision and differentiation with respect to these various actions.[3]

Let us now examine some elements of our method, and their place and function within the analytic procedure.

An essential condition for analytic work is that the patient have the necessary confidence in the analyst's ability to abide by the tacit contract between them. On the patient's side, this contract demands complete frankness; on the analyst's, total discretion and that he act exclusively in the interest of the patient's recovery. Indeed, analysis may be jeopardized if the patient believes that the analyst uses his confidence for other than therapeutic purposes. Such trust is contingent upon a consistent behavior of the analyst, which is not part of the analytic technique proper but an equivalent of specific actions by the analyst.

Some interventions and the rules of their application aim at the *creation of initial rapport* (beginning of transference): listening, understanding, giving hope of relief from suffering. But sometimes this function may be performed by a beginning of clarification, by preparation for future interpretation, or even by interpretation itself.[4] Other interventions *prepare the patient for analytic treatment:* explanations about its nature, discussion of fees, of hours, etc., which may minimize later resistances. The practical rules governing certain interventions are designed to *facilitate the later analysis of transference,* or to *forestall future difficulties* or even unsurmountable obstacles to a favorable termination of the treatment.

Some interventions serve to *create the most propitious conditions for following the fundamental rule and for the gaining of reality testing for psychic processes,* e.g., the request that the patient maintain the recumbent position. Others again have the purpose of *keeping the intensity of psychic conflicts at its optimal value,* e.g., imposing the rule of abstinence, or creating a reality situation that may diminish over-intense conflicts and acting out. A most important condition for the successful outcome of the analysis is *not to gratify transference*

---

3. Some authors indeed have defined certain actions of the analyst more precisely. Devereaux (1951) discusses confrontations as distinct from interpretations. E. Bibring (1954), describing several types of interventions that occur during the process of analysis, discriminates between "suggestion," "manipulation," "clarification" (a term introduced by Carl Rogers), and "interpretation."

4. In exceptional cases and situations, by going to see the patient (M. Kris; E. Kronold [in A. Freud 1954]).

phenomena within the analytic situation, be they manifestations of positive or of negative transference.[5]

Turning to variations in the application of the more general technical rules, we see an important example in the degree of anonymity maintained by the analyst. This obviously is far less complete in small communities, in institutions, in training analyses (when the analyst is also an instructor and administrator of the school), or in the case of a patient who knows a relative of the analyst, for instance. We are aware that while analysis is possible even under these conditions, it may be seriously hampered by difficulties arising from such lack of anonymity. Of course, the analyst's anonymity is being preserved also by his position where the patient does not see him, and by the fact that the patient's questions or remarks about him usually remain unanswered. Some patients at the beginning or at certain points of the analysis may be so disturbed by this artificially imposed diminution of their ability to test psychological realities, to distinguish fantasies about the analyst from his real attitude towards them,[6] as to necessitate changes in this respect. In certain extreme situations it may become necessary to have the patient temporarily abandon the recumbent position and face the analyst.

Gitelson (1932) has described situations in which the analyst found it appropriate to acknowledge his personal motives for certain actions toward the patient. Recently Bouvet, Marty, and Sauguet (1956) reported some instances where valuable results ensued from confirming that the patient's guess about some action of the analyst during a session had been correct. In all these cases the abandonment of a small area of anonymity, under particular and well-defined conditions, favored the analysis of transference phenomena.

There also are cases, especially if sexual curiosity was seriously interfered with in childhood, where the patient may need gradual preparation before he can tolerate having his questions remain unanswered so that he may be able to analyze them. Variation of the analyst's behavior in these areas is sometimes imperative to avoid deep and harmful hurts, since the psychological situation in some adult cases resembles that which we encounter in the analysis of children and adolescents.

5. This is what is meant by the "rule of abstinence" in the strict sense of the term.

6. We must assume that testing of "social realities" may perform the function, among others, of countercathexis against drive discharge.

Indeed, great caution and tact must be applied in the use of the rule of abstinence. This is true even with regard to acting out, in full view of the aim that the patient replace action by thought. E. Jacobson (in an unpublished paper) has described the necessity to permit token gratifications in order to make the patient's behavior analyzable. I remember once surprising a young candidate when I advised him at first not systematically to refuse all the small gifts his patient would present to him. To the near-borderline patient, his acceptance of a gift meant that she was accepted by the analyst as a worthwhile person; thus it facilitated the analysis of her very seriously disturbed object relationships. In short, maximal frustration is not always the most favorable condition for analytical work.

The applicability of a rule in a given case or at a given moment will depend on the patient's psychological state and on our estimate of the effect its application might have upon him at such time or in the future. One well-known intervention or "parameter" consists in advising phobic patients to brave their phobic restrictions. Obviously this recommendation should be made only if the anxiety thus provoked will not become intolerable or incompatible with the continuance of analysis. Besides, such a procedure may sometimes be completely unnecessary or even contrary to the patient's best interest, depending on the meaning of the phobia in a given case. The analyst, in deciding whether this intervention is indicated, will be guided by his understanding of its individual effects. A recommendation to brave the phobic situation may indeed serve to achieve various results. (1) By increasing anxiety in the patient, it may help him to bring psychic material to the fore that would not emerge otherwise. (2) It may express confidence in the patient's ability to master reality on his own, to act without the protecting love that prevailed in the early childhood situations which were the prototypes of his phobic restrictions. (3) It may break off the analyst's participation in the epinosic gain which the patient derives from the phobic situation.[7]

Sometimes a variation of technique is the inevitable and expected result ensuing from the application of a rule. A striking example of this

7. It may be due to the absence of too much epinosic gain from their phobic restrictions that some patients are able to overcome them during analysis without such encouragement by the analyst. This may also be due to the way in which these patients had overcome the infantile prototype situations; how they overcame the overprotective behavior of the mother (transforming passivity into activity).

kind was described by Anna Freud (1954): It had been necessary to advise a homosexual patient to refrain from sexual gratification, and this recommendation led to such intense anxiety that she chose to be available to this patient at any hour of the day or night.

In most of the instances cited above, the variations in application of analytical rules refer mainly to quantitative factors. On the other hand, variation of some kind is inevitable whenever the use of some established rule precludes the use of another one in the future. To give an example: A man of about forty consulted me because of a conflict centering around his unsatisfactory love life. He had been contemplating divorce for many years, but was unable to carry out his intention. Each time, as soon as he came close to legal procedure, he was seized by a state of violent anxiety at the idea of being alone. The patient since adolescence had been suffering from anxiety states when left alone, particularly at night. In one of the first interviews, while we were discussing the advisability of analysis of him, he asked ironically whether he would be expected not to make a definite decision with regard to his divorce until the end of the treatment. I replied that I did not expect him to refrain from making any major decision during his analysis. Had I followed the general rule in this case, I would have drastically reinforced the patient's phobic restrictions, making it impossible later to recommend that he brave them.

If in the use of such rules we must guard against jeopardizing the future progress of an analysis, the same obviously holds true with regard to variations of technique. I am thinking, for instance, of actions on the analyst's part that might be helpful in the beginning, but which later on would affect his objectivity toward the patient or preclude that degree of anonymity which we cannot quantitatively define but consider to be most favorable for effective analytic work.

The variations described thus far do not refer to the truly essential and fundamental steps in the analytic process. Important though they may be, all these interventions play only a nonspecific role in it. The specific tool of the psychoanalyst is the interpretation. To illustrate the situation, we might imagine an intestinal ailment requiring treatment by an antibiotic that can be carried to the diseased portion of the intestine only by certain vehicles having no specific curative effect in themselves. In this analogy the antibiotic represents the interpretations, or rather, the insights resulting from interpretations. The vehicles stand for the various other steps which the analyst must take in order that he can interpret correctly, i.e., understand his patient and enable him to benefit from it: in other words, so as to make interpretation effective. This is merely a crude comparison, of course. The analytic process is much more complicated, since all the steps in it are usually contingent upon each other and completely intertwined.

The two essential steps here involved, which are characteristic for the psychoanalytic process, consist in understanding the patient and in conveying this understanding to him in a way that will enable him to gain insight into his own conflicts. Variations may occur (1) in the means by which the patient presents and the analyst acquires the psychic material necessary to such understanding, and (2) in the way the analyst conveys the results of his understanding to the patient in order to promote the latter's insight.

Schematically, one can say that the analyst's first task is to enable the patient to follow the fundamental rule. But the way of achieving this varies from one case to another. It may require the entire range of the analyst's tools; which of them he will use and when depends on the individual type of the patient's difficulty with regard to this rule. In a general way it depends on the nature of the neurotic disturbance, since the way in which a person's pathogenic conflicts were constituted and dealt with enters into the way he behaves in analysis. His particular difficulty in following the fundamental rule is a part or an indirect continuation of the pathogenic conflicts that had led to his neurosis. Such difficulties reflect specific defense mechanisms as well as the drives they are warding off, and can thus be understood and overcome by various analytical means (A. Freud 1936).

There are, however, considerable variations in cultural and individual factors, beside the psychopathological ones, which influence the way a patient gradually learns to follow the fundamental rule as well as the particular style of expression he finally acquires. Equally important are the various means by which the analyst must teach his patients to follow the rule and the particular ways in which he must understand their modes of expression. We need only remember the different ways of making use of the patient's body movements or posture or of their dreams or, for example, the various ways in which we may try to understand and deal with their silences.

Although the aim of the analyst on the whole is to promote the patient's ability to follow the fundamental rule, at times it is necessary to interrupt the flow of associations; for instance, in order to obtain an exact description of some symptom or fantasy, to get associations to some dream elements, or to ask questions about important dates in the patient's life, such as the time sequence of some events or the circumstances under which certain symptoms appeared. Perhaps the best known example of this kind may be found in Freud's case history of the "Rat Man" (1909). You will recall that before Freud could correctly interpret this patient's obsession concerning rats, he had to ask him three times in the course of the analysis to recount the events during the military maneuvers that had preceded the onset of the symptom. It is useful to follow this method also in some instances where isolated symptoms appear during the analysis. In one such case, only my insistence that the patient describe the details of a situation preceding an anxiety attack elicited the admission that he suspected his wife of being unfaithful to him.[8]

I have found it valuable to ask the patients for more detailed descriptions of situations, events or thoughts in two other types of situation:

(*a*) When a patient's repeated descriptions of conflicts or arguments with some other person remain unvaried or fail to yield any new details after attempts have been made to interpret the underlying motives for these disagreements.

(*b*) When patients misuse the fundamental rule by complying as far as they believe the analyst expects it of them, while avoiding to mention some other thoughts that occur to them. But such patients will, for instance, easily agree with interpretations without ever voicing any contradiction or any indirect confirmation, such as the recollection of some other hitherto uncommunicated event or dream.[9]

8. E. Bibring (1937) has pointed out that generally it is of importance for the analyst before giving interpretations to get a satisfactory description from the patient of his thoughts and the events in his life, in order to avoid erroneous conclusions.

9. The fundamental rule is based upon elimination of the conscious trend to remember only what one wants to remember (aim-directed thinking of the conscious). Thus, it gives entrance to preconscious elements and later even to unconscious ones. Under the influence of analysis, preconscious (or unconscious) resistances may use a different path: not forgetting, but forgetting to tell. It is a defense against a coherent, understandable whole. But under prodding by the analyst, the conscious or preconscious intention to remember leads the patient to tell missing details. As long as a thought or an affect has not been verbalized, it remains in isolation and but incompletely available to the System Cs, or, to put it more precisely, to the dynamic processes which lead towards insight (cf., Loewenstein 1956).

Needless to say, any such interruptions of the patient's flow of associations should be made only sparingly and not in the initial stage of analysis.

Most striking are the variations in the ways by which the analyst must communicate his understanding to the patient. While each undoubtedly has his own personal style of analyzing, it is equally certain that he varies his way of working with each patient and even in different phases of the same analysis. Each patient, being a unique individual with a unique combination of traits and problems, will present a unique combination of patterns of behaving in analysis. He will display his personal mode in the presentation of material, in resistances, in transference manifestations, in the way he gains insight or utilizes it to find healthier ways of solving his pathogenic conflicts. Hence each has to be understood in an individual way and dealt with accordingly. These individual differences among patients account for the various ways in which we must understand the material and accomplish the long preparatory work, so that our interpretations may favor the gaining of insight. Hence the difficulty of formulating general rules for interpretation. Psychoanalysis nevertheless has discovered a general framework of principles governing the interpretative work in analysis. However, within this general framework a large number of variations are inevitable.

Interpretations are not the only means, of course, by which an analyst may convey his knowledge to a patient. There are confrontation and clarification, as well as other steps that contribute to the analyst's complicated work preliminary to interpretation. It is not as if the analyst knew everything and merely had to convey this knowledge via interpretations, according to rigidly established rules. In actual fact, during the analytic process the analyst gradually learns from his patient while attempting to convey to him what he thus learns, so that the process of gaining insight and conveying it is reciprocal to some extent. There is a constant interplay, an intertwinement between the work of the patient and that of the analyst.

The problem of variations in an analyst's way of interpreting may be approached from different standpoints, e.g., of the correctness of interpretations or of their efficacy in producing insight and leading ultimately to a healthy solution of pathogenic conflicts.

The correctness of interpretations is contingent upon what Bernfeld (1932) called the "science of traces": the fact that past psychic processes leave traces behind them. As a technique, psychoanalysis proceeds to uncover the traces, to bring them to the fore and to interpret them correctly. As a body of knowledge, it enables the analyst to reconstruct past psychic processes out of such traces. These two steps—the finding of traces and their interpretation—constitute a long drawn-out process in which each, in turn, influences the other. And the work of interpretation itself, as we have said, must be painstakingly and patiently prepared, so that both analyst and patient may gain the insight needed to ensure not only the correctness of interpretations but also their efficacy (Loewenstein 1957).

We are bound to distinguish types of interpretations according to their place and function within the analytic process. Freud (1937) differentiated between interpretations proper, such as those of a dream or a parapraxis, and "genetic" interpretations or reconstructions of a remote and warded-off event or fantasy or impulse or reaction that had left its imprint on the patient's life. One can also distinguish a type of interpretation, which I have proposed to call "reconstruction upwards," aiming at the eliciting of comparatively recent material from more remote events. One may likewise discriminate interpretations that have a "tactical" value, so to speak, from those having a "strategic" value (Loewenstein 1951a), or oppose interpretations with "short-range" impact to those exerting a "long-range" influence. Interpretations sometimes may have a direct effect in terms of recall, of insight, or even of therapeutic change. But often their impact is a more indirect one, and they have what Hartmann (1951) termed a "multiple appeal."

The pathways by which interpretations effect various changes in the patient are not sufficiently known to us. In fact, we must recognize that we possess only very incomplete information with regard to the various types of interpretations and to their place and functions within the analytic process. Therefore we have little theoretical knowledge about the reasons why an analyst feels compelled to use one type of interpretation in preference to another at different moments of an analysis, even though we have practical knowledge to guide us in these matters.

To be sure, we are aware of some conditions to which interpretations must be subordinated in order to produce insight. We know that dynamic, economic, structural, and genetic points of view must be taken into consideration in formulating interpretations. However, the value of interpretations will depend on the following conditions (Loewenstein 1951a):

(a) On the *optimal distance from the surface,* i.e., from the present, from what is known, already worked out, or from what one might say is "on the agenda." We observe that the usual method which Freud advised us to follow, namely, to proceed from the surface to the depth, must be adjusted to individual peculiarities of our patients. In some cases, the attempt to analyze recent or present conflicts proves ineffective as long as some important past situation remains unanalyzed. In others, on the contrary, any attempt at understanding of childhood or puberty conflicts appears fruitless without a detailed and thorough analysis of recent or current conflicts and symptoms. While we maintain the general principle always to consider both past and present and their interrelation, such individual differences seem to determine somewhat divergent pathways in the analytic work.

(b) The effectiveness of interpretations depends also on their *sequence or hierarchy.* There are a few well-founded, empirical rules which govern this hierarchy to some extent. This precedence is always given to interpretation of resistance before other aspects of the material. A related but not identical rule gives precedence to interpretations of the ego and its mechanisms before those of id derivatives. However, these two rules may conflict with one another if the resistance happens to be at the service of the id.

Another very important empirical rule calls for the interpretation of transference manifestations in preference to other parts of the material. There exist differences of opinion on this point. Some analysts consider this rule valid for all transference phenomena. Others believe that merely transference resistance should be analyzed first, whereas the remaining transference phenomena should be analyzed only toward the end of the analysis. In a few rare cases, however, neither view seems applicable. Manifestations of very violent, ambivalent transference resistance, particularly such as repeat habitual modes of behavior towards other persons, may prove completely unanalyzable when approached directly. A detour over less intensely cathected reactions outside the transference area may be required to overcome this type of resistance.

(c) Closely related to the sequence of interpretations is another condition of their efficacy; i.e., the right *timing.* Its importance rests on the fact that analysis, like neurosis, is a process. Indeed, it takes time to undo the effect of developmental forces and to start their work all over again. During this process, there occur moments which the analyst finds propitious for communicating some interpretation to the patient. It appears that some interpretations have to be imparted at certain moments when the patient seems "ripe" to hear them; not before, but frequently also not later, lest they lose their impact or it be "too late" to make them. What accounts for this "ripeness" or lack of it in the patient has never been satisfactorily defined theoretically. In deciding that the time is right for certain interpretations we are guided by what Freud called *tact* in analysis. By its vagueness and intuitive quality the term reveals our lack of knowledge in this respect, and therefore implies that variety exists in the timing of different types of interpretations.

Tact in analysis also involves: understanding one's own unconscious or preconscious motivation in deciding to make a particular interpretation (Loewenstein 1930–31, 1951a, 1951b); keeping "in tune," "in step," with the patient's problems and also with what is relevant in a given moment;[10] evaluating the indirect impact of interpretations on other parts of the dynamic structure; and finding the right pathways—taking into account the patient's autonomous ego and the transference—to "convince" the patient, i.e., lead him toward insight.

A great deal more could be said, of course, about the conditions that favor the effectiveness of interpretations in a therapeutic analysis.[11] A more detailed description of these conditions would point up the various ways whereby an analyst must try to approach his patient and to deal with both the conflict-laden and the more or less "conflictless" part of his personality (Hartmann 1939).

But summarily one might say that variation in the mode and timing of interpretations is based upon the different relations in each case, between defensive and what Hartmann (1939, 1950) called "autonomous ego functions." This means that such variation will depend on the various types of defenses, on the role of each in forming the "defensive organization" (Hoffer 1954; Kris 1956), on the way in which defenses influence autonomous ego functions (i.e., on the nature of "intrasystemic conflicts" [Hartmann 1951]), and how the autonomous functions are influenced also by id forces, by the superego and by reality (e.g., in

10. This aspect of tact in psychoanalysis was stressed by D. Rapaport in a recent discussion.

11. As to the role of wording, cf., E. Kris (1951), Loewenstein (1951a, 1957).

the transference). It will further depend on individual peculiarities of autonomous ego functions (i.e., talents, abilities) and their role in reaching the areas involved in conflict. I refer here to such factors as sense of humor; capacity for object thinking, for neutralization and for "controlled regression" (Kris 1950); relative intactness of self-observation and of reality testing for mental phenomena; and the ability to use that combination of the "expressive and cognitive functions of speech" (Loewenstein 1956) which is essential for analytic insight.

Some of the rules concerning interpretation, which were mentioned earlier, serve the aim of increasing the tolerance of the patient's ego for his pathogenic conflicts by trying first to bring his resistances or his defenses under the sway of his autonomous ego functions. The analyst lends his own autonomous ego, one might say, to reinforce the patient's autonomous ego (Loewenstein 1954). The latter has been partly weakened, some of its functions being inhibited or impaired by the impact of conflicts between the id, the superego, and the defensive parts of the ego. Which autonomous ego functions have been affected by pathogenic conflicts and in what way, therefore, will determine what pathways and modes of approach are open or closed to the analyst when he tries, for instance, to subject the defensive forces to insight. Or putting it differently: psychic material warded off by the various defense mechanisms is being maintained in its warded-off state by interaction with some autonomous ego functions, whether these act as a countercathexis or not. To mention but two examples: repression is maintained at the expense of the function of memory, reaction formation against aggression by the reinforcement of the (normal) function of empathy. Thus the choice of interpretations and their characteristics will be determined, among other things, by the nature of the defense mechanism that keeps the psychic material in a warded-off state. The interpretative work will vary according to whether we deal, for instance, with a repression or with a reaction formation. We may even assume that to each defense mechanism there corresponds a distinctive mechanism for the emergence of the warded-off material into the Systems Pcs-Cs (cf., also Waelder 1951).

As I mentioned before, in the interpretation of resistance it is important to consider how the defensive functions of the ego have influenced the autonomous functions. For instance, A Freud (1936) advises in the analysis of character neuroses to choose the point where there is still mobile conflict. This means the point where some part of the autonomous ego functions still has access to defensive functions. One may also call it the point where the autonomous function of self-awareness extends to remnants of defenses and id derivatives. In this example, an intact fragment of the autonomous function is chosen to help it regain its sway over lost ground.

In other cases the analyst may utilize particular gifts of his patient so as to convey his interpretation in a special, convincing way. We know that the right joke, told at the right moment, may be used instead of an interpretation when a patient's sense of humor makes him accessible to a particular type of joke. Yet there are many instances when a joke not only falls flat, but even may have the opposite effect on a patient. Not long ago, Ernst Kris remarked that it would never occur to him to tell any joke to certain patients. We can think of several reasons that might make it inadvisable. Some persons lack a sense of humor or do not respond to a particular type of humor. Some patients react to jokes as if the analyst were callously making fun of them, others as if to a veiled seduction. And the analyst had best beware of using this approach with those who themselves like to tell jokes in analysis; either the patient knows the joke already, or it will become a competition between them, or a mutual seduction. Generalizing this last point, one might say that the analyst should refrain in analysis from using the same defense mechanisms as his patient.

Although the sense of humor is a secondary autonomous ego function (Hartmann 1950), its exercise actually encompasses psychic processes of various kinds, involving not the ego alone, but also the id and the superego. Hence a variety of effects may ensue when a patient's sense of humor is used for the purpose of conveying something to him by the short-cut of a joke instead of interpretation. The analyst's tact thus may be employed in weighing the various possible effects on the drives, on the superego, or on the various parts of the ego, which might result from telling a given joke to a given patient at a given moment in the analysis. Similar considerations always apply when the analyst is faced with the complex problems involved in the choice, the mode, the wording and the timing of interpretations, that is to say, throughout his work.

I am fully aware that by this presentation of some variations in what we call classical psychoanalytic technique, I have raised many more questions than I have been able to answer. Should it succeed, nevertheless, in eliciting controversy and discussion, I shall consider its function to be fulfilled, for it will have drawn our attention anew to a number of complicated and important problems of psychoanalysis.

REFERENCES

Bernfeld, S. (1932). Der Begriff der "Deutung" in der Psychoanalyse. *Ztschr. f. ang. Psychol.* 42:448–97.

Bibring, E. (1937). On the theory of the therapeutic results of psychoanalysis. *Int. J. Psychoanal.*, 18:170–89.

—— (1954). Psychoanalysis and the dynamic psychotherapies. *J. Amer. Psychoanal. Assn.*, 2:745–70.

Bouvet, M., Marty, P. & Sauguet, H. (1956). Transfert, contre-transfert et réalité. *Rev. Franç. Psychanal.*, 20:494–516.

Devereux, G. (1951). Some criteria for the timing of confrontations and interpretations. *Int. J. Psychoanal.*, 32:19–24.

Eissler, K. R. (1953). The effect of the structure of the ego on psychoanalytic technique. *J. Amer. Psychoanal. Assn.*, 1:104–43.

Freud, A. (1936). *The Ego and the Mechanisms of Defense.* London: Hogarth Press.

—— (1954). Problems of technique in adult analysis. *Bull. Philadelphia Assn. for Psychoanal.*, 4:44–70.

Freud, S. (1909). Notes upon a case of obsessional neurosis. *Coll. Papers* 3.

—— (1937). Constructions in analysis. *Coll. Papers* 5.

Gitelson, M. (1932). Emotional position of the analyst in the psychoanalytic situation. *Int. J. Psychoanal.*, 33:1–10.

Greenacre, P. (1956). Reevaluation of the process of working through. *Int. J. Psychoanal.*, 37:439–44.

Hartmann, H. (1939). Ich-Psychologie und Anpassungsproblem. *Int. Ztschr. Psa. und Imago*, 24:62–135.

—— (1950). Comments on the psychoanalytic theory of the ego. *Psychoanal. Study Child*, 5:74–96.

—— (1951). Technical implications of ego psychology. *Psychoanal. Q.*, 20:31–43.

Hoffer, W. (1954). Defensive process and defensive organization; their place in psychoanalytic technique. *Int. J. Psychoanal.*, 35:194–98.

Kris, E. (1950). On preconscious mental processes. *Psychoanal. Q.*, 19:540–60.

—— (1951). Ego psychology and interpretation in psychoanalytic therapy. *Psychoanal. Q.*, 20:15–30.

—— (1956). The recovery of childhood memories in psychoanalysis. *Psychoanal. Study Child*, 11:54–88.

Loewenstein, R. M. (1930–31). Le tact dans la technique psychanalytique. *Rev. Franç. Psychanal.*, 4:267–75.

_____ (1951a). The problem of interpretation. *Psychoanal. Q.*, 20:1–14.

_____ (1951b). Ego development and psychoanalytic technique. *Amer. J. Psychiat.*, 107:617–22.

_____ (1954). Some remarks on defenses, autonomous ego, and psychoanalytic technique. *Int. J. Psychoanal.*, 35:188–93.

_____ (1956). Some remarks on the role of speech in psychoanalytic technique. *Int. J. Psychoanal.*, 37:460–68.

_____ (1957). Some thoughts on interpretation in the theory and practice of psychoanalysis. *Psychoanal. Study Child*, 12:127–50.

Stone, L. (1954). The widening scope of indications for psychoanalysis. *J. Amer. Psychoanal. Assn.*, 2:567–94.

Waelder, R. (1951). The structure of paranoid ideas. *Int. J. Psychoanal.*, 32:167–77.

9

Variations in Classical Technique: Concluding Remarks

It is impossible, for obvious reasons, to render justice to all the many interesting contributions made by the various discussants.

Bouvet stressed an important facet of the analysis of transference phenomena by the use of the term "distance." This term, as he said, stands for many complex psychic processes involved in the transference and in the way of analyzing it. Hence it may often be important for the purpose of clear description in a given case to spell out its various components concretely. A case in point is Annie Reich's beautiful case presentation. In this instance the use of the term "distance" would not have been as illuminating as was her description of the technical changes to which she had to resort. It is a moot question whether the technique used in this case should come under the heading of modifications or of variations of psychoanalytic technique.

S. Nacht's contribution deals with problems centering around the anonymity of the analyst and the optimal degree of frustration. He rightly reminds us of the fact that many a patient's resistance makes use of the very essentials of psychoanalytic treatment, moreover, that this type of resistance may become so difficult to surmount as to necessitate changes in the use of certain practical rules otherwise beneficial to the treatment. Nacht also describes cases in which a "reparative gift" on the part of the analyst is required to enable the patient to give up his self-destructive behavior. He further alludes to some cases where the analyst, in order to achieve what he terms a "restructurization" of the

Concluding remarks on the main presentations in the panel discussion "Variations in Classical Psychoanalytical Technique" read before the 20th Congress of the International Psychoanalytical Association, Paris, July–August 1957.

ego, has to abandon his usual neutrality and replace it by an attitude of "presence." Nacht acknowledges the origin of this term in its use by Racamier in a paper on schizophrenia. This confirms the impression one gains that the patients here referred to are afflicted with severe ego disturbances, probably exceeding the limits of a neurosis. In such cases, indeed, considerable variations or even modifications of our technique are necessary. No objection can be raised against an analyst's decision to modify his technique in order to help a patient to recover, rather than to deprive the patient of a possible cure for the sake of guarding the "gold of analysis" from being alloyed.

I know that had I used the term "flexibility" instead of the term "variations" of analytic technique, as Anna Freud suggests, I might have avoided some objections to my presentation. However, I prefer to maintain this terminology for a specific reason. The term "flexibility" has been used by some authors as opposed to an alleged "rigidity" of the classical psychoanalytic technique; moreover, what some of them designated as flexibility were technical procedures far removed from what either Anna Freud or I would call standard psychoanalysis at all. Thus, by choosing the term "variations" I wanted to stress that I do not share the views of those authors.

Miss Freud discussed another important point relevant to the whole problem of psychoanalytic technique and its variations. If I understood her correctly, she meant that the analyst should first explore the patient's use of *his own* ego in the analytic process, before he considers lending *his* (the analyst's) ego to the patient as an aid in dealing with the defensive part of the latter's ego. The cursory way in which I had just mentioned the interplay between some of the analyst's and some of the analysand's autonomous ego functions must have lent itself to being thus misunderstood. I had described this point in somewhat greater detail in a previous paper [reprinted here as chapter 3]. Obviously, no psychoanalysis is possible without the active presence and participation of the patient's autonomous ego. It is only to some deficient or temporarily disturbed functions of the latter that the analyst, provisionally, must "lend" some of his own in the course of the treatment. Indeed, without the analyst's knowledge of unconscious psychic processes, without his intact capacity for testing psychic realities, without his ability to recall what the patient himself tends not to remember, a patient would never be able to use his ego to gain insight into his unconscious conflicts.

Kurt Eissler, likewise objecting to my use of this formulation, argued that according to Anna Freud the mother-child relationship is based on such lending of the mother's autonomous ego to the infant, and that the psychological situation between a patient and his analyst is not comparable with that between infant and mother. To this objection I might reply that the analytic situation is also quite different from any other learning situation in which a teacher not only imparts knowledge to a student but also teaches him to think independently. Yet there, too, the teacher temporarily lends some of his autonomous ego functions to his pupil. None of these situations—mother-child, teacher-student, analyst-patient—can be wholly described in mere terms of an interplay of autonomous ego functions. And as to the part of these situations which can be thus described, not the same autonomous functions are involved in each of them.

Eissler has touched upon many problems relating to variations in technique, which deserve a thorough discussion. I regret I cannot do full justice to them but must limit myself to but a few. I shall start with his discussion of repression and memory. He objects to my observation about the effects of various defenses on various autonomous ego functions and particularly to my remark that repression is maintained at the expense of memory. His fine examples confirm, indeed, what we well know; namely, that repression may affect the function of memory in various ways. His objections notwithstanding, repression affects recollection, i.e., the function of memory, whereas reaction formation exerts an influence on empathy.

A part of Eissler's remarks deals with the relationship between interpretations and interventions or what he prefers to call parameters. In his discussion he introduced—for the first time, as far I know—a very fine and useful distinction between interventions and those actions of the analyst which he terms "pseudo-parameters." The latter tools implicitly perform the function of interpretations, even though on the surface they may seem to be very different from them. Eissler uses these examples for a number of valuable metapsychological considerations. In spite of obvious divergences of opinion concerning the relationship between interpretation and intervention, there is some basic agreement between us. He admits, albeit reluctantly, that in practice no analysis has ever been carried out without a single intervention, but he would like, if possible, to do away with all of them. I myself believe that the more successfully and elegantly analysis can be carried out with a minimum of intervention, the better. But since in fact there always are interventions, let us acknowledge their existence and examine their functions.

In one of his case descriptions Eissler illustrates my discussion about the use of the "parameter" that consists in advising a patient to brave his phobic restrictions. In my paper [reprinted here as chapter 8] I outlined some situations where this advice is unnecessary or even contrary to the best interests of the patient. Eissler's example adds to our knowledge of such situations in which intervention can be dispensed with and interpretations alone are sufficient for the progress of treatment.

Eissler dwells a great deal on the problem of the analyst asking questions of the patient, and he would prefer to replace all such questions by some sort of interpretations. I am tempted to speculate how Freud would have reacted had it been suggested to him that he might have done better by not asking the Rat Man to repeat his story of the maneuvers and suggesting to the patient instead that he must have slurred over some details of the story. From what we know of Freud and of his very unrigid way of analyzing, we can surmise what his answer might have been. He probably would have replied that this different approach might well have led to the same result. But Freud might have added, I believe, that there is nothing wrong in asking a patient some questions, and that sometimes it may even be better to do so because it is preferable for the analyst to be spontaneous rather than systematically to disguise his inquiries.

The problem of interpretation versus intervention also occupies the main part of H. Rosenfeld's discussion. However, his thoughts lead in a direction other than those expressed by Eissler. The latter defines classical technique as "the one in which interpretation remains the exclusive or leading or prevailing tool of operation." Rosenfeld apparently agrees only with the first part of this definition and describes the "classical technique of analysis" as the one "relying entirely on interpretations." I can only repeat that although interpretation is the essential and specific tool of classical psychoanalytic technique, I doubt whether anyone has ever carried an analysis through to a therapeutically successful end without having done anything but interpreting.

Viewing the problem of classical analysis in a historical perspective, Rosenfeld wonders whether the technique, as described, albeit very incompletely, by Freud forty-five years ago, has remained unchanged. He adds that even then there may have been differences between individual analysts, e.g. that Karl Abraham is supposed to have talked a great deal and Hanns Sachs to have been rather silent. I do not know on what information Rosenfeld bases this comparison. But I had the opportunity to attend discussions on technique led by Abraham as well as by Sachs, in which both of them expressed the view that the frequency of interpretations or the length of the analyst's silence should be entirely contingent upon the individual needs and peculiarities of the given patient. Thus some variations in the mode of interpretation were considered necessary by these two analysts.

Rosenfeld defines the main features of psychoanalytic technique and illustrates his definition by a clinical example. That the latter is a fine sample of classical analytic technique, as it was taught by Freud, every experienced analyst today would undoubtedly affirm. His definition of psychoanalytic technique, I think, in the main would also find unanimous agreement among analysts, except perhaps for a certain undertone of rigidity in his formulations and from his ban on any use of humor in analysis. If "strictly adhered to," these formulations might lead to a sterile regimentation of our technique.

We know that Freud himself not infrequently did use jokes while analyzing. To be sure, not every analyst is inclined or able to employ humor as an indirect means of expressing or understanding some psychological truth. And we certainly must guard against the possible misuse of humor in analysis as an unconscious seduction of the patient, as I mentioned in my paper. On the other hand, as Nacht rightly reminds us, any part of the analytic procedure might be unconsciously experienced by a patient as seduction and be misused by his resistance.

Essentially Rosenfeld's definition of psychoanalytic technique adheres to the classical formulations of Freud. However, it is couched in terms so general as to obscure important controversial issues. These issues become apparent only when such a definition is translated into concrete clinical terms. For instance, some of the phenomena which Rosenfeld and other adherents of Melanie Klein describe as transference are not invariably thus understood by every analyst. The same difference of opinion certainly exists with regard to the manner in which transference phenomena should be interpreted.

There can be no doubt that our increased knowledge of the development of the human mind has enriched and improved our therapeutic technique. Thus, Melanie Klein and her followers have unquestionably contributed to our knowledge and our skill. For the same reason I should assume that Freud's technique must have been influenced by his discoveries in the field of ego psychology and that his discoveries, in turn, to some extent were made possible by a refinement of his technique. I can only speculate, of course, as far as Freud's technique is concerned. But one might try to infer his attitude towards this development of psychoanalysis from the last paper in which he dealt with technical problems. In "Analysis Terminable and Interminable," he stressed once more that the analyst cannot content himself with the role of uncovering early childhood conflicts; that a complete analytic work must encompass all the gradual vicissitudes and transformations of the early pathogenic conflicts throughout childhood, youth, and adult life, to permit us to understand and analyze a patient; and that this is possible if we are able to analyze the interplay of the drives, of the ego, and the superego not only in their earliest forms, but through all stages of human development.

There has been a considerable progress in our technique in the last twenty-five years, and this progress is due to the discoveries in the field of ego psychology. In my opinion, the most important contribution in this direction was made by Anna Freud's systematic exploration and analysis of the ego's defense mechanisms. The work of others[1] in the area of ego psychology, as it applies to technique, since then has considerably contributed to our understanding and improved use of psychoanalysis. While it is true that ego psychology has not added anything fundamentally different to the classical technique,[2] its influence has led to a certain shift of emphasis which in some cases makes the whole difference between failure and success.

Coming back once more to variations within the framework of standard technique, they are not to be confused with its modifications. They are to be found, as a matter of fact, in the practical work of every analyst. The problem still remains how to describe them in terms of their rationale and proper use. Undoubtedly the opinions expressed by the various discussants on these questions will prove of great value for the advancement of our knowledge and the increasing effectiveness of our therapeutic skill.

1. Most of those I have in mind are cited in the [reference section of chapter 8].

2. I have tried to describe this development in one of my papers [reprinted here as chapter 2].

10

The Silent Patient

INTRODUCTION

It is a great pleasure and privilege to chair a panel composed of such distinguished members of the American Psychoanalytic Association—a panel, moreover, on a subject of such fascinating interest and importance as the one we shall discuss today.

The psychoanalytic process reflects the preexisting neurotic process, inasmuch as it forms a continuation of it and achieves in favorable cases to modify its outcome. Everything that happens to the patient in analysis is under the simultaneous sway of two apparently opposite forces. One moves him to communicate the data relevant to his neurosis, while the other compels him to resist such communication. Both are constantly operative, but mixed in varying proportions. It is only in some extreme, exceptional moments that one or the other force alone seems to be at work. Indeed, even when the patient's resistance appears maximized, when he refuses to communicate or even is ready to interrupt his treatment, the very motives of his resistance reveal the nature of his neurotic conflict and thus must be understood as a communication—by repetition—of the warded off conflict. And even in moments when the resistance seems at a minimum, when insight is being gained during what Kris (1956) called "the good psychoanalytic hour," this insight actually integrates the interplay between drives and defenses. Indeed, without resistance the psychoanalytic process is not possible.

Panel held at the Midwinter Meeting of the American Psychoanalytic Association, December 6, 1958.

While the analytic process thus consists in an interaction between communication and resistance, this does not describe it completely, for it is at the same time a therapeutic process. The gradual overcoming of the resistances and the gathering of insight into the nature of the neurotic conflicts lead ultimately to a change, to a different solution of these conflicts.

Let us take a familiar example. A male patient is in analysis with a male analyst. At some point he becomes silent, discouraged, and ready to interrupt his treatment. If he can be brought to express the hostile or critical thought which he tried to conceal through silence, we have the essential constituents of the phenomena I just described. The patient, by giving in to the resistance, reenacts and repeats his oedipal conflict whose outcome had been the relinquishment of competition with his father in favor of passivity and illness. His silence thus is both a resistance against communication and a nonverbal expression of the conflicting forces. By leading this patient to overcome his resistance and to verbalize his hostile thought, the analyst enables him to take a definite step in the therapeutic process.

Hence, when we distinguish between resistance and communication or when we contrast resistance with insight, progress, change, we merely underscore the relative importance of one or the other at a given moment of analysis; we stress their quantitative aspect or their operational relevance.

Essentially, the analytic process takes place in the realm of speech, and we understand silence in a patient as being a part or a form of speech. The patient may be, may remain, or may become silent at any point of his analysis, for any length of time, and in any of innumerable ways. Indeed, in analysis silence is as inevitable and as significant as speech. It is a positive or negative mode of communication. It is a phase in the curative process.

In a paper some years ago (Loewenstein 1956), I attempted to describe the various functions of speech in the analytic process by using the general classification devised by Karl Buehler (1934). Speech, according to him, encompasses three functions between the addressor and the addressee: they may speak of objects and their relationships; or the addressor may express—i.e., communicate—what is in himself; or he may appeal to the addressee. The act of speech therefore comprises: (1) what Buehler called the *Darstellungsfunktion*, which could be translated as *function of representation* or as *cognitive function*, since it refers to the knowledge and description of things or objects and the connections between them; (2) the *function of expression*, by which the speaker expresses something about himself; and (3) the *function of appeal*, encompassing all those speech acts which appeal to the addressee to do something or to respond in some way (e.g., imploring, commanding, forbidding, seducing, etc.).

In the analytic situation, we may at first expect the patient's speech to be mainly confined to the expressive function and to that facet of the function of representation which deals mostly with the description of events. But our experience shows that very soon the patient's thoughts lead him to exercise the third function as well, namely, when his interest begins to center on the analyst.

The analyst, in accordance with the rules of analytic technique, has two tasks. He refrains from responding to the appeal function which manifests itself as transference reactions. Furthermore, the analyst aims at transforming the appeal function of the patient's speech into the expressive function by showing the patient, through interpretations, how the latter expresses or describes something about himself when he speaks of persons or things outside himself. In his own speech the analyst will exclude both the function of appeal and the expressive function, limiting himself specifically to the cognitive function in relation to facts concerning his present addressee: the patient. He will thus, in turn, promote the expressive function of the patient, since the interpretation will communicate to the patient knowledge about himself that will favor his recall and expression of hitherto unavailable facts about himself.

However, at the same time, the patient's knowledge about himself will enhance one particular aspect of the cognitive function, which we believe to have a special importance in the curative effect of analysis. Indeed, there must exist a difference between the application of the cognitive function to the nonself and its application to the self. In the latter case, the cognitive and expressive functions are intertwined in a very significant way. Speech in the analytic process serves as a means of discharge and a binding of affects; it adds to thoughts and memories a degree of perceptual and social reality; it leads to an objectification of inner processes; it permits the differentiation of past and present, the testing of psychic realities, and makes psychoanalytic insight possible. It promotes the integrative processes to which we ascribe the major part of the therapeutic effectiveness of psychoanalysis.

The various secondary functions of speech in analysis then can be subsumed under these three. They will be brought out in this panel, either directly or by their disturbance when the patient is silent.

Speech and its counterpart, silence, are the essential foundation of social intercourse. In the peculiar relationship between the analytic patient and his analyst, both speech and silence are slanted in a particular way not encountered in any other situation. Indeed, the patient is expected to talk without restraint, not to withhold anything that occurs to him, to say things which no one is expected to express in any normal social situation. Nor does his interlocutor behave in the way others do. He is not seen, and his contribution to this dialogue is very different. Indeed, the particular distribution of the various functions of speech between patient and analyst might help us to understand why silence plays a so much greater role in some patients than in others or in certain periods of an analysis than in others.

But perhaps two aspects of speech, as they appear in analysis, cannot be fitted quite satisfactorily into Buehler's classification. One is the particular form of the integrative function of speech to which we attribute the therapeutic effect of bringing psychic content to consciousness or of psychoanalytic insight. The other is the role and significance of speech within the framework of object relations.

Outside the analytic situation, speech is only one among various ways in which the patient's object relations are revealed and expressed. Yet in the analysis he is expected to translate all facets of his past and present object relations into speech. Small wonder then that some of their aspects cannot find expression in spoken language but manifest themselves by a disturbance of verbalization or by a nonverbal communication: by silence.

Today we shall hear important contributions to the clinical, theoretical, and technical problems raised by the patient's silence. They will once more remind us that these are complex and difficult problems. Before calling upon the first speaker, may I add one more remark. I do not mean to say that silence, which may appear as a difficulty in analysis, need always be a symptom of disordered object relations. Aside from the analytic setting, object relations may well involve deeds rather than words or may be ruled by the adage that silence is golden. In fact, we can think of some object relations whose severe disturbance reveals itself through untoward verbal outpourings. Our culture, for better or for worse, puts a premium on verbal expression. But in discussing the silent patient, let us not forget that silence, in analysis as well as outside of it, is at times a necessary mode of object relationship.

REFERENCES

Buehler, K. (1934). *Sprachtheorie. Die Darstellungsfunktion der Sprache.* Jena: Fischer.

Kris, E. (1956). On some vicissitudes of insight in psychoanalysis. *Int. J. Psychoanal.*, 37:445–55.

Loewenstein, R. M. (1956). Some remarks on the role of speech in psychoanalytic technique. *Int. J. Psychoanal.*, 37:460–68.

11

Some Considerations on Free Association

I

In this paper I shall attempt to review some of the phenomena which can be observed in the patient during the analytic process, describing them as they appear when the psychoanalytic technique is being used. In addition, I propose to review some principles that were found to underlie these phenomena, and to bring to the fore some conclusions which may be drawn from them.

The development of the psychoanalytic method is familiar to us from Freud's own descriptions. In the last decade, valuable contributions on its historical background were published (Bellak 1961; Jones 1953; Zilboorg 1952). Without going into the details of this development, I must recall some of its highlights in order to underscore certain significant shifts in approach.

After abandoning hypnosis, Freud used at first a method based on the expectation that the warded-off memories of traumatic events would emerge if the patient "concentrated" on recapturing recollections connected with his symptoms. The patients were helped in this procedure by Freud's insistence that they would remember and by reconstructions, as we would say today, which he based upon the derivative memories and associations they produced. The emergence of forgotten memories or of the intermediate associations would follow a *starting point* chosen by the analyst, namely, the patient's symptom or a detail of it. In the method of *free association*, which Freud later developed

Paper presented at the Tenth Anniversary Meeting of the Western New England Psychoanalytic Society, New Haven, October 20, 1962, and at the Midwinter Meeting of the American Psychoanalytic Association, New York, December 9, 1962.

and which we have been using since, the patient is expected to start with anything that occurs to him. When thought or speech are freed from their usual conscious, aim-directed character, the unconscious or concealed "purposive ideas" will exert determining effects on them (Freud 1900).

In *A General Introduction to Psychoanalysis*, Freud (1916–17) defined the fundamental rule for the patient as follows:

> ... we require the patient to put himself into a condition of calm self-observation, without trying to think of anything, and then to communicate everything which he becomes inwardly aware of, feelings, thoughts, remembrances, in the order in which they arise in his mind. We expressly warn him against giving way to any kind of motive which would cause him to select from or to exclude any of the ideas (associations), whether because they are too "disagreeable," or too "indiscreet" to be mentioned, or too "unimportant" or "irrelevant" or "nonsensical" to be worth saying. We impress upon him that he has only to attend to what is on the surface consciously in his mind, and to abandon all objection to whatever he finds, no matter what form they take. [P. 253f.]

This definition, very close to the last one given by Freud in *An Outline of Psychoanalysis* (1938), was sometimes interpreted in a particular way: namely, that *resistances* were unwanted obstacles to the smooth functioning of free association. That happened even at a time when Freud himself viewed resistances in a very different light.[1]

According to this approach, not everything which the patient said in free association had the same relevance and value. Resistances were merely obstacles to the rise of drive impulses; the latter were the real stuff that mattered, the only thing analysts were interested in.

Yet Freud had long ago expressed a different view: although the fundamental rule itself becomes the target of resistances, and although they hamper the flow of free association, resistances are inevitable, an essential part of every analysis, the obverse of the defensive side of the unconscious pathogenic conflicts. Thus, for example, transference resistances are the most serious hindrance to a successful cure, and yet their correct analytic understanding and interpretation are the most powerful therapeutic tool of the psychoanalyst.

---

1. E.g., Fenichel (1935) wrote that the patient "is not to tell us selected things. In fact, he is not to be active at all; he is to do nothing except make an effort not to prevent giving expression to impulses which rise within him."

Another, though less clearly defined idea of the basic rule existed among analysts. Fenichel (1935) wrote: " 'To tell everything' is difficult. There are individuals [obsessional neurotics] who never learn to apply the basic rule. . . . Their 'basic resistance' cannot be swept away by injunction to tell everything." Terms like "breaking down" of resistance, which can be found in many publications, are not merely literary approximations. They reveal an underlying approach to the problem of patients trying to apply the basic rule, which led Ernst Kris to coin the term "angry analyst."

Some patients, confronted with the task of "telling everything" that occurs to them, will soon be able to prove to the analyst that it is an impossible endeavor. They no sooner start to recount an event than another recollection will interfere with the narration of the first one, and so on. Although we will see in this behavior a "resistance" based on the patient's wish to prove the absurdity of analysis, it correctly reflects a factual state of affairs. One might wonder then if the task of teaching patients to follow the fundamental rule can ever succeed: if it is possible at all for a patient to free-associate, really, in the sense of telling everything that occurs to him? When the question is couched in these terms, an answer is not easy to find.

An important shift in the approach to the patient's free associations resulted from a systematic and fruitful application of Freud's ego psychology to the psychoanalytic technique. Anna Freud (1936) in *The Ego and the Mechanisms of Defense* presented a modified picture of what we expect to learn from a patient attempting to comply with the fundamental rule. It is significant that she started her book by reminding the reader that some analysts considered it outside the sphere of psychoanalysis to study or observe anything in the human mind outside the id, the instinctual drives, and their derivatives. In contrast to this point of view, she stressed that "the proper field for our observation is always the ego. It is, so to speak, the medium through which we try to get a picture of the other two institutions [the id and the superego]" (p. 6). According to the technical procedure based on ego-psychological principles, the analyst is equally interested in all free associations of his patient, whether they be determined by id, ego, or superego elements. She states that

> . . . many beginners in analysis have an idea that it is essential to succeed in inducing their patients really and invariably to give all their associations without modification or inhibition, i.e., to obey implicitly the fundamental rule

of analysis. But, even if this ideal were realized, it would not represent an advance, for after all it would simply mean the conjuring-up again of the now obsolete situation of hypnosis, with its one-sided concentration on the part of the physician upon the id. Fortunately ... such docility in the patient is in practice impossible. The fundamental rule can never be followed beyond a certain point. [P. 13] [And, further on, she adds that] what concerns us is not simply the enforcement of the fundamental rule of analysis for its own sake but the conflict to which this gives rise. [P. 15]

In other words, for the analysis it is as important to have the patient say what occurs to him as it is to observe how and why he is unable to do so. Not only does the analyst pay equal attention to id, ego, and superego manifestations, but even the patient is expected to observe and express his emerging thoughts as well as his reluctance to perceive or verbalize them. Actually this approach is but the logical outcome of Freud's discovery of the paramount significance of unconscious psychic conflicts, and of his insistence on the importance of analyzing resistances.

In defining the role of the ego in the analytic method, it became necessary to distinguish different types of ego functions, i.e., defensive from various autonomous ego functions (Hartmann 1939a, 1950). As we shall see later, such distinctions are helpful also in the study of free association.

We may now try once more to describe what we mean by the basic rule, and what kind of phenomena or processes we expect to be elicited in the patient when he attempts to follow it. While the fundamental rule leaves him free to choose what he wants to start with, it requires him to be candid and to try not to eliminate from his communications such thoughts as occur to him or those which may interfere with what he is telling. His possibility of complying with such a request is severely limited, not only by inner obstacles, i.e., by resistances, but even by the duration of a session and by the need for intelligibility of his communications (Kris 1956).

This description is valid only approximately, and even so only for the beginning of analytic treatment. As the process of analysis unfolds, we do not expect the analysand to remain continually in "a condition of calm self-observation." On the contrary, we expect him to be carried away to some extent by his thoughts and emotions. We further expect that at a later time, another type of behavior will make its appearance in him: a more active one, culminating ultimately in analytic insight.

II

The process of free association has a twofold effect. One is its direct effect on the patient and on his ability to continue with it. The other effect is on the analyst, but the results of this are ultimately communicated to the patient in the form of interpretations, and thus affect the latter in turn. These two modes in which the free associations exert their influence are distinguished here for the sake of clarity. Actually, they are so interdependent that neither can exist without the other.

In favorable cases the use of free association has the effect of facilitating the emergence of new material, particularly when some initial obstacles have been overcome with the help of the analyst. One might say that in these favorable but rare cases, the free association grows on itself. However, this does not lead very far without the interventions and interpretations made by the analyst, which are necessary for the analytic process to continue.

For the analyst, the patient's free associations are the main source of information about the latter's life, about his memories, thoughts and feelings, wishes and fears, the people in his past and present environment, etc. True, Freud from the very beginning of his analytic work paid attention to the nonverbal components of the patient's communications, to the tone of voice, facial expression, gestures, posture, symptomatic actions and other forms of behavior, and considered them an important and relevant part of analytic material (cf., Kanzer 1961) (e.g., in the Rat Man). However, verbal communication, speech, is the essential and irreplaceable vehicle of the analytic process. The information conveyed in the manifest content of a patient's words and behavior is not everything we expect to learn from the free association. As Freud (1909) put it, the analyst must listen not only to the manifest message imparted to him, but also to a concealed one unknown even to its bearer. He learns only gradually in each individual case to understand this hidden message and its relation to the manifest one. Without going into the details of the psychic processes that operate in the analyst during his work, it must be stressed here that his mode of listening is an indispensable counterpart of the patient's free association. The analyst listens to various aspects of the patient's speech. One may describe it by enumerating them in a schematic way: listening to what is being said; to how it is being said, when and in what context it is being said; to what is not said, but deliberately or unwittingly omitted;

and finally, to the absence of communication—listening to silence.

The understanding of the concealed message thus gradually conveyed to the analyst is made possible alone by the condition under which a psychoanalysis is undertaken and conducted. Freud defined this as follows (1938, p. 63):

> The analytical physician and the weakened ego of the patient, basing themselves upon the real external world, are to combine against the enemies, the instinctual demands of the id, and the moral demands of the superego. We form a pact with each other. The patient's sick ego promises us the most complete candor, promises, that is, to put at our disposal all of the material which his self-perception provides; we, on the other hand, assure him of the strictest discretion and put at his service our experience in interpreting material that has been influenced by the unconscious. Our knowledge shall compensate for his ignorance and shall give his ego once more mastery over the lost provinces of his mental life. This pact constitutes the analytic situation.

By discretion we must, I believe, understand not only the promise never to divulge the patient's private life and his secrets. It means more than that: it is a promise that this secret knowledge, which the analyst is authorized to acquire by the patient's compliance with the fundamental rule, shall be used for the exclusive benefit of the patient.

Within the framework of the analytic situation, as just described, the patient's associations are expected to develop into a process that ultimately leads to the unfolding of warded-off pathogenic conflicts. Again we must remember that such an outcome is contingent upon the interpretative work of the analyst, but the process of free association provides the means of achieving it.

Freud (1900) stressed that the patient's associations, if understood correctly, always reveal that they center around his neurosis, his unconscious conflicts, and around the person of the analyst. Psychoanalytic experience proves that even the stimulations he receives from external reality shed light, to some extent, upon the patient's unconscious conflicts. His relation to persons or situations in the outside world has always been involved in these conflicts. To be sure, fortuitous events can become new centers of stimuli for association, but they may reawaken or redirect preexisting conflicts. Such happenings may even have been codetermined by the patient's unconscious tendencies. Moreover, the patient's choice of the events which he recounts is indicative of the interaction between unconscious determinants and external reality.

The same is true, as we know, regarding his reactions to the analyst. In the transference, peculiarities of the latter's personality or behavior gradually evoke a variety of reactions determined by some warded-off conflicts in the patient. Correctly perceived characteristics of the analyst are either seized upon, or are tendentiously disregarded or misinterpreted; or both methods may appear combined.

It seems useful for our purpose to separate and to describe, as distinct from the preceding, a further source of influence on the patient's free associations, namely, the actuality of the analytic setting. This particular setting contributes in a specific way to the patient's behavior. Most important among its components are the requirements surrounding the basic rule. The usual behavior and actions of the patient are intentionally inhibited by the prone position on the couch. His perceptions of the analyst are curtailed as well, since the analyst is more or less invisible and much more silent than the usual interlocutor in a conversation, who would respond in a visible and audible way. The resulting psychic phenomena in the patient have been likened to a dreamlike state, which is only very remotely true. Free association was variously compared with daydreaming, or thinking aloud, or the stream of consciousness. None actually is equivalent to the process involved in free association, which eliminates the wish-fulfilling (Hartmann 1927) or purposive or solitary character of the others.

These peculiarities of the analytic setting aim indeed at a partial curtailment of action and perception of external reality in order to induce processes of self-observation, displacement, and projection, i.e., a shifting in reality testing (Kris 1950; Loewenstein 1951). And the requirement, moreover, to curtail censorship and yet to verbalize, to tell all the resulting self-observations to another person, makes the psychic processes of the analysand different from anything else in his life.

The patient is expected to perform these complex processes entailing the temporary and partial suspension by the ego of some of its functions (Hartmann 1939a, 1939b) and the sharpening of others, e.g., of self-observation and communication to the analyst. And the latter, in his behavior, imposes some amount of deprivation on the patient by not being seen and by not responding in the way interlocutors usually do. These deprivations are partly balanced, however, by his listening, his interest, and his understanding. Through this behavior, which is specific for the analyst, he contributes to the analytic setting which exerts its influence upon the patient's state and upon his associations.

In addition, the analytic process gradually becomes the focal plane onto which the innumerable past and present experiences of the patient are refracted, and where they are reintegrated in such a way as to lead to their insightful understanding and ultimately to a favorable solution of pathogenic conflicts. These processes, as we know, require the ability to withstand a certain amount of instinctual frustration and also presuppose the intactness of a number of ego functions.

Actually it is not surprising that the fundamental rule should be the foremost and continuous target of resistance (Freud 1916–17). Nor is it surprising that patients should act out in the analytic situation or outside it. Not only is "repeating" a primitive form of telling something to another person, particularly when something unconscious is being conveyed, but action is for many people a more natural way of behavior than merely to observe their own reaction or reflect upon it and communicate it to someone.

I said before that the process of free association tends to grow on itself, as it were, by its own momentum. But it equally tends to run down, so that the analysis comes to a stop. A continual oscillating between these two tendencies is characteristic for the whole analytic process.

III

What are the conditions favoring one or the other of the opposite tendencies just mentioned? They can be briefly summarized as follows.

The free associations are facilitated by the uplift trend inherent in the drives (A. Freud 1936; Freud 1920) whose derivatives tend to come to the fore in the form of wishes, affects, or related thoughts. Provided the analyst's work, i.e., his effort to analyze the patient's resistances, is successful, the analytic process will unfold and lead to a favorable outcome. This statement has to be qualified, however. Many authors, starting with Freud himself, have pointed out that certain other, tacit conditions must be fulfilled in order that the analytic process may develop and issue in a satisfactory conclusion.

Aside from such general preconditions as analyzability of the patient and correct work by the analyst, which lie outside the framework of this presentation, these conditions are mainly that the patient be able to cooperate, i.e., to maintain a positive, confident attitude toward the analyst and a therapeutic alliance with him (Freud 1937). On the other hand, the latter must be able to inspire it by his consistent concern with the patient's ultimate well-being (Stone 1961). Without this "analytic atmosphere" it is hardly possible to conduct an analysis to a satisfactory outcome. The presence of these tacit conditions is what differentiates a therapeutic from a purely investigative analysis.

The factors or forces obstructing analysis are numerous. According to Freud, everything that stands in the way of a patient's cure is to be considered a manifestation of resistance. This definition was so broadly framed that it required further elucidation. Freud classified resistances according to their origins in the substructures of the mental apparatus; that is to say, he distinguished resistances stemming from the ego, from the id, and from the superego. Ego resistances are expressions of the various defensive mechanisms that were at work in the pathogenic conflict, and which continue to be at work in the patient's life and his neurosis. The superego resistances stem from the self-punitive tendencies of the patient. Id resistances, which determine his need to suffer, are active intrapsychically; Freud (1924) referred to them in speaking of "masochism of the ego" and "sadism of the superego."

It would be in agreement with Freud's view to place under the heading of id resistances also those phenomena opposing the curative effect of analysis which are based on individual peculiarities of the instinctual drives. Freud (1937) mentioned, for instance, an intensity of free intrapsychic aggression inducing a proclivity to conflict, the stickiness of the libido in some people, intolerance to passivity in some men, and the irreducibility of penis envy in some women. Resistances due to the epinosic gain may stem, in my opinion, not alone from the ego, but sometimes also from the instinctual drives or the superego. As a factor limiting the effectiveness of psychoanalytic treatment, Freud also stressed the strength of drives relative to that of the ego. Here some qualifying remarks are necessary. One can no longer consider ego strength or weakness in a global way. First of all, a distinction must be made between defensive and autonomous functions. Furthermore, within each category the various functions play different roles in the treatment, which can only partly be described in quantitative terms.

In other words, the character and intensity of resistances will depend not only on intersystemic but also on intrasystemic conflicts (Hartmann 1951). And the interplay of these conflicts emerges with striking clarity in the patient's efforts to follow the fundamental rule.

The strength or weakness of instinctual drives depends, in addition, on the particular distribution of drive components and on the stage of drive development at which fixation points occurred. For instance, the strength or weakness of the phallic components of the sexual drive relative to that of its pregenital components, the comparative distribution and interaction of aggressive and libidinal drives, and their effect on the intensity of sadistic or masochistic proclivities, may be decisive for the character of resistances and hence for the outcome of an analysis.

Resistances so far have been classified only with respect to substructures of the mental apparatus whence they originate. However, they may also be viewed from other angles; for instance, according to their intensity, their impact, or their consequences. A detailed classification of the various clinical forms of resistance would contribute greatly to our understanding, but I can make only a limited and tentative attempt at describing some of them.

Some resistances may first appear as insurmountable unwillingness to start treatment, and they may diminish at a later time to such a degree that analysis becomes acceptable to the patient and can even be favorably completed. In some instances these shifts can be accounted for by various changes in the patient's reality situation and their effects on the dynamic balance within the neurosis.

Fluctuations in intensity of resistances, due to similar reasons, are observable also within the course of an analysis. On the other hand, we know that resistances grow more intense when the analysis comes closer to some unconscious conflict, and diminish again after it has been analyzed.

Aside from the fluctuations just mentioned, differences in the impact of resistances may depend on the *positional value*[2] of the particular unconscious conflict underlying them. For instance, one patient's difficulty in expressing a hostile thought about the analyst may have only peripheral importance within his neurosis, whereas in another patient such a resistance, if not analyzed, might endanger the whole treatment because ambivalence conflicts play a central role in his neurosis.

2. This term was used by E. Kris to characterize the variety of effects of interpretation; see Loewenstein (1951).

There are still other peculiarities of resistances that must be taken into consideration. For example, resistances against verbalizing a particular thought or feeling are a very different matter than those stemming from the patient's symptoms, or from the make-up of his personality or character. The patient may be suffering, for instance, from a neurotic inhibition of verbal expression, or from neurotic affectlessness; or he may be unable to communicate anything having to do with his daydreams or masturbatory fantasies. These resistances are of a different order of magnitude from the common ones. The task of overcoming them is a long-range problem, and its achievement also represents a major therapeutic success.

To repeat, Freud stressed that the fundamental rule remains under attack by resistance throughout the whole analytic treatment. One might raise the question, however, whether all resistances manifest themselves only as obstacles to free association. This is not the case. Indeed, Freud distinguished resistances against the fundamental rule itself from those which oppose the curative effect of analysis. We know that in most cases the latter will appear, at some time or other, as resistances against free association. And yet, there are cases where the particular pathogenic makeup of the instinctual drives, the ego, or the superego, or a generalized psychic inertia (Freud 1937), does not interfere with free association, does not take the fundamental rule as its target.

A similar "state of affairs can be observed in transference phenomena. These may present two kinds of resistances: against expressing thoughts or feelings about the analyst, and against realizing that these transferred reactions are but repetitions of past, warded-off, responses to other persons. The latter kind of resistance does not necessarily create obstacles to compliance with the basic rule.

In short, not all resistances manifest themselves as disturbances of free association. Are all obstacles to free association caused by resistances? If we use the latter term in its strict sense, as referring only to forces involved in the pathogenic conflict, then we must qualify Freud's statement that everything which stands in the way of an analysis has to be considered a resistance.

Not every human being is capable of performing the complex ego functions required of an analysand: we know that children are unable to free-associate; that there are some adult persons, and not only psychotics, incapable of using these various functions under conditions involved in the analytic process; moreover, that nearly all patients require not only time, but also some analytic work in preparation, before acquiring the ability to follow the fundamental rule.

In practice we frequently succeed in overcoming such difficulties of the patient by analyzing them. And our increased knowledge of ego psychology, of object relations, and particularly of their early development, has thus broadened the field of applicability of analysis.

IV

The basic rule requires a shift in the intersystemic and intrasystemic balance of forces that usually exists when one talks to someone about oneself. What is demanded from the analysand is that one part of his ego shift its usual allegiances and oppositions vis-à-vis other parts. As I stated before, the ego temporarily suspends some of its functions.[3]

A part of the original compact between analyst and analysand is the implied request that the latter postpone his legitimate expectation of therapeutic results until they both understand his neurosis. On the other hand, in requesting the patient to follow the basic rule, we expect him to set aside the ego functions that deal with understanding himself. And we know resistances stemming precisely from the difficulty which patients experience in eliminating these functions. They rebel against having to express nonsensical or unrelated thoughts, and some have the greatest difficulty in desisting from constant watchfulness over the analyst as well as over their own thoughts and feelings.

The simultaneous operation of logical thinking and fantasying is normally impossible. A similar intrasystemic conflict also exists for the patient while he follows the basic rule. Indeed, here this difficulty is magnified by the fact that he is not in possession of the data which would permit him to understand himself and that he is, moreover, unconsciously unwilling to know them. The basic rule enjoins the pa-

3. Sterba (1934) described what he called the "dissociation of the ego" as a result of the analyst's interpretative work. The concept of a conflictless sphere emphasizes that such division of functions within the ego exists normally even outside the analytic situation. With the new concepts introduced by Hartmann, we can describe the intrasystemic conflicts sharpened by the analytic situation as existing not only between autonomous and defensive functions of the ego, but even between different groups of autonomous functions (Loewenstein 1954).

tient to suspend logical thinking about himself in favor of uncritical self-observation.

But while the analysand is required to suspend these ego functions during the analytic sessions, the analyst temporarily exercises them for him. They are assigned to the analyst because his ability to understand the patient is presumably intact, while the latter's self-knowledge is impaired by his pathogenic conflicts.

Part of the analyst's work thus chiefly serves to maintain free association, to overcome the patient's resistances against the fundamental rule. But he soon makes interpretations as well, which aim at helping the analysand to gain insight into the warded-off conflicts. Through this type of interpretations we now want to foster what we had asked the patient to set aside: his understanding of himself.

Freud (1916-17) mentioned a type of patients who seem to associate perfectly well, but in whose analysis nothing seems to happen. They harbor an attitude of hidden doubt toward the analysis, which is at the basis of their resistance. We all know the patient who responds to any and every interpretation with some remark that reveals his constant rejection of the analyst's ideas. Others seem not to react to them at all, but will neither reject nor accept any. Still others give lip service to our interpretations, but their responses remain purely intellectual and are not accompanied by any emotional reaction. Nor do they ever show any attempt at understanding, any insight, although they seem to comply perfectly well with the basic rule.

No matter what the underlying motives for this behavior may be (and they can usually be uncovered when the behavior as such is subjected to analysis), it represents resistances against an aspect of the analytic method which is not contained in the wording of the basic rule, as conveyed to the patient, namely, the requirement to cooperate with the analyst by reflecting upon himself on the basis of hitherto warded-off data. This type of cognitive activity of the patient culminates in those phenomena of the analytic process which we call "dynamic insight" (Loewenstein 1951).

We must here raise the question whether these phenomena should be viewed as distinct from or as comprised in the processes of free association. In one sense the activity of insight is the opposite of free association, and thus might well deserve to be put under a different heading. On the other hand, these activities are intertwined so closely, and are both so necessary in the psychoanalytic process, that I prefer to consider them as two aspects of the basic analytic method.

There is, of course, a third aspect in every analysis: the various activities of the analyst, without which the other two would not exist. But for the sake of clarity I must refrain from detailing the role which the analyst plays in the analytic process. Even while deliberately limiting this presentation to processes within the analysand, it has been unduly simplified. Indeed, a great many things happen to a patient between his attempt to follow the basic rule and his experience of what Kris (1956) called the "good analytic hour."

From the initial pact, in which the patient promises to observe the fundamental rule and the analyst vouches discretion, the psychoanalytic situation develops into a complex series of subtle interactions between them. These have been extensively described in the literature, most recently by Bellak (1961), Gitelson (1962), Khan (1962), Menninger (1958), Stone (1961), and Tarachow (1962). Powerful forces enter into play in the patient; old or recent conflicts are being reactivated with great urgency, and some of them are being intensely experienced toward the analyst and toward the analytic procedure itself. The patient is driven to relive and repeat what he is unable to remember, with the analyst as object, and he tenaciously resists the analytic task of translating this repetitive behavior into thought, recall, and speech.

It takes all the skill of the analyst to harness these forces for the benefit of the analysand. He must combine two seemingly opposite trends in the analytic method: on the one hand, to open up the gates to warded-off and forgotten drives, emotions, fantasies, modes of experiencing, primary-process thinking, or what Rubinfine (in an unpublished paper) calls "archaic ego states"; on the other hand, to control these forces and to transform them into secondary-process thought, i.e., verbalization, recall, and insight. Hartmann (1939a) has stressed that in an analysis there occurs not only a reestablishment of disrupted connections, but a veritable discovering of connections, comparable to what happens in scientific discoveries.

All the processes taking place during an analysis are made possible, as far as the analysand is concerned, by the intrapsychic shifts resulting from compliance with the fundamental rule. In free-associating the patient breaks with the preexisting state of affairs within the mental apparatus, which consisted of counter-cathexes erected against both the warded-off drives and the defensive ego functions. In analyzing, he is being invited to counteract this by directing his perceptions toward these warded-off elements of both ego and id. The change in the interaction of autonomous functions brings about a shift in the balance of forces between autonomous and defensive functions within the ego, and hence between ego and id.

I said before that this shift in the intrapsychic balance of forces in the analysand is fruitful because some of them are temporarily taken over by the analyst. Moreover, the whole process is made possible only by the fact that phenomena resulting from this shift in the intrapsychic balance are being communicated to the analyst. His presence and some aspects of the analytic setting itself provide the condition of security permitting the analysand thus to disrupt his inner balance. Indeed, the recumbent position tends to inhibit action, and this inhibition is power-fully reinforced by the conviction that the analyst will not get actually involved by the patient's aggressive or sexual impulses. The security derived from this protective defense makes it possible to overcome other defenses (Loewenstein 1954).

To repeat, Freud stressed time and again (Freud 1937) that a particular positive attitude toward the analyst is essential for the con-duct of an analysis, namely, one of trust and confidence that whatever the analyst may do will be consistently done for the ultimate benefit of the patient. The patient's therapeutic alliance with his analyst hinges upon this. Gitelson (1962) recently stated: "The analyst is 'on trial' as much as the patient." Unfortunately, it happens sometimes that the analyst does not pass the test. Stone, in a penetrating study of the psychoanalytic situation (Stone 1961), developed a similar idea, namely, that the analytic process becomes possible only through the physician-patient relationship underlying it.[4]

The existence of this underlying stable object relationship to the analyst, which is based upon aim-inhibited drives, enables the patient to develop intense transference reactions at times and yet to withstand their nongratification, so that they can be analyzed.

Greenacre (1954) as well as Stone (1961) have stressed that the child-mother relationship is the ultimate paradigm which the patient is driven to repeat by transferring it onto the analytic situation. It is characteristic of this transferred relation that when it appears, nonver-bal elements of free associations tend to prevail. Not only is this due to

---

4. Stone rightly mentions that the ability to maintain this type of relationship is not the exclusive attribute of medical doctors.

the preverbal stage of development which is being relived at such moments, but it also expresses the longing to be understood by the analyst without talking, as the infant was by the mother.

All this tends to remind us, if we were inclined to forget it, that the processes taking place in the patient while he undergoes analysis cannot be completely understood without considering the role of object relations in his mental life. The fundamental rule contains the essential requirement, namely, that the patient communicate his thoughts to the analyst. The patient's verbalizations in the analytic situation are the carriers of the complex object relations existing between him and the analyst. The example of the infant-mother paradigm of the analytic situation illustrates that verbal communication in analysis promotes both closeness to the object and distance from it. Stone (1961) speaks of "deprivation-in-intimacy." The closeness is enhanced, in addition, by the fact that the patient as an infant had learned to talk from his mother (Loewenstein 1956), whereas the distance is emphasized by the analytic requirement to verbalize in order to be understood. As the parents were for the child, the analyst is a temporary auxiliary autonomous ego for the patient (Loewenstein 1954). And like the child, the patient gradually learns to use his own ego and to dispense with that of his analyst.

V

In the course of this presentation, a number of problems were touched upon or adumbrated which would require greater attention and elaboration. It is impossible to do justice to all aspects of the analytic method that are inseparably connected with my central subject. However, I should like to consider more closely one particularly important aspect of the analytic process reflected in the patient's associations, namely, speech.

Some years ago I published a paper which dealt in more detail with the functions of speech and verbalization within the psychoanalytic process (Loewenstein 1956).[5] I stated that we use the term speech in the sense specified by Ferdinand de Saussure (1916): to denote spoken language, which is considered one of the two inseparable aspects of language (*la langue et la parole*). He defined the overall con-

---

5. Cf. also Hartmann (1951) and Loewenstein (1951).

cept of language (*langue*) as a system of distinct signs corresponding to distinct ideas. According to Buehler (1934), speech encompasses three functions between addressor and addressee. They may speak of objects and their relationships; this is the function of representation, or cognitive[6] function (*Darstellungsfunktion*). When speech serves to communicate—express—what is in oneself, it has the function of expression. And finally, it has the function of appeal when the speaker appeals to the addressee to do something or to respond in some way.

In psychoanalysis speech plays a paramount role, since it is the main and essential carrier of information and also the sole manifest vehicle of object relation between patient and analyst. Inevitably, all three functions of speech will come to be used by the patient in his analysis.

Inasmuch as speech is the vehicle of object relations, the patient uses it for the discharge of his instinctual drives while reliving and remembering his most regressive nad primitive wishes and states of mind. These processes do not consist of actual behavior, but are expressed through speech. The patient's primary-process thinking is being reactivated, but he communicates it in words, thus imparting to the primary process important characteristics of secondary-process thinking. No matter how he might be carried away by the verbal discharge of affects, the patient's speech creates an outside reality shared with the analyst: a social, objective, and binding reality (Hartmann 1951; Loewenstein 1951, 1956). We know that in the analytic process all emotional, instinctual, and regressive phenomena are as necessary as those pertaining to insight, to the autonomous functions of the ego.

It is generally accepted among psychoanalysts that language, speech, is an autonomous function of the ego. But Stone (1961) states that "its autonomy is relative, . . . susceptible to regression, to invasion by conflict." What can be meant by this?

The relations between autonomous ego functions, on the one hand, and defensive functions or superego functions or id derivatives, on the other, can be very complicated. We know that autonomous functions even can be placed at the service of the instinctual drives or can be used by them. For example, obsessional thinking can serve as an unconscious equivalent of masturbatory fantasies, perception can be

6. A term suggested by Roman Jakobson in a personal communication.

erotized, etc. (Hartmann, Kris & Loewenstein 1946). Language is used even more extensively in this way than are other autonomous functions of the ego. Nevertheless, in these instances one cannot speak of a regression of the autonomous functions, but only of their use in the service of functions which are not autonomous.

Hartmann (1950) stressed the possibility of regression in secondary autonomous functions of the ego. How can this concept be applied to speech? Leaving aside disorders due to brain damage, loss of speech is observable in some small children. It may be only the ability to speak that disappears, not the understanding of spoken language; or the loss in some instances may be complete. In either case, we can use the term regression in the sense of a loss of a function.

How can we understand the idea of regression of the speech function? If speech, as we assume, is the use of a "signifying," i.e., of a word, to designate a "signified," i.e., the idea of an object—or, in Freud's terminology, the use of a "word representation" to designate a "thing representation"—what can the regression of speech represent? It can mean the partial or total loss of it, and the return to a state where the child had not yet learned the use of language for communication with other people. I do not think that we observe such regression in analyses of neurotics, although patients at times tend to replace words by nonverbal communication or by silence.

There exists, however, a particular form of "regressive invasion" of speech by conflict. In these cases the movements of lips, tongue, and throat in speech acquire a primitive significance centering around the libidinal and aggressive use of the mouth, so overwhelmingly important in early childhood (Stone 1961). The analytic situations to which this refers give the impression that what the patient says is less important than what he expresses by the movements of his mouth. Again, even in these cases, it is not the faculty of speech that is regressed but the bodily activity of speaking; it is not the psychological function but the physiological mechanism of speech which becomes the carrier of libidinal and aggressive drive discharge.

The function itself, of designating a "signified" by a "signifying," cannot be traced back to any form of drive vicissitude or instinctual behavior, whether centering around the mouth or not, either libidinal or aggressive.[7] Such an approach, moreover, would fail to discriminate

---

7. Language is indeed one of the primary autonomous functions of the ego.

between genetic continuity and change of function, and would thus reintroduce an old element of confusion in our conceptual framework which Hartmann (1934b) was able to dispel.

The idea of regressive alteration of the speech function can be applied to one kind of phenomena in analysis. It refers to an altered relation between the "signifying" and "signified." These phenomena are easily observable and well known in psychoses. Either the meaning of a word is changed, or even a neologism is coined to designate this altered connection. As we know, altered relations between "signifying" and "signified" exist in the unconscious symbolic meanings of images and words, in dreams and in neurotic symptoms, or in the language of wit and in that of courtship; and thus we deal with them during the analytic process. However, the speech function itself is preserved in these instances; only the vocabulary is partially modified. Moreover, we must not forget that a great many of the nonautonomous uses of language are not actually regressive but are part of the psychic equipment of the normal adult. However, it is in the nature of the analytic process to trace all these phenomena back to their sources. This is why their regressive antecedents will be brought to the fore during analysis.

If it is essential for the outcome of an analysis that regressive uses or misuses of speech occur, it is equally essential that they be "in the service of the ego," as Kris put it. The requirement of verbalization of the analysand's thoughts and emotions is a prerequisite for these controlled regressions, and hence also for insight.

REFERENCES

Bellak, L. (1961). Free association: conceptual and clinical aspects. *Int. J. Psychoanal.*, 42:9–20.

Buehler, K. (1934). *Sprachtheorie. Die Darstellungsfunktion der Sprache.* Jena: Fischer.

Fenichel, O. (1935). Psychoanalytic method. In *The Collected Papers of Otto Fenichel.* New York: Norton, 1953, pp. 318–30.

———— (1945). *The Psychoanalytic Theory of Neurosis.* New York: Norton.

Freud, A. (1936). *The Ego and the Mechanisms of Defense.* New York: Int. Univ. Press, 1947.

Freud, S. (1900). The interpretation of dreams. *S.E.*, 4/5.

———— (1909). Notes upon a case of obsessional neurosis. *S.E.*, 10.

———— (1916–17). *A General Introduction to Psychoanalysis.* Garden City, N.Y.: Garden City Publ. Co., 1943.

———— (1920). Beyond the pleasure principle. *S.E.*, 18.

———— (1924). The economic principle of masochism. *S.E.*, 19.

———— (1937). Analysis terminable and interminable. *Coll. Papers* 5.

———— (1938). *An Outline of Psychoanalysis.* New York: Norton, 1948.

Gitelson, M. (1962). The curative factors in psychoanalysis. I. The first phase of psychoanalysis. *Int. J. Psychoanal.*, 43:194–205.

Glover, E. (1928, 1938). *The Technique of Psychoanalysis.* New York: Int. Univ. Press, 1955.

Greenacre, P. (1954). The role of transference: practical considerations in relation to psychoanalytic therapy. *J. Amer. Psychoanal. Assn.*, 2:671–84.

Hartmann, H. (1927). *Die Grundlagen der Psychoanalyse.* Leipzig: Georg Thieme.

———— (1939a). *Ego Psychology and the Problem of Adaptation.* New York: Int. Univ. Press, 1958.

———— (1939b). Psychoanalysis and the concept of health. *Int. J. Psychoanal.*, 20:308–21.

———— (1950). Comments on the psychoanalytic theory of the ego. *Psychoanal. Study Child,* 5:74–96.

———— (1951). Technical implications of ego psychology. *Psychoanal. Q.*, 20:31–43.

———— (1955). Notes on the theory of sublimation. *Psychoanal. Study Child,* 10:9–29.

———— Kris, E. & Loewenstein, R. M. (1946). Comments on the formation of psychic structure. *Psychoanal. Study Child,* 2:11–38.

Hartmann, H. & Loewenstein, R. M. (1962). Notes on the superego. *Psychoanal. Study Child,* 17:42–81.

Jones, E. (1953). *The Life and Work of Sigmund Freud. Vol. 1. The Formative Years and the Great Discoveries.* New York: Basic Books.

Kanzer, M. (1958). Image formation during free association. *Psychoanal. Q.*, 27:465–84.

———— (1961). Verbal and nonverbal aspects of free association. *Psychoanal. Q.*, 30:327–50.

Khan, M. M. R. (1962). Dream psychology and the evolution of the psychoanalytic situation. *Int. J. Psychoanal.*, 43:21–31.

Kris, E. (1950). On preconscious mental processes. *Psychoanal. Q.*, 19:540–60.

———— (1955). Neutralization and sublimation: observations on young children. *Psychoanal. Study Child,* 10:30–46.

———— (1956). On some vicissitudes on insight in psychoanalysis. *Int. J. Psychoanal.*, 37:445–55.

Loewenstein, R. M. (1951). The problem of interpretation. *Psychoanal. Q.*, 20:1–14.

―――― (1954). Some remarks on defenses, autonomous ego, and psychoanalytic technique. *Int. J. Psychoanal.*, 35:188–93.

―――― (1956). Some remarks on the role of speech in psychoanalytic technique. *Int. J. Psychoanal.*, 37:460–68.

―――― (1957). Some thoughts on interpretation in the theory and practice of psychoanalysis. *Psychoanal. Study Child*, 12:127–50.

Menninger, K. A. (1958). *Theory of Psychoanalytic Technique.* New York: Basic Books.

Rapaport, D. & Gill, M. M. (1959). The points of view and assumptions of metapsychology. *Int. J. Psychoanal.*, 40:153–62.

Rosen, V. H. (1958). Abstract thinking and object relations: with specific reference to the use of abstraction as a regressive defense in highly gifted individuals. *J. Amer. Psychoanal. Assn.*, 6:653–71.

Saussure, F. de. (1916). *Cours de Linguistique Générale.* Lausanne & Paris: Payot.

Sterba, R. F. (1934). The fate of the ego in psychoanalytic therapy. *Int. J. Psychoanal.*, 15:117–26.

Stone, L. (1961). *The Psychoanalytic Situation. An Examination of Its Development and Essential Nature.* New York: Int. Univ. Press.

Tarachow, S. (1962). The problem of reality and the therapeutic task. *J. Hillside Hosp.*, 11:21–28.

Zilboorg, G. (1952). Some sidelights on free associations. *Int. J. Psychoanal.*, 33:489–95.

12

Defensive Organization and Autonomous Ego Functions

I

This panel takes place at a time when it is proper and right to remember that thirty years ago, Anna Freud published *The Ego and the Mechanisms of Defense* (1936). That work was a milestone and a turning point in the history of psychoanalytic clinical theory and technique.

As clinical theory, it spelled out and enlarged what had been known, before then, about defenses and their mechanisms. Anna Freud observed and described not only defenses which the ego erects against drives and their derivatives; her conception also encompassed defenses against affects, defenses against objective dangers. Nor did she limit herself to a description of single mechanisms; she also described more complex phenomena: e.g., the effect of defenses on drive derivatives, on affects, and on parts of the personality encompassing nondefensive areas of the ego, such as "restrictions of the ego" and complex behavior patterns of "identification with the aggressor" and "altruistic surrender."

Anna Freud made the important observation that individuals use similar defense mechanisms in their resistances and in their neurotic behavior. The favorable impact which her work had on technique cannot be stressed enough. The general technical advice Freud had given long before, to analyze resistances, has in the last thirty years acquired concretely applicable form.

A somewhat shorter version of this paper was presented in the panel on "Defense Organization of the Ego and Psychoanalytic Technique" at the Annual Meeting of the American Psychoanalytic Association, Atlantic City, May 7, 1966.

II

The complexity of the phenomena that have since become known as defenses of the ego has given rise to many theoretical and technical studies and contributions. Only some of them will be mentioned in this presentation.

The function of particular defense mechanisms within the framework of an individual's psychic makeup appears less simple to us now than it may have done at first. For example, Waelder (1951) pointed to the simultaneous action of several such mechanisms in a defensive process. He used the term "isomorphism" to underline the similarity of these mechanisms in individual development and in symptom formation. Kris spoke of specific patterns of defense against specific drive patterns as being characteristic of certain individuals and of their neurotic symptoms, and he called them the "defensive system" (Kris 1951, 1956b). Long before, Freud had pointed to the preponderance of certain defenses in particular mental disorders: repression in hysteria; repression plus regression, undoing and isolation in obsessive-compulsive neurosis; projection in paranoid disorders. However, significant as these correlations between defensive mechanisms and types of neuroses are, they have not led to further or new satisfactory classifications.

In her pioneering study, Anna Freud also carefully examined the processes of defense "according to the source of anxiety and danger," thereby following Freud's formulations. Defenses can express the ego's protection against instinctual demands, for instance; or they may originate in the child's wish to please the parents; or at a later stage of development, they may express the compliance with internalized moral prohibitions: the superego. As Freud and others have pointed out, defenses appear successively with the gradual development and maturation of the ego.

III

An important problem, which has both theoretical and therapeutic implications, is that of the pathogenicity of defensive mechanisms. Although Freud defines mechanisms of defense as part of the potentially pathogenic factors in neuroses, a one-sided view has considered them to be pathogenic or morbid in themselves. To be sure, where there is pathology, defensive mechanisms as well as instinctual drives play a role in the pathogenic processes, but this does not mean that either defenses or drives are always pathogenic. Both instinctual drives and defenses against them are essential parts of the normal human mind (cf., Glover 1947; Hartmann 1950; Nunberg 1932).

What then accounts for their being a part in a pathogenic process? Freud spoke of the inappropriateness of some defense mechanisms involved in pathology. This peculiarity might be viewed as deriving from problems of chronology described by Anna Freud (1936) and those, less well known, concerning the origins and gradual development of defenses (cf., Glover 1947; Hartmann 1950; Nunberg 1932). In regard to their pathogenicity, one can say that some defensive mechanisms either may be too weak in relation to some drives (Freud 1937), or may be too strong in relation to some other types of drives. However, it would seem preferable to speak of "effectiveness" or "ineffectiveness" of defenses, rather than strength or weakness. Some defense mechanisms are inappropriate in respect to the ego and to the reality situation of a given individual. Their rigidity at various developmental stages and in the light of changing reality situations can make them pathogenic.

One other point of view must be stressed in respect to the potential pathogenicity of defense mechanisms; namely, its possible pervasive effect on character formation, on object relations, and its intertwinement with other defenses and with drive derivatives. Let us take a concrete example:

The turning of passivity into activity is one of the most important adaptive mechanisms of normal maturation and development. The child gradually learns to make use of it in order to become independent of his mother, but also in order to master the frustrations or disappointments inevitably experienced while growing up. This mechanism also enters into the normal development of moral autonomy; the child takes over the parental prohibitions and commands during the formation of his superego.

Clinical observations show pathological outcomes of this normal mechanism when it is secondarily used for purposes of defense. Among the best known is the so-called "sour grapes" reaction. When this type of reaction appears consistently in the form of "I don't care" in relation to a love object, it may express considerable disturbances of affectivity and character. An outgrowth of these developments may be similar reactions of "sour grapes," or even of "bitter grapes," when this defense mechanism is already used in an anticipatory way, giving rise to a behavior pattern characterized by the colloquialism "to quit before one is fired." Patients who react in this fashion start hating not only the actually, but even the potentially rejecting object. These disorders, of various severity, are based on vicissitudes of this particular mechanism, usually combined with other defenses, such as isolation.

Since these defense mechanisms exist in normal human beings, the question arises why only some people suffer from severe neurotic disorders based to a considerable extent on such defenses. One can say that pathology occurs when these mechanisms become generalized; i.e., when the behavior they elicit is not limited to a specific person, but appears in a stereotyped form in regard to most people. One can formulate this also by saying that pathogenicity here is based on the inappropriateness of these defenses in regard to the reality situation. Pathogenicity is also intensified when the defenses are generalized so as to include other affects in various life situations. This may take the form of a general inhibition of affectivity, and hence, severe disturbances of object relations.

Usually an additional factor is involved in such serious disturbances: the combination, the entwinement, of defense mechanisms with instinctual gratifications. This occurs mainly when the "sour grapes" defense is simultaneously used for the purpose of warding off libidinal wishes and for the gratification of aggressive, vengeful reactions to an anticipated rebuff by the potentially loved object. The original defense mechanism in these cases becomes pathogenic due to this complex spread and intertwinement with instinctual derivatives—or, one could say more generally, when defenses also subserve instinctual gratifications. Such cases make for particularly difficult therapeutic problems.

Certain defense mechanisms become directed against superego demands (Freud 1923). This presents unusual problems in analysis, since it can often lead to moral or sexual masochism. Absence of guilt feelings or remorse on a conscious level—those signals of conflict between ego and superego—impairs the ability to deal with superego demands by confronting present and anticipating future reality situations. Such defenses against the superego frequently result in an alternation between impulsive actions and self-punitive behavior. Since the signal function of guilt feelings is inhibited, the warning role of the superego is curtailed (Hartmann & Loewenstein 1962; Loewenstein 1966).

The psychoanalytic process aims at a correction of these unfavorable quantitative or qualitative relations between the defenses of the ego, the demands of the drives, the exigencies of the superego, the functioning of the autonomous ego, and the potentialities and necessities of outer reality.

IV

Schur (1953, 1958) clarified the processes underlying anxiety and defense. He showed the existence of ego regression in the ego's responses to danger, as distinct from its evaluation of danger situations. According to his reformulation of "ego regression in anxiety, every state of anxiety, whatever its kind or degree, has its genetic link to old dangers and traumatic situations" (Schur 1953, p. 94).

The concept of a *defensive organization* of the ego was first used, as far as I know, by Hoffer (1954). He aptly delimited a psychic organization forming part of the ego, whose general organization comprehends defensive mechanisms, the individual character structure, as well as what Hartmann defined as the "conflict-free sphere"; i.e., all the primary and secondary autonomous functions of the ego. It is clear that the defensive organization influences the autonomous aspect of the ego, and that the latter in turn participates decisively in the formation, development, and functioning of the defensive organization.

Hartmann (1950, 1953) stressed the importance of the autonomous ego's ability to create stable and effective defenses. He ascribes the disorders of defense mechanisms in schizophrenia to disordered autonomous ego functions, impaired due to a lack of neutralization of psychic energy at the disposal of defense.

In Hoffer's view (1967), the defensive organization has as its major function anxiety regulation. Hence its genesis and vicissitudes can be traced back to the developmental and maturational changes of the "inner world" in interrelation with the "outside world." This organization can also be thought of as involved in intersystemic and intrasystemic aspects of the ego, and in some of the latter's autonomous and drive regulatory functions. As a result of these interactions the defensive organization must be credited with positive achievements and sublimated, often positively creative activities of the ego.

Defenses are phenomena serving to protect the integrity of the ego organization (Freud 1926). Thus their function is implicitly one of adaptation (Hartmann 1939). Even a neurotic symptom resulting from an interaction between drive derivatives and defensive processes can be viewed as reflecting the ego's function of adaptation. One can state that the processes that resulted in a neurosis were *adaptational*, i.e., guided by the function of adaptation, although they did not end up being *adaptive* in the usual sense of the term. It is worth noting that Hoffer's description of the defensive organization stresses truly adaptive counterparts of a neurosis; these various character traits and productive activities of neurotics are based on the very defenses involved in their symptomatology.

There is great merit in this view of defenses as a complex organization. It gives the analyst a deeper and much wider understanding of his patients, and hence increased sureness and clarity in his therapeutic endeavor.

The psychoanalyst uses essentially his patient's intact autonomous functions to initiate and further the analytic process, and to assist in leading it to a satisfactory result. Even in order to follow the fundamental rule, the patient must have at his disposal a number of complex autonomous ego functions, such as anticipation, reality testing in a wide sense, speech, self-observation, as well as relatively stable object relations. And those of his functions which are in any way inhibited or disturbed by resistances—i.e., in some part by the defenses—must be assisted by the activities of the analyst. It is correct to say, I believe, that in this respect the analyst has the function of a temporary, auxiliary autonomous ego for his patient (Loewenstein 1954, 1956).

V

We must distinguish between two sides of the psychoanalytic technique: on the one hand, the method and procedures and specific technical rules; on the other hand, the use of psychoanalytic knowledge in order to implement this method, so that the analytic process can unfold and lead to a satisfactory termination. For example, free association could never proceed beyond a certain point if the analyst were not able to interpret its disturbance as the result of some specific preconscious or unconscious resistance.

Progress in ego psychology has not changed the fundamental principle, namely, to transform unconscious phenomena into conscious ones. However, there may be more change in the empirical technical rules that Freud had stressed over the years.

One of them is that the analyst should not interpret strongly warded-off instinctual impulses without first analyzing the resistances, the motives for defense that had left them in the warded-off state. This rule is sometimes couched in terms of the advice to analyze "resistance before content." This formulation may lead to misunderstandings, because all derivatives, whether of drives or of defenses, appear during analysis as contents. What distinguishes one from the other, identifying one content as a drive derivative and another as a defense derivative, are their functional characteristics. It may also be confusing to think of defenses as always closer to the "surface" than drives. Actually, one or the other, or even a derivative of the superego demands, can be at the "surface" at a given time in the analysis; so that usually the one "on the agenda" is being brought to the attention of the patient, and in most cases interpretations encompass more than that. They usually include both defense and drive derivatives, and often superego demands as well. The empirical rule of "analyzing resistance before content" also refers to the statement that resistances, particularly transference resistances, should be interpreted before attempting reconstructions of forgotten biographical data. This is mostly a sound practice, but not always. In cases where intense emotional reactions toward the analyst thwart all progress of the treatment, only a correct reconstruction of the warded-off event that is being relived in the transference enables the patient to overcome his resistance.

One might think there is nothing new in analytic technique. But if we compare, let us say, the technique used by Freud in the Dora case with some examples described by Anna Freud, the difference is extremely striking. The principle of analyzing resistance existed before 1936, but its implementation had never before been spelled out. Anna Freud also formulated a reevaluation of the fundamental rule. As opposed to the idea—described, e.g., by Fenichel (1935) as late as 1935—that one should pay attention only to impulses coming to the fore among free associations, she stressed the importance of observing the way in which a patient is unable to follow the basic rule, and emphasized that equal attention must be given to the id, the ego, and the superego.

By the same token, Hartmann's introduction of the concept of ego autonomy has not changed the essential psychoanalytic method and procedure. We continue to use the same method, but some of us, hopefully, with the sense that we understand better than before what happens in our patients when we analyze them.

A distinction must be drawn between resistances and defenses. For the sake of clarity, it is useful to limit the term resistance to the phenomena that oppose the analytic process (Loewenstein 1954). Defenses are phenomena which exist in the individual whether he is in analysis or not. Moreover, resistances are not all due to defenses of the ego. Freud (1926) described various types of resistance as having their seat in the ego, in the id, or in the superego, and added others, some of which, such as "psychic inertia" and "adhesiveness of the libido," cannot be clearly attributed to one or another of these psychic agencies (Freud 1937).

Although disturbances in free association are chiefly determined by resistance, some may be due to other causes. The inability of children to associate can be ascribed to differences between ego functions of children and of adults.

The following explanations have been offered to account for the inability of children to associate freely in the same way as adults. The first two (in personal communications to the author) ascribed it to incomplete maturation or development of the autonomous ego in the child.

Heinz Hartmann thought that some autonomous functions, in particular those entering the secondary process, are still too unstable in the child when exposed to the inevitable impact of the primary process in analytic treatment.

Elisabeth Geleerd suggested that in children, the functions of introspection and reflection upon oneself are still insufficiently developed. Instead, quite naturally, they tend to play, to play-act, and to act out.

Anna Freud (1965), referring to the child's inability and unwillingness to associate freely, ascribes it to the immature ego's need to keep defenses up more rigidly because it is insecurely balanced between pressures from within and without.

Perhaps some obstacles to free association in adults arise from similar insufficiencies or from other, still unknown, conditions (Loewenstein 1963).

VI

In the panel on "Defense Mechanisms and Psychoanalytic Technique" (Zetzel 1954), various problems concerning ego defenses were subjected to discussion. One of these was the fate of defenses as a result of psychoanalytic treatment. Two views were presented. Some panelists were of the opinion that defensive mechanisms should disappear as a result of analytic treatment. Some others, including myself, stressed rather the modification of defenses in the analytic process, their adjustment to current psychic and external reality. The same opinion had been expressed by Hoffer (1954) and by me (1954) in the symposium on "Mechanisms of Defence and Their Place in Psychoanalytic Technique." It is in connection with these issues that the term "defensive organization," which Hoffer introduced on that occasion, appears especially valuable. Hoffer took issue more particularly with the technical implications of the viewpoint that defenses are, as it were, unwanted, morbid, and neurotic, and must be made to disappear in analysis. He quoted an author whose name he did not mention: "'the analytic work is exclusively directed against the defences; they have to be handled with determination and the aim to be achieved is their dissolution; they have to be broken up under the impact of the analyst's interpretations'" (Hoffer 1954, p. 195). Hoffer is in thorough disagreement with this point of view, and so am I. In fact, such a "dissolution" of defenses does not take place as a result of analysis—whether one considers it desirable or not.

A closely related problem is that of the unconscious character of the defense mechanisms. Of course, these mechanisms are scientific concepts or constructs. We assume, however, that specific unconscious psychic phenomena exist, which have the characteristics we ascribe to them; e.g., of inhibiting particular actions, of distorting certain memories of one's own past, of disturbing even perception, in the various ways described in the psychoanalytic literature. We infer their existence from clinical observations, as well as from human behavior and some conscious phenomena subserving similar functions, such as self-control, suppression, trying not to think of unpleasant things, etc. We conceive the characteristics of unconscious mechanisms to some extent in the image of these conscious defensive reactions, as *homologous* to them (Loewenstein 1965).[1] One might put it in the following

1. In contrast, some other concepts or constructs in psychoanalytic theory, such as id,

way, for example: if repression were conscious, it could be translated in terms similar to what we call suppression.

What is the correlation between unconscious and conscious defenses? What, in particular, is the fate of unconscious defenses when they have been made conscious through analysis? Undoubtedly they must undergo some modification as a result of having become conscious. But not all of them do become conscious, or remain so after analysis. In this respect, modifications of the defensive organization can be compared with modifications imparted to the drive organization as a result of the analytic process.

Hoffer rightly points to the counterpart of defenses in other areas of the personality—in achievements, sublimations, object relations, character traits—and to the fact that these correlates can have highly valuable features. Therefore he warns against directing interpretive activity indiscriminately "against" all defenses, instead of carefully distinguishing those which had a part in pathology from others, often newly formed, that are valuable for an integrated defensive organization.

Moreover, we must not forget that psychoanalytic treatment can achieve results only if one essential defense is maintained during treatment: namely, that against action and gratification in analysis. Only by virtue of this can other defenses, after they have become conscious, be overcome or partly lifted. Indeed, patients can become conscious of their unconscious conflicts only if their sexual and aggressive transference reactions are not gratified in the analysis, and are not responded to in a similar way by the analyst, but are analyzed by him (Loewenstein 1954).

VII

The analytic method can be said to aim at the mobilization of warded-off material and at its expression in speech, thus submitting primary-process phenomena to secondary-process thinking and control. And the analyst's interpretations can be described as working in the same direction: they assist the patient's memory, reality testing, and under-

---

ego, superego, psychic energy, can never be observed or even construed in the image of actual behavior or conscious thought; they are *heterologous* to them (Loewenstein 1965).

standing of inner and outer reality. Moreover, they are not usually directed only at defenses, or only at drives or at the superego. They encompass and take into account the patient's entire thought and emotional processes. Thus, they include essential autonomous processes as well. To interpret is to translate into secondary-process thinking what was distorted by primary-process phenomena. The analyst reconstructs past events and elicits "archaic ego states" (Rubinfine 1967)—modes of thinking and experiencing—in the patient. He thus reconstructs not "drive derivatives" or "defensive mechanisms" alone, but complex psychic phenomena encompassing all that and the conflict-free sphere (Loewenstein 1951a, 1957).

I should like to illustrate some of my statements by a few examples.

1. A female patient suffering from depressive states and frigidity presented typical reactions to what she experienced as rejection by a man. Since a certain period in childhood she had hated and despised her father and felt intense admiration and devotion for her mother. In her relation to her husband, an initial admiration soon gave way to a similar contempt for which she subtly adduced justification. Her transference reactions likewise presented oscillations between love and subtle contempt and resentment. The analysis of transference resistances repeatedly showed her regressive attachment to the mother as resulting from what she felt to be rebuffs in a triangular situation. Her jealous rage, however, was invariably directed against the man, and her love toward the woman. The analysis of this complicated but typical mechanism had no therapeutic effect until she realized that what might have been an appropriate reaction in childhood was no longer appropriate in her adult life. Once she became aware of her tendency to displace a regressive defense against sexual wishes from an incestuous object to all men and to all sexuality, an impressive change rapidly ensued.

2. A young man presented, among other symptoms, a compulsive need to drive through red lights on the road, an action often followed by anxiety and guilt feelings. His frequent "toying with danger" fulfilled his impulse to defy prohibitions, as well as inviting punishment. As a rule, the ability to differentiate between what is considered morally wrong and what is dangerous develops only gradually in childhood, and it presupposes a high degree of ego development as well as a formed

superego. This differentiation is performed by the autonomous functions of the ego. The patient in question reacted to red traffic lights as if they were moral injunctions and not signals of danger. The unconscious motives of this confusion were highly complex, but the patient's ability to gain insight into them was based on his essentially intact superego and ego functions.

3. My last example concerns a patient whose character neurosis was built to a considerable degree on the mechanism of isolation and repression of affect, aside from other defenses. Although he was a man of highly sophisticated intelligence and sensitivity, he was not aware, for instance, of ever having been jealous, or of ever having wanted to be loved by his mother. All his life he had lived, to use his own words, in the illusion of being the preferred child of his parents. Once, in a situation where he imagined that I might take sides with an adversary of his, he brought up the "illusion of communion" with the analyst and hesitantly spoke of feelings of jealousy. I remarked that his sentence was not complete. Reluctantly, and with a disbelieving chuckle, he finished the sentence which expressed that he wanted to be loved by his analyst. This wish had never occurred to him before uttering these words. (Needless to add that when the patient was reminded of this incident a week later, it had been forgotten by him.) Here, one might say, words carried to the surface of conscious awareness a thought and an affect which had previously been unconscious. In these instances, language performs the function of a kind of scaffolding that permits conscious thought to be built inside. Here the power of language, the inner logic of the half-formed sentence, allowed a warded-off feeling to be brought to consciousness.

For the sake of brevity, I chose only a few out of many examples which would show the import of autonomous ego functions for psychoanalytic technique.

SUMMARY

The developments of the concepts of "defense" and "ego" in the last thirty years are surveyed. The question of pathogenicity of defense mechanisms is examined; their organization and role in normal psychic life and in adaptation are noted. The role of the defensive organization and of autonomous ego functions is discussed from the standpoint of technique. In psychoanalytic technique the difference is stressed between fundamental principles, practical rules, and the body of psychoanalytic knowledge. Some clinical vignettes illustrate the author's views.

REFERENCES

Eissler, K. R. (1953). The effect of the structure of the ego on psychoanalytic technique. *J. Amer. Psychoanal. Assn.*, 1:104–43.

Fenichel, O. (1935). Psychoanalytic method. In *The Collected Papers of Otto Fenichel*. New York: Norton, 1953.

French, T. M. (1938). Defense and synthesis in the function of the ego. Some observations stimulated by Anna Freud's *The Ego and the Mechanisms of Defense*. *Psychoanal. Q.*, 7:537–53.

Freud, A. (1936). *The Ego and the Mechanisms of Defense*. New York: Int. Univ. Press, 1967.

——— (1954). Problems of technique in adult analysis. *Bull. Philadelphia Assn. for Psychoanal.*, 4:44–70.

——— (1965). *Normality and Pathology in Childhood: Assessments of Development*. New York: Int. Univ. Press.

Freud, S. (1923). The ego and the id. *S.E.*, 19.

——— (1926). Inhibitions, symptoms, and anxiety. *S.E.*, 20.

——— (1937). Analysis terminable and interminable. *S.E.*, 23.

Geleerd, E. R. (1965). Two kinds of denial: neurotic denial and denial in the service of the need to survive. In *Drives, Affects, Behavior, II*, ed. M. Schur. New York: Int. Univ. Press, pp. 118–27.

Gero, G. (1951). The concept of defense. *Psychoanal. Q.*, 20:565–78.

——— (1953). Defenses in symptom formation. *J. Amer. Psychoanal. Assn.*, 1:87–103.

Glover, E. (1947). Basic mental concepts, their clinical and theoretical value. *Psychoanal. Q.*, 16:482–506.

Greenson, R. R. (1958). Variations in classical psychoanalytic technique. *Int. J. Psychoanal.*, 29:200–01.

——— (1960). Problems of dosage, timing, and tact in interpretation. *Bull. Philadelphia Assn. for Psychoanal.*, 10:23–24.

Hartmann, H. (1939). *Ego Psychology and the Problem of Adaptation*. New York: Int. Univ. Press, 1958.

——— (1950). Comments on the psychoanalytic theory of the ego. *Psychoanal. Study Child*, 5:74–96.

——— (1951). Technical implications of ego psychology. *Psychoanal. Q.*, 20:31–43.

———— (1953). Contribution to the metapsychology of schizophrenia. *Psychoanal. Study Child*, 8:177–98.

———— (1960). *Psychoanalysis and Moral Values.* New York: Int. Univ. Press.

———— & Loewenstein, R. M. (1962). Notes on the superego. *Psychoanal. Study Child*, 17:42–81.

Hoffer, W. (1954). Defensive process and defensive organization: their place in psychoanalytic technique. *Int. J. Psychoanal.*, 35:194–98.

———— (1967). Bemerkungen zur abwehrlehre. In *Hoofdstukken uit de hedendaagse psychoanalyse*, ed. P. J. van der Leeuw, E. C. M. Frijling-Schreuder & P. C. Kuiper. Arnheim: Van Loghum Slaterus, pp. 20–30.

Kris, E. (1951). Ego psychology and interpretation in psychoanalytic therapy. *Psychoanal. Q.*, 20:15–30.

———— (1956a). On some vicissitudes of insight in psychoanalysis. *Int. J. Psychoanal.*, 37:445–55.

———— (1956b). The recovery of childhood memories in psychoanalysis. *Psychoanal. Study Child*, 11:54–88.

Lampl-de Groot, J. (1957). On defenses and development: normal and pathological. *Psychoanal. Study Child*, 12:114–26.

Loewenstein, R. M. (1951a). The problem of interpretation. *Psychoanal. Q.*, 20:1–14.

———— (1951b). Ego development and psychoanalytic technique. *Amer. J. Psychiat.*, 107:617–22.

———— (1954). Some remarks on defenses, autonomous ego, and psychoanalytic technique. *Int. J. Psychoanal.*, 35:188–93.

———— (1956). Some remarks on the role of speech in psychoanalytic technique. *Int. J. Psychoanal.*, 37:460–68.

———— (1957). Some thoughts on interpretation in the theory and practice of psychoanalysis. *Psychoanal. Study Child*, 12:127–50.

———— (1963). Some considerations on free association. *J. Amer. Psychoanal. Assn.*, 11:451–73.

———— (1965). Observational data and theory in psychoanalysis. In *Drives, Affects, Behavior, II*, ed. M. Schur. New York: Int. Univ. Press, pp. 38–59.

———— (1966). On the theory of the superego: a discussion. In *Psychoanalysis—A General Psychology: Essays in Honor of Heinz Hartmann*, ed. R. M. Loewenstein, L. M. Newman, M. Schur & A. J. Solnit. New York: Int. Univ. Press, pp. 298–314.

Nunberg, H. (1932). *Principles of Psychoanalysis: Their Application to the Neuroses.* New York: Int. Univ. Press, 1956.

Pfeffer, A. Z. (1963). Panel report: Analysis terminable and interminable—twenty-five years later. *J. Amer. Psychoanal. Assn.*, 11:131–42.

Rubinfine, D. L. (1967). Notes on a theory of reconstruction. *Brit. J. Med. Psychol.*, 40:195–206.

Schur, M. (1953). The ego in anxiety. In *Drives, Affects, Behavior, I,* ed. R. M. Loewenstein. New York: Int. Univ. Press, pp. 67–103.

———— (1958). The ego and the id in anxiety. *Psychoanal. Study Child,* 13:190–220.

Waelder, R. (1930). The principle of multiple function: observations on over-determination. *Psychoanal. Q.,* 5:45–62.

———— (1951). The structure of paranoid ideas: a critical survey of various theories. *Int. J. Psychoanal.,* 32:117–77.

Zetzel, E. R. (1954). Panel report: Defense mechanisms and psychoanalytic technique. *J. Amer. Psychoanal. Assn.,* 2:318–26.

13

Ego Autonomy and Psychoanalytic Technique

When asked to give a paper in memory of Heinz Hartmann, I felt that it would be redundant to present once again his theoretical contributions to psychoanalysis, for which he is most famous. I have chosen instead to speak about his ideas in the area of psychoanalytic technique, which are less well known. Indeed Hartmann published only a single paper on this subject, "Technical Implications of Ego Psychology" (1951), to which I shall refer further on. It is a highly important paper, based upon his views concerning psychic structure and particularly the structure of the ego. It reveals his unusual clinical acumen and his mastery of psychoanalytic technique.

Hartmann's theoretical discoveries and formulations stem mainly from a period in the history of psychoanalysis that started with Freud's renewed interest in ego psychology and especially with his introduction of the structural point of view. By this approach Freud resolved the dilemma arising from important clinical observations that could not be satisfactorily explained in terms of his topographical theory. That earlier theory had formulated conflicts between drives and defenses in terms of distinctions between the characteristics of preconsciousness and consciousness as opposed to the unconscious. What did not fit into this formulation was the clinical finding of unconscious resistances and unconscious moral demands. Freud had to choose between functional characteristics and qualities of consciousness or unconsciousness in a neurotic conflict. He decided therefore to describe the psychic ap-

Paper presented at the Heinz Hartmann Memorial Meeting of the New York Psychoanalytic Society and Institute, October 21, 1971, and at a scientific meeting of the Boston Psychoanalytic Society, December 1, 1971.

paratus in terms of structure and function, rather than in degrees of consciousness.

The second important reformulation of psychoanalytic theory by Freud was his new theory of anxiety. He had formerly regarded anxiety as the result of prevented discharge of libidinal tensions. This "toxic" theory of anxiety he replaced by that of a reaction of the ego to internal or external danger: a "biological" theory, as it were, encompassing normal as well as pathological anxiety. The new theory included also a reconstruction of a ubiquitous developmental series of danger situations to which the child reacts with anxiety and defense. This well-known series comprises fear of loss of object, fear of loss of the object's love, castration anxiety, and superego anxiety. Here, for the first time, Freud described an aspect of ego development which, although it is involved in conflict, is not the result of conflict.

But it was Hartmann who, later on, referred to developmental characteristics of this type as autonomous ego development. Stressing that many of the functions involved in this autonomous development and in the "conflict-free sphere" of the ego are relatively independent of drive-defense conflict, he described them as primary autonomous ego functions. Among these primary autonomous functions he included control of motility, perception, anticipation, thinking, reality testing, recall phenomena, object comprehension, and language.

Hartmann extended the study of ego autonomy to behavior that has become known as secondary autonomy: to certain strivings in man which we call ego interests, e.g., those concerned with social status, influence, power, professional status, wealth, etc. They can be traced back to their instinctual sources, such as the wish to be loved and admired, competitive tendencies, sadistic impulses, and narcissism. But it is characteristic for these strivings that, despite their instinctual genetic precursors, they come to be unquestionably in the service of the ego after the structuralization of the psychic apparatus has taken place. However, they are only a part of the ego, and it is very important to distinguish these secondary autonomous phenomena from other activities of the ego.

Other examples of secondary autonomy are certain character formations; thus the well-known traits of the so-called anal character, such as extreme punctiliousness, stubbornness, and orderliness, which are due, as Freud described, to reaction-formations against early anal erotic interests. These early instinctual precursors are observable in dreams and in neurotic and psychotic symptoms, as well as in the analytic treatment, but in general such character traits are independent of them. The degree of independence of these character traits, their relative irreversibility, is certainly a measure of secondary autonomy and mental health.

Hartmann's contributions widened the psychoanalytic understanding of the total personality. Besides looking at the human being from the point of view of symptomatology and neurosis, now we also pay greater attention to character, adaptedness, talents, and achievements. This approach has considerable influence on our clinical work. Hartmann added to our perspective the nonconflictual counterpart of conflict. He stressed, however, that conflict must not be equated with pathology, nor autonomy with health. They are not mutually exclusive.

I started by defining briefly the concept of autonomy in Hartmann's work. After the publication of Freud's "The Ego and the Id" (1923) and "Inhibitions, Symptoms, and Anxiety" (1926), some authors tried to describe analysis in terms of the total personality. But only since the addition of the study of ego autonomy has it become possible to speak of analysis of the total personality.

The concept of ego autonomy has important bearing upon the theory of psychoanalytic technique. In every analysis the relationship between theory and technique is a very close one. Our technique is based, first of all, on understanding the patient's neurosis as well as the healthy aspects of his personality.

Anna Freud (1936) made the important statement that the patient's ego is the medium through which analysis takes place and which permits us to observe with equal attention manifestations of his ego, id, and superego. Actually the specific medium through which we observe these three substructures of the mental apparatus is the autonomous ego of the patient. The interactions and conflicts in which we are interested take place not only between ego, id, and superego, but also within the ego itself. The requirement of the basic rule accentuates the conflict between autonomous functions and defensive functions of the ego. In addition, it accentuates certain autonomous functions—self-observation, verbalization—while inhibiting others, e.g., purposive thinking. Thus the basic rule influences even conflicts between drives and defenses. One can say that if the main (though not exclusive) interest of psychoanalysis is the study of conflict in man, the *tools* of this study are the autonomous functions. And last, but not least, *these tools themselves* become objects of the analyst's interest.

In his conceptualization of autonomous functions, Hartmann always tried to follow the most precise interaction not only of dynamic, economic, and genetic factors, but equally of functional and structural elements. These distinctions are particularly important in order to understand the formation of secondary autonomy. In conceptualizing these developments he introduced a biological term into psychoanalysis: "change of function." This concept is of great help in many different technical problems. The analytic situation is partly determined by a displacement of forces involved in various vicissitudes of conflicts. In such instances, the conflicts may present themselves in paradoxical sequences in which the resistance is determined not by the defenses of the ego but by drive derivatives.

Hartmann extended the concept of conflict from the well-known conflict between drive and defense to conflicts within the ego itself. The latter he called *intra*systemic, as opposed to *inter*systemic, conflicts. The question has been raised whether these two types of conflicts may be legitimately juxtaposed. It is true that the forces involved in them are not the same. But one can assume that the conflicts within the ego acquire a certain import and intensity when they are linked to intersystemic conflicts of the ego with id or superego. The stimulus for this linkage, however, may originate either in the id or in the ego, or in their relations to each other, such as those elicited by compliance with the fundamental rule.

Ego autonomy enters the field of technique in still other forms. Only patients with some degree of integrity of the ego are accessible to psychoanalytic treatment. This means intactness not alone of some defenses, but also of autonomous functions. The very prerequisites of the analytic situation hinge upon them. The autonomous ego is the medium through which patients communicate to the analyst what they observe in themselves. We require the patient not to censor and not to omit certain thoughts, while placing him so that he cannot observe the analyst's reactions. These requirements lead to complicated shifts within the autonomous functions of the patient, which have significant effects on his free associations. The analytic setting contributes in a specific way to the patient's behavior. Some of his behavior and reactions are inhibited by the recumbent position on the couch. Moreover, the analyst does not respond to his patient's verbalization in the same way as ordinary interlocutors would do.

These peculiarities of the setting are designed to achieve a partial curtailment of action and perception of external reality, so as to foster processes of self-observation. But they also increase the mechanisms of displacement and projection, thereby shifting the patient's perception from the outer to the inner world. Besides, they encourage a relative increase of primary process thinking; and yet the basic rule also requires the patient to communicate all his resulting self-observations in a way that is intelligible, as only secondary process allows it. In brief, the patient is expected to perform these complicated processes entailing the temporary and partial suspension by the ego of some of its own functions and the sharpening of others, especially those of self-observation and communication to the analyst (Loewenstein 1963, p. 458). By mentioning the psychoanalytic "setting" in such detail I merely take into account that it is one of the basic constituents of the psychoanalytic situation.

The patient's autonomous ego, whose alliance with the analyst is essential for the success of the treatment, enables him to overcome his unconscious resistances. Indeed, it is necessary that the patient have relatively intact memory, thinking, perceptions, reality testing, capacity for self-observation and for verbal expression. On the other hand, we know that our alliance with his autonomous ego would be precarious without the transference. It is in the analytic situation that one best observes how greatly some aspects of autonomous functions can be enhanced or, on the contrary, impaired by unconscious influences of the defensive organization and of the id.

In recent years some analysts have come to emphasize the treatment alliance as being in the forefront of analytic tools. Such an alliance is indeed indispensable for psychoanalytic therapy. But we must not forget that things are more complicated; autonomous functions may actually come to be used in the service of resistance. For example, some patients are very eager to cooperate with the analyst, to help him by presenting as much material as possible, and yet their behavior betrays that they are "resisting against resistances." There are periods when they struggle against the emergence of unwelcome transference reactions. Only when this apparently conflictless cooperation is disturbed and gives place to transference resistances, can a new step forward be made in the analysis.

Some aspects of autonomous functions act as a resistance in still other situations. A well-known illustration of conflicts within the autonomous ego is resistance by means of intellectualization, such as

Anna Freud (1936) described in adolescents. Here the gradual development of the thinking function is used not only for analytic understanding, but also against it. We saw that Hartmann explained these shifts by formulating the concept of *change of function*, which is very important for the understanding of many puzzling aspects of psychic development. As I mentioned, it also plays a considerable role in certain clinical and technical situations.

There are well-known phenomena in which changes of function chronically modify and impair the autonomy of thinking; they are among the best-known characteristics of obsessive-compulsive neurotics. These patients present obsessive forms of thinking and compulsive doubting, symptoms which also are stubborn obstacles to analysis. Their compulsive logic is used as a defense against fantasy and ambiguity in thinking, which the analytic process is designed to foster.

We assume that these impairments of the thinking process in such patients are due to the regressive influence of unconscious conflicts. In other words, drive derivatives, defenses, and superego demands have achieved a reinstinctualization of the thinking process. Inhibitions or disorders of autonomous functions exist in most neurotic symptomatology. But in some patients the deneutralization of autonomy manifests itself mainly during some periods of their analysis; it happens under the impact of the transference, and leads to regressive reactivations of drive derivatives as well as regressions of ego functions.

Every analyst has seen patients whose apparently willing cooperation in the treatment takes the form of using analytic terms, and we all know how difficult it often is to analyze the defenses which this behavior represents and conceals. These cases demonstrate the importance of speech in psychoanalysis, both for the patient and for the analyst. Sometimes a simple reformulation of the patient's analytic jargon into everyday language may have considerable effect. An example used in an earlier paper (Loewenstein 1954) is particularly apt.

A patient described how when he brought home newly purchased books, he had to hide them from his wife. He said sadly: "My wife is castrating me." I reformulated this by suggesting that he actually doubted whether his wife loved him. As a matter of fact, the patient's own words were not without symbolic validity. But they were not in the right place psychologically, so to say, and by this pseudoscientific statement he certainly avoided the expression of feelings. It was interesting that a few days later, he started a session by telling me that his older brother (who was suspected of having tuberculosis) had regularly been given cream to drink by their mother, whereas he himself (the youngest child) never got any. When he related this he burst into tears. He continued to sob throughout the hour, and ended by saying that he had never cried in his previous analysis.

The examples I have given show that there are complicated interactions among the autonomous functions as well as between them and the defensive organization of the ego.

Ego psychology opened up a new area of observation, which had been closed to us before; namely, the observation of speech in psychoanalysis.

Hartmann formulated the role of language in the analytic treatment in very felicitous terms; I therefore quote him at length.

Freud found that in the transition from the unconscious to the preconscious state, a cathexis of verbal presentations is added to the thing-cathexis. Later, Nunberg [1937], already thinking along structural lines, described the role of the synthetic function of the ego in this process toward binding and assimilation. One may add that the function of the verbal element in the analytic situation is not limited to verbal cathexis and integration, but also comprises expression. I am referring to the specific role of speech in the analytic situation. This, too, contributes toward fixing the previously unconscious element in the preconscious or conscious mind of the patient. Another structural function of the same process is due to the fact that the fixing of verbal symbols is in the development of the child linked with concept formation and represents one main road toward objectivation; it plays a similar role in the analytic situation. It facilitates the patient's way to a better grasp of physical as well as psychic reality. Besides, the action of speaking has also a specific social meaning inasmuch as it serves communication, and in this respect becomes the object of the analysis of transference. There is also, of course, in speech the aspect of emotional discharge or abreaction. Finally the influence of the superego on speech and language is familiar to us, especially from psychopathology. This is to say that the different aspects of speech and language, as described by psychologists and philosophers, become coherent and meaningful if viewed from the angle of our structural model, and that in this case actually all the structural implications have today become relevant for our handling of the analytic situation. In trying to clarify the technical aspects of the problems involved, we are actually following the lead of structural psychology. [Hartmann 1951, pp. 149–50]

This general formulation permits us also to understand specific peculiarities of our patients' speech in the area of vocabulary, syntax, and grammar, which may reveal important unconscious reactions. I have commented on the misuse of analytic terminology, and also mentioned patients who are habitually or occasionally unable to express any emotional aspects of what they tell us: they can *describe,* but cannot *express.* We also see patients in whom the opposite prevails: who can *express* but not *describe.* A use of specific words, which are foreign to the speaker's subculture, may be very significant. For example, when a young patient of conventional Anglo-Saxon background, in analysis with a Jew, suddenly uses the Yiddish word *shmuck* to criticize a third person, it says a great deal about his unconscious attitude toward the analyst.[1]

While most distortions of free associations are resistances expressive of unconscious conflicts, there are some disturbing phenomena which may have to be explained differently.

From a paper I wrote some time ago, I should like to quote here a passage concerning the fact that children do not free associate in analysis:

The following explanations have been offered to account for the inability of children to associate freely in the same way as adults. The first two (in personal communications to the author) ascribed it to incomplete maturation or development of the autonomous ego in the child.

Heinz Hartmann thought that some autonomous functions, in particular those entering the secondary-process thinking, are still too unstable in the child when exposed to the inevitable impact of the primary process in analytic treatment.

Elisabeth Geleerd suggested that in children, the functions of introspection and reflection upon oneself are still insufficiently developed. Instead, quite naturally, they [children] tend to play, to play-act, and to act out.

Anna Freud [1965], referring to the child's inability and unwillingness to associate freely, ascribes it to the immature ego's need to keep defenses up more rigidly because it is insecurely balanced between pressures from within and without. [Loewenstein 1967, pp. 802–03][2]

In addition, one must also consider that children have a lesser ability than adults to postpone action, and therefore greater difficulty in replacing action by thought and speech. Delay of action is an auton-

---

1. This incident was related to me by Dr. Milton H. Horowitz. Soon after, one of my own patients used the same word in a like way.

2. Similar explanations had been given earlier by Berta Bornstein (1951) in her paper, "On Latency."

omous ego function. It appears early in childhood, but takes years to become fully developed.

In my opinion, some obstacles to free association in adults arise from similar insufficiencies. These insufficiencies may be temporary. They interfere with free association in certain patients in the midst of intense transference reactions in which the regression of ego functions makes patients literally behave like children. They are unable to free associate because the developmental inability is reconstituted. The technical effort in such situations has to be directed toward the ego regression and not merely toward the "resistance" (cf., Stone 1961; Loewenstein 1963).

These and other observations confirm Hartmann's interesting idea that while analysis has used psychopathology for the study of normal psychology, the reverse can also be fruitful. As we have just seen, the knowledge of normal childhood development may explain pathological phenomena in adult disturbances of free association.

Hartmann approached the discussion of important technical problems from the side of psychoanalytic theory. The advantage of the structural theory from a technical point of view is that our understanding of the patient's psychological problems comprises the whole of the mental apparatus. The latter is seen as an integrated whole divided into centers of mental functioning, which allows a multidimensional approach to psychic phenomena. As far as technique is concerned, it has generally been accepted that the structural-functional approach is

more useful in giving account of the dynamic and economic properties of mental life. In technique the concept of stratification proved very useful and still is, insofar as making unconscious processes conscious by way of the preconscious is clearly one main and constant factor responsible for our technical results. However, based on the concept of layers and on resistance analysis ... the concept of historical stratification was developed by Wilhelm Reich [1933], and with it a picture of personality that is definitely prestructural, in terms of the development of psychoanalytic psychology. [Hartmann 1951, p. 147]

Further on, Hartmann points out:

'Good' theory helps us to discover the facts (for instance, to recognize a resistance as such), and it helps us to see the connections among facts. This part of our psychology also gives a deeper understanding of the forms and mechanisms of defense, and a more exact consideration of the details of the patient's inner experience and behavior; corresponding to this, on the side of technique, is a tendency toward more concrete, more specific interpretation. This approach includes in its scope the infinite variety of individual characteristics, and a degree of differentiation which had not been accessible to the previous, somewhat shadowy knowledge of ego functions. It also sharpened our eyes to the frequent identity of patterns in often widely divergent fields of an individual's behavior as described by Anna Freud. [Hartmann 1951, p. 149]

Unlike Freud, Hartmann in his writings made no practical technical recommendations. Rather, he followed Freud's example in employing analysis as a method of investigation. Psychoanalysis reaches its therapeutic goals and has achieved most of its scientific discoveries through investigating all aspects of the patient's mind. As Hartmann put it, the theoretical approach has the advantage of brevity. I think it has the further advantage of being applicable to many more concrete clinical situations than any practical recommendation can be. This bent in Hartmann's thinking accounts for the fact that he considered every psychoanalysis, aside from its therapeutic function, as a scientific investigation by both patient and analyst. He believed that analysis did more than merely reconnect what had been disconnected and distorted by defenses. Psychoanalysis, in some instances, leads to real scientific discoveries.

For example, when a patient finds out that some strange, anxiety-provoking behavior of his mother when he was three years old was due to a miscarriage she had at that time, this is a new discovery for him. In fact it is highly unlikely that a three-year-old child would know and understand his mother's early manifestations of pregnancy and, even less, the symptoms and nature of a miscarriage. This raises the very complicated question of how such a discovery is made in analytic treatment. It certainly has to do with the general problem of learning. Analytic theory does not include a theory of learning, but thanks to the concept of ego autonomy, we can understand a little better than before how a patient learns about himself in his analysis.

It has been assumed that he gradually does so through a process of identification with the analyst. This hypothesis may indeed explain the reliving in the transference of very early mental states of identification with the parents, through which the child acquired important developmental gains. But the explanation of learning through identification with the analyst is not precise enough. Some consequences of such identification are the opposite of learning. They represent a regressive *imitation of the analyst's person* as the patient imagines him to be. If it persists, imitation solidifies the neurosis by crystallizing some aspects of the transference. What the patient learns from his analyst is to allow certain thoughts to become available to himself, and to look at them from a point of view acquired from the analyst. The analytic approach to his thoughts and feelings, by learning through identification with the analyst's *function*, leads to nonconflictual insight. Identification with the analyst *as a person* perpetuates conflict.[3]

Patients who use psychoanalytic terms instead of expressing their genuine thoughts and emotions imitate and often caricature an imaginary analyst. Such imitations serve not learning, but resistance through unconscious drive gratification and defense.

I now return to the example of a patient using a Yiddish word ostensibly to criticize a third person. This is relevant in the present context. The patient used the word to establish a libidinal link with his Jewish analyst, as well as to deny the aggressive character of the transference. What counts is not only the content of words, but how and when they are used. Here a specific word was used by the patient in an *imitative transference* context. He was not identifying with the analyst's *functioning*.

The clinical-technical differences between these two processes were beautifully illustrated by Ernst Kris (1956) in his paper, "On Some Vicissitudes of Insight in Psychoanalysis." Kris described three types of insight: (1) insight motivated by competitive transference; (2) an insight determined by a libidinal transference; and (3) insight in which transferential motivation is absent. In the latter, insight has risen to a successful identification with the functioning of the analyst and is a shared "understanding." It has become a truly autonomous achievement of learning.

By applying our understanding of ego autonomy to certain malfunctions of the superego, we may clarify some puzzling features of self-punishment. I am referring here not merely to the symptomatology of certain forms of moral masochism, but also to occasional self-punitive acts.

---

3. As Dr. Milton Horowitz formulated it in a recent conversation, the spectrum of regression in such identifications ranges from *learning* to *imitation*.

In a patient whom I analyzed some time ago, I noticed a particular, striking absence of affect. After approximately a year of analysis, I mentioned to him that in my opinion he had more guilt feelings than he was aware of. He reacted by saying: "I? Guilt feelings? If I had them, I would be a decent man." This response alone was proof that he had them—and also a manifestation of moral masochism. Instead of conscious guilt feelings he experienced severe anxiety states. His feeling of guilt was not displaced to another context, as in isolation of affect; rather, it was warded off.

Such warding off of superego demands may take other forms as well. It is part of complex dynamic and structural connections in the relationship between ego and superego, which may have considerable consequences for psychopathology. I am referring here to consequences of the "disregard of superego demands." They may be neurotic symptoms, psychosomatic disorders, self-inflicted punishment, all of which enter into the symptomatology of moral masochism and in all of which the absence of conscious guilt feelings may be an important factor (cf., Loewenstein 1954).

The functions of guilt feeling are not identical in childhood and in adults. In early childhood, guilt feelings are closely linked to expectation of punishment after the commitment of a forbidden act. After the formation of the superego, guilt feeling begins to appear also in connection with internal prohibition and punishment. And gradually it acquires the function of signaling and warning against future forbidden acts and thoughts. *Signal guilt feeling*, like signal anxiety, elicits defenses at the mere anticipation of danger—in this case, moral danger. It is a secondary autonomous ego function. What Freud called "superego anxiety" may apply to this form of warning before the act, as well as to remorse and guilt as punishment following the act.[4]

The warning function of the superego, however, presupposes a faultless anticipatory functioning of the ego. If the primary autonomous functions of anticipatory thinking and reality testing fall prey to instinctualization or regression, the results may include a defect in judgment. This can lead in turn to a situation of failure and punishment. Here we have a variety of mechanisms showing how some persons

---

4. Certain anticipated actions elicit a tentative punitive reaction in the superego, a *warning*, to which the ego responds in turn with a *signal guilt feeling* normally leading to a defense, e.g., stoppage or delay of such actions.

arrive at self-punishment apparently meted out by unforeseeable circumstances. In all these mechanisms the conflict is not only between superego and ego, but between all subsystems of the human mind.

The patient to whom I referred did not ward off guilt feelings alone. He was also unable to recognize in himself any feelings of jealousy or even the wish to be loved. His denial of these emotions resulted from repressing his resentment against his dead parents. Instead of experiencing these emotions he suffered from anxieties. An incident during the terminal phase of his very long analysis clearly illustrated the self-punishing mechanisms in this patient. He fantasied during a session that he would sit with me at an excellent meal, the table beautifully set, while he would sharpen his long carving knife, preparing himself with relish to puncture my abdomen in order to deflate me utterly. At this point of the fantasy he suddenly became aware that his knife was turned against his own abdomen. Assailed by a terrible anxiety, he stopped his daydream. He remained shattered for several days. In this patient, intense aggression against a rival—his father—turned against himself, and his unconscious guilt feelings were replaced by overwhelming anxiety.

I should like now to present clinical vignettes of two other patients in whom warded-off guilt feeling was significant, and who made precipitous, potentially self-damaging decisions under its influence. The ego regression, however, was not identical in both cases.

In the first example, a patient remarked one day that he heard a very close friend had incurred severe injuries in a car accident. He was greatly worried whether the friend would survive his injuries, and also what impact his possible death might have on his wife and children. Suddenly the patient added, in a resentful tone, that his friend had frequently taken unnecessary risks while driving. He implied that the accident served his friend right for being foolhardy and showing poor judgment. I was struck by the fact that the patient manifested no guilt whatsoever, which would have attenuated the impression he gave of cold anger in talking about his friend. A few days later, he told me that he had made a rash and risky decision in his business, and that he felt intensely ashamed and anxious about the consequences of this decision. He could not understand how he, an experienced businessman, could have been so rash and impulsive. Fortunately his fears did not materialize, and he was able to redress the situation. Only some days later did he remember a similar angry reaction at the death of his mother several years ago. He felt resentment toward her for not having taken care of her health, and it seemed to him that she showed poor judgment in these matters. When she died he felt that she had abandoned him. Now, at last, the patient felt very guilty for having harbored such hostile thoughts about his mother. It became clear to him in the analysis that these three incidents were closely interconnected: his angry criticism first of his mother and then of his friend, followed by the same risky behavior of which he had accused them.

This patient was not really a moral masochist, although he was capable of intense sympathy and feelings of guilt. On the other hand, since childhood he had also tended to withdraw vindictively from those who hurt him by what he experienced as indifference toward him.

From the events just summarized we can see that his repression of guilt was linked to ambivalence toward both mother and friend. Therefore his guilt feeling and need for self-punishment remained unconsciously active, exerting a regressive pull upon his ego. Instead of feeling consciously guilty, he identified with the poor judgment of his mother and friend, thereby trying to punish himself.

I am indebted to Dr. Nicholas Young for the second clinical vignette. It lends itself to an illustration of mechanisms of self-punishment which, though similar, are unlike those described in the preceding example.

A young man wanted to buy some expensive sports equipment and thought of getting it at wholesale prices with the help of his aunt. He hesitated somewhat, in view of her generally uncooperative behavior and unpleasant character. Nevertheless, he decided to ask her, and she reluctantly agreed to let him use her name in the matter. The order was filled incorrectly, but to return the merchandise he needed his aunt's signature. Afraid to expose himself again to her criticism, he precipitately forged her signature. He felt no guilt about it, although he had always been a scrupulously honest young man. One is reminded of a sudden naughty act of a usually well-behaved child. But he was crushed by the consequences when his forgery was discovered by the store and by the aunt.

In my opinion, this patient was not a moral masochist either. The poor judgment he exercised in this matter did not derive from unconscious guilt feelings to begin with, as in the previous example, but rather from an ego regression. It was the consequence of a conflict between his fear of the aunt and his regressively instinctualized wish to buy something immediately and cheaply. This poor judgment led him to disregard or even ward off the anticipatory guilt feeling which would have prevented him from committing forgery and hence inviting punishment. Here too, the defect of judgment is seen as the consequence of a complex regression involving several psychic systems.

Both cases illustrate complex mechanisms by means of which some people arrive at failure and self-punishment in interaction with external reality conditions. They are not able to create these reality conditions, but can unconsciously utilize them in many subtle ways.

In the course of analytic treatment we do not expect our patients to exercise the same autonomous functions in the same way at all times. At first their free associations are geared to what Freud called "calm self-observation" and communication to the analyst. It is only later that the patient takes a more active approach to the understanding of his feelings, thoughts, and memories. This leads gradually to an integration and restructuring of his self-knowledge in moments of analytic insight. During all these periods of the analytic process some other aspects of autonomous functions may be used as a resistance, as I have discussed before. We know that patients differ from each other in the use of particular defense mechanisms. The characteristics of their defenses impinge upon various autonomous functions and cause them to be impaired in the service of resistance. Certain forms of autonomous functions are more susceptible than others to being drawn into id-ego conflicts. They seem to be endowed with features that lead more easily to an alliance with the defensive organization of the ego. Conversely, some forms of autonomous functions, which play a role in creative talents, may facilitate healthy solutions of potentially pathogenic conflicts. These complicated interactions between various ego functions or even some of their particular aspects, at various stages of the analysis, have not yet been sufficiently explored.

At the end of his paper, "Technical Implications of Ego Psychology," Hartmann makes a number of important remarks. He points out that the analyst who scrutinizes the patient's material, taking into account all psychic systems with equal attention, is able to distinguish situations where generally accepted technical principles may have to be modified. Hartmann states that analysts encounter situations in which even the familiar opposition of drive and defense loses "much of its absolute character." He alludes here to unexpected and sometimes highly troublesome quantitative or qualitative side effects of interpretation. . . . If such incidental effects occur, our dosage or timing may have been wrong. But it may also be . . . that we have missed some structural implications though correctly following quantitative economic principles. It may be that we have considered this quantitative aspect of a resistance only and have not considered precisely enough how the same quantity may involve the various functions of the ego and the superego in a different degree. [Hartmann 1951, pp. 150–51]

Recognizing that psychoanalytic technique is somewhat lagging behind our theoretical knowledge, Hartmann points here to the technical problems presented by unexpected incidental reactions to interpretation. These reactions often transcend our immediate interest in the drive-defense area. He adds that in trying to account for these and similar observations stemming from various clinical sources, we can speak of a process set in motion by a stimulus; in this case, by an interpretation. This stimulus, according to him, "produces not only . . . 'local' reactions. It goes, beyond . . ., changing the balance of mental energies and affecting a variety of aspects of the dynamic system. The process activates or sets in a state of preparedness elements functionally and genetically connected with it" (Hartmann pp. 152–53). Further on, he notes that this "principle of multiple appeal," as he calls it, has "not yet been taken sufficiently into account by our theory or technique" (Hartmann p. 154).

Expectations of analytic results are now, paradoxically, more modest and yet more far reaching. Hartmann's widened view of psychoanalysis has not so much enlarged the variety of conditions to be treated, but rather our understanding of the infinite complexity of the individual personality.

Freud's elegant dictum that where id was, ego shall be, must be prosaically modified to include: where there is conflictual ego, the autonomous ego should acquire increased control.

SUMMARY

An attempt is made to describe briefly the role played in psychoanalytic technique by primary and secondary autonomous ego functions, concepts introduced and developed by Hartmann. The analytic process takes place mainly within the autonomous ego. The method of free association hinges upon a variety of autonomous functions. Under the regressive pull of drives and defenses, however, some of these may become reinstinctualized so as to act in the service of resistances (e.g., intellectualization). Intersystemic conflicts between drive derivatives and defenses are complicated by intrasystemic conflicts within the ego and even between different autonomous functions. The study of ego autonomy has added new perspectives to our understanding of the human mind; e.g., the nonconflictual counterpart of conflict, the observation of speech in psychoanalysis.

Hartmann approached psychoanalytic technique from the side of theory. Compared to the descriptive approach, "good" theory has the advantage of brevity as well as of applicability to a larger variety of clinical situations. To think in terms of autonomy versus conflict-laden phenomena allows a better grasp of the problem how patients learn through analysis. By identifying with the analyst's functioning rather than with his person, they achieve autonomous self-understanding as opposed to transference-laden imitation.

In conflicts with the superego the autonomy of ego functions assures favorable solutions, whereas repression of signal guilt feelings may contribute to self-punitive behavior in moral-masochistic neurotics as well as to occasional self-destructive acts in others.

REFERENCES

Blanck, G. (1966). Some technical implications of ego psychology. *Int. J. Psychoanal.*, 47:6–13.

Bornstein, B. (1951). On latency. *Psychoanal. Study Child*, 6:279–85.

Eissler, K. R. (1953). The effect of the structure of the ego on psychoanalytic technique. *J. Amer. Psychoanal. Assn.*, 1:104–43.

Freud, A. (1936). *The Ego and the Mechanisms of Defense*. New York: Int. Univ. Press, 1946.

———— (1965). *Normality and Pathology in Childhood. Assessments of Development*. New York: Int. Univ. Press.

Freud, S. (1923). The ego and the id. *S.E.*, 19.

———— (1926). Inhibitions, symptoms, and anxiety. *S.E.*, 20.

Hartmann, H. (1939a). *Ego Psychology and the Problem of Adaptation*. New York: Int. Univ. Press, 1958.

———— (1939b). Psychoanalysis and the concept of health. In *Essays on Ego Psychology. Selected Problems in Psychoanalytic Theory*. New York: Int. Univ. Press, 1964, pp. 3–18.

――――― (1947). On rational and irrational action. In *Essays on Ego Psychology. Selected Problems in Psychoanalytic Theory.* New York: Int. Univ. Press, 1964, pp. 37–68.

――――― (1950). Comments on the psychoanalytic theory of the ego. In *Essays on Ego Psychology. Selected Problems in Psychoanalytic Theory.* New York: Int. Univ. Press, 1964, pp. 113–41.

――――― (1951). Technical implications of ego psychology. In *Essays on Ego Psychology. Selected Problems in Psychoanalytic Theory.* New York: Int. Univ. Press, 1964, pp. 142–54. (Originally published in *Psychoanal. Q.,* 20:31–43.)

――――― (1953). Contributions to the metapsychology of schizophrenia. In *Essays on Ego Psychology. Selected Problems in Psychoanalytic Theory.* New York: Int. Univ. Press, 1964, pp. 182–206.

――――― & Loewenstein, R. M. (1962). Notes on the superego. *Psychoanal. Study Child,* 17:42–81.

Kris, E. (1951). Ego psychology and interpretation in psychoanalytic therapy. *Psychoanal. Q.,* 20:15–30.

――――― (1956). On some vicissitudes of insight in psychoanalysis. *Int. J. Psychoanal.,* 37:445–55.

Loewenstein, R. M. (1951a). The problem of interpretation. *Psychoanal. Q.,* 20:1–14.

――――― (1951b). Ego development and psychoanalytic technique. *Amer. J. Psychiat.,* 107:617–22.

――――― (1954). Some remarks on defenses, autonomous ego, and psychoanalytic technique. *Int. J. Psychoanal.,* 35:188–93.

――――― (1956). Some remarks on the role of speech in psychoanalytic technique. *Int. J. Psychoanal.,* 37:460–68.

――――― (1963). Some considerations on free association. *J. Amer. Psychoanal. Assn.,* 11:451–73.

――――― (1966). On the theory of the superego: a discussion. In *Psychoanalysis—A General Psychology. Essays in Honor of Heinz Hartmann,* ed. R. M. Loewenstein, L. M. Newman, M. Schur & A. J. Solnit. New York: Int. Univ. Press, pp. 298–314.

――――― (1967). Defensive organization and autonomous ego functions. *J. Amer. Psychoanal. Assn.,* 15:795–809.

Stone, L. (1954). The widening scope on indications for psychoanalysis. *J. Amer. Psychoanal. Assn.,* 2:567–94.

――――― (1961). *The Psychoanalytic Situation. An Examination of Its Development and Essential Nature.* New York: Int. Univ. Press.

Bibliography of
Rudolph M. Loewenstein
(Writings, 1923–1972)

1923

Zur Psychoanalyse der schwarzen Messen. *Imago*, 9:73–82.

1927

Le transfert affectif. Remarques sur la technique psychiatrique. *L'Évolution Psychiatrique*, 2:75–90.

1928

La technique psychanalytique. *Rev. Franç. Psychanal.*, 2:113–14.

1930

La conception psychanalytique des névroses. *L'Évolution Psychiatrique*.
Remarques sur le tact dans la technique psychanalytique. *Rev. Franç. Psychanal.*, 4:267–75.

1932

D'un mécanisme auto-punitif. *Rev. Franç. Psychoanal.*, 5:141–51.
Un cas de jalousie pathologique. *Rev. Franç. Psychoanal.*, 5:554–85.
La technique psychanalytique. *Journal Médical Français*.

1933

La conception psychanalitique de l'hystérie (with G. Parcheminey). *L'Encéphale*, 28:312–30.

1935

Translation (with M. Bonaparte) of S. Freud, *Les Cinq Psychanalyses (Fünf Krankengeschichten)*. Paris: Denoël & Steele.

Phallic passivity in men. *Int. J. Psychoanal.*, 16:334–40. (De la passivité phal-
lique chez l'homme. *Rev. Franç. Psychanal.*, 8:36–43. Die phallische
Passivität beim Manne. *Int. Ztschr. Psa.*, 21:20–36.)
La psychanalyse des troubles de la puissance chez l'homme. *Rev. Franç.
Psychanal.*, 8:538–600.

1936
De l'impuissance génitale (with M. Cénac). *L'Évolution Psychiatrique.*

1937
Bemerkungen zur theorie des therapeutischen Vorgangs der Psychoanalyse.
Int. Ztschr. Psa., 23:560–65.

1938
L'origine du masochisme et la théorie des pulsions. *Rev. Franç. Psychanal.*,
10:293–321.

1940
The vital and somatic instincts. *Int. J. Psychoanal.*, 21:377–400. (Von den
vitalen oder somatischen Trieben. *Int. Ztschr. Psa. und Imago*, 25:174–96.
Des pulsions vitales ou somatiques. *Rev. Franç. Psychanal.*, 14:106–28,
1950.)

1945
A special form of self-punishment. *Psychoanal. Q.*, 14:46–51. (Reprinted in *The
Yearbook of Psychoanalysis, II.* New York: Int. Univ. Press, 1946, pp. 143–
57.)

1946
In memoriam: Otto Fenichel. *Psychoanal. Q.*, 15:139–40.
Comments on the formation of psychic structure (with H. Hartmann and E.
Kris). *Psychoanal. Study Child*, 2:11–38. (Reprinted in *Papers on
Psychoanalytic Psychology*, Psychological Issues, Monograph 14. New York:
Int. Univ. Press, 1964, pp. 27–55. Comentarios sobre la formación de la
estructura psíquiqua. *Rev. de Psicoanálisis*, 8:222–48, 1951.)

1947
In memoriam: Hanns Sachs. *Psychoanal. Q.*, 16:151–53.
The historical and cultural roots of anti-semitism. In *Psychoanalysis and the
Social Sciences, I.* New York: Int. Univ. Press, pp. 46–61. (Reprinted in *The
Yearbook of Psychoanalysis, IV.* New York: Int. Univ. Press, 1949, pp.
226–62.)

1948

Les tendances de la psychanalyse. *L'Évolution Psychiatrique*, pp. 41–58.

1949

Notes on the theory of aggression (with H. Hartmann and E. Kris). *Psychoanal. Study Child*, 3/4:9–36. (Reprinted in *Papers on Psychoanalytic Psychology*, Psychological Issues, Monograph 14. New York: Int. Univ. Press, 1964, pp. 56–85.)

Some controversial issues in sex education. *Child Study Magazine*, 26:103ff.

A posttraumatic dream. *Psychoanal. Q.*, 18:449–54. (Reprinted in *The Yearbook of Psychoanalysis*, VI. New York: Int. Univ. Press, 1950, pp. 118–22.)

1950

Conflict and autonomous ego development during the phallic phase. *Psychoanal. Study Child*, 5:47–52.

1951

The problem of interpretation. *Psychoanal. Q.*, 20:1–14. (Das Problem der Deutung. *Psyche*, 22:187–98, 1968.)

Ego development and psychoanalytic technique. *Amer. J. Psychiat.*, 107:617–22.

Freud: Man and Scientist. The first Freud Anniversary Lecture. New York: Int. Univ. Press. (Reprinted in the *Bulletin of the New York Academy of Medicine*, 27:623–37.)

Christians and Jews: A Psychoanalytic Study. New York: Int. Univ. Press. (Republished: Delta Book No. 1273, New York: Dell Publ. Co., 1963. *Psychanalyse de L'Antisémitisme*. Paris: Presses Universitaires de France, 1952. *Christenen en Joden*. Amsterdam: Polak & Van Genep, 1966. *Estudio Psicoanalitico del Antisemitismo*. Buenos Aires: Ediciones Hor, é S.A.E., 1966. *Psychoanalyse des Antisemitismus*. Frankfurt am Main: Suhrkamp Verlag, 1967.)

Some psychoanalytic comments on "culture and personality" (with H. Hartmann and E. Kris). In *Psychoanalysis and Culture*. New York: Int. Univ. Press, pp. 3–31. (Reprinted in *Papers on Psychoanalytic Psychology*, Psychological Issues, Monograph 14. New York: Int. Univ. Press, 1964, pp. 86–116.)

1953

Editor of *Drives, Affects, Behavior, I.* New York: Int. Univ. Press.

The function of theory in psychoanalysis (with H. Hartmann and E. Kris). In *Drives, Affects, Behavior, I*, ed. R. M. Loewenstein. New York: Int. Univ. Press, pp. 1–37. (Reprinted in *Papers on Psychoanalytic Psychology*,

Psychological Issues, Monograph 14. New York: Int. Univ. Press, 1964, pp. 117–43.)

1954

Some remarks on defenses, autonomous ego, and psychoanalytic technique. *Int. J. Psychoanal.*, 35:188–93.

Some reflections on the development of sado-masochistic fantasies (summary of a paper presented before the Philadelphia Association for Psychoanalysis). *Bull. of the Philadelphia Assn. for Psychoanal.*, 4:20.

1956

Réflexions sur le traitement d'un cas de névrose compulsionnelle. *Rev. Franç. Psychanal.*, 20:384–404. (Reflections on the treatment of a case of obsessional neurosis. In *Troubled Women*, ed. L. Freeman. Cleveland & New York: World Publ. Co., 1959, pp. 295–316.)

Some remarks on the role of speech in psychoanalytic technique. *Int. J. Psychoanal.*, 37:460–68. (Reprinted in *Readings in Psychoanalytic Psychology*, ed. M. Levitt. New York: Appleton-Century-Crofts, 1959, pp. 248–61.)

1957

A contribution to the psychoanalytic theory of masochism. *J. Amer. Psychoanal. Assn.*, 5:197–234.

Some thoughts on interpretation in the theory and practice of psychoanalysis. *Psychoanal. Study Child*, 12:127–50. (Reprinted in *Psychoanalytic Clinical Interpretation*, ed. L. Paul. New York: Macmillan & Free Press, 1963, pp. 162–88.)

In memoriam: Ernst Kris. *J. Amer. Psychoanal. Assn.*, 5:741–43. (French translation: *Rev. Franç. Psychanal.*, 22:136–40, 1958.)

1958

Remarks on some variations in psychoanalytic technique. *Int. J. Psychoanal.*, 39:202–10. (Bemerkungen über einige Variationen der psychoanalytischen Technik. *Psyche*, 13:594–608, 1960.)

Variations in classical technique: concluding remarks. *Int. J. Psychoanal.*, 39:240–42. (Schlussbemerkungen. *Psyche*, 13:637–40, 1960.)

Discussion of *Influences of Early Mother-Child Interaction on Identification Processes* by Samuel Ritvo and Albert J. Solnit. *Psychoanal. Study Child*, 13:86–87.

1959

Problems of indications as viewed by a psychoanalyst. *Diseases of the Nervous System*, 20:84–88.

1961

Introduction to panel: The Silent Patient. *J. Amer. Psychoanal. Assn.*, 9:2–6.

1962

Notes on the superego (with H. Hartmann). *Psychoanal. Study Child,* 17:42–81. (Reprinted in *Papers on Psychoanalytic Psychology,* Psychological Issues, Monograph 14. New York: Int. Univ. Press, 1964, pp. 144–81. Notes sur le surmoi. *Rev. Franç. Psychanal.,* 28:639–87, 1964.)

1963

Some considerations on free association. *J. Amer. Psychoanal. Assn.*, 11:451–73.
In memoriam: Marie Bonaparte. *J. Amer. Psychoanal. Assn.*, 11:861–63.

1964

Symptom formation and character formation. Contribution to discussion of prepublished papers. *Int. J. Psychoanal.,* 45:155–57. (French translation: *Rev. Franç. Psychanal.,* 30:243–47, 1966.)

1965

Hommage à la mémoire de Marie Bonaparte. *Rev. Franç. Psychanal.,* 29:7–10.
Observational data and theory in psychoanalysis. In *Drives, Affects, Behavior, II,* ed. M. Schur. New York: Int. Univ. Press, pp. 38–59.

1966

Heinz Hartmann. Psychology of the ego. In *Psychoanalytic Pioneers,* ed. F. Alexander, S. Eisenstein & M. Grotjahn. New York: Basic Books, pp. 469–83.
On the theory of the superego: A discussion. In *Psychoanalysis—A General Psychology. Essays in Honor of Heinz Hartmann,* ed. R. M. Loewenstein, L. M. Newman, M. Schur & A. J. Solnit. New York: Int. Univ. Press, pp. 298–314.
Rapport sur la psychologie psychanalytique de H. Hartmann, E. Kris et R. Loewenstein. *Rev. Franç. Psychanal.,* 30:775–820.

1967

Defensive organization and autonomous ego functions. *J. Amer. Psychoanal. Assn.*, 15:795–809.

1968

Psychoanalytic theory and the teaching of dynamic psychiatry. In *The Teach-*

ing of Dynamic Psychiatry, ed. G. L. Bibring. New York: Int. Univ. Press, pp. 104–14.

Psychoanalysis: Therapeutic methods. In *International Encyclopedia of the Social Sciences, XIII.* New York: Macmillan & Free Press, pp. 31–37.

Comments on *Short Term Effects as Indicators of the Role of Interpretation in Psychoanalysis* by James Naiman. *Int. J. Psychoanal.*, 49:356–57.

1969

Developments in the theory of transference in the last fifty years. *Int. J. Psychoanal.*, 50:583–88.

1970

In memoriam: Heinz Hartmann. *Int. J. Psychoanal.*, 51:417–19.

In memoriam: Heinz Hartmann. *Psychoanal. Study Child*, 25:12–15.

1971

The basic rule: Free association—reconsideration. Panel report by H. Seidenberg. *J. Amer. Psychoanal. Assn.*, 19:98–109.

1972

Ego autonomy and psychoanalytic technique. *Psychoanal. Q.*, 41:1–22.

Index

Abraham, Karl, 168

Acting out, 27-28, 45, 120-21, 150, 152, 182

Action, 182, 189; speech as substitute for, 57, 59

Adaptation, 9, 48, 201

Adolescents, 17, 45, 216

Affects, 57, 59-60

Aggression, 57, 91, 94, 96; discharge of, 83, 87-89, 95; expression of, 88-90, 92, 95

Alexander, Franz, 41

Analysis. *See* Psychoanalysis

Analyst: actions of, 19, 58-59, 143, 150-52, 161 (*see also* Interventions); anonymity of, 151, 164; attitude of, 11, 18, 19, 165; distrust of, 109, 111; and free association, 179-80; and functions of speech, 56, 172; intellectual integrity of, 116; intuition of, 6-7, 14, 131; lends patient his ego, 42, 55, 58-59, 160, 165-66, 187, 189, 190, 201; patient's identification with, 220-21; personal style of, 6, 8, 13, 156; role of, 54-55, 58-59, 181-82, 183, 187, 188, 189; questioning of patient by, 154-55, 167. *See also* Interpretations; Therapeutic alliance

Analyst/patient interaction, 12-13, 27-28, 36, 141, 156, 173, 188, 189

"Analytic atmosphere," 18, 183

Analytic data, 6-7, 9-10, 12, 14-15, 124, 128, 143-44; and psychoanalytic theory, 2-3

Analytic method. *See* Psychoanalytic technique

Analytic setting, 181-82, 189, 214-15

Analytic situation, 8, 19, 54-55, 180, 188, 214, 215; child-mother relation paradigm for, 11, 189-90; defense in, 41-42, 43; frustration in, 13, 152, 164, 182

Anticipation, 201, 212, 222

Anxiety, 30-31, 40-41, 45, 70-71, 212, 222; and defense, 197, 200; and masochism, 70-71, 77

Appeal (function of speech), 55-56, 62

"Archaic ego states," 206

August, Harry E., 83

Basic rule. *See* Fundamental rule

Bibring, E., 59, 150n3, 155n8

Bisexuality, 77-78

Bonaparte, Marie, 92

Bornstein, Berta, 26, 36

Bouvet, M., 151, 164

Bowlby, John, 132

Bringing to consciousness, 40, 42, 60, 64-65, 173; term, 34, 53-54

Brunswik, Egon, 127n3

Buehler, Karl, 55, 143, 171, 173

Burlingham, Dorothy, 132

Cassirer, Ernst, 59

Castration fear, 30, 69, 70, 71, 72, 77, 91, 96, 212

Catharsis (concept), 9, 56, 57

"Change of function" (concept), 214, 216

Character formation, 96, 198-99, 212-13

Child-mother relationship, 11, 189-90

Children, 17, 45, 88-89, 90-91, 185; inability of, to free associate, 203, 218-19;